MUSIC IN THERAPY

Music in Therapy

EDITED BY

E. Thayer Gaston, Ph.D.

PROFESSOR OF MUSIC EDUCATION

DIRECTOR OF MUSIC THERAPY

DEPARTMENT OF MUSIC EDUCATION

UNIVERSITY OF KANSAS

The Macmillan Company, NEW YORK

Collier-Macmillan Limited, LONDON

TO THOSE OF EVERY TIME AND CULTURE

WHO HAVE USED MUSIC AS A MEANS OF

HELPING THE SICK AND THE HANDICAPPED

TO HAPPIER LIVES OF GREATER CREATIVITY

© Copyright, The Macmillan Company, 1968

First Printing

Library of Congress catalog card number: 68–10106

THE MACMILLAN COMPANY, NEW YORK
COLLIER-MACMILLAN CANADA, LTD., TORONTO, ONTARIO

Printed in the United States of America

FOREWORD

Music in Therapy starts with the contemplation, in sharp focus, of three principles that form much of the foundation of music therapy. Evidence of the fundamentality of these principles comes from the fact that the operation of each principle is a common experience of all music therapists. Enunciations of these basic principles are found whether one studies man and his music, the processes of music, research in music therapy, clinical practice, descriptions of the needs of patients, community-centered therapy, or the prescriptions and recommendations of psychiatrists. Wherever we look, these principles are a primary source of direction in music therapy.

Not at any time, from the planning to the completion of this book, were suggestions made to any contributor as to the specific content of his writing. Clinicians were asked to write and present case histories from their particular fields of expertness. The treatment aims of psychiatrists and therapeutic teams had been stated before descriptions of clinical practice or case histories were written. Considering these conditions, it is remarkable that so many sources should agree so precisely about the importance of the three principles of music therapy:

1. *The establishment or reestablishment of interpersonal relationships*
2. *The bringing about of self-esteem through self-actualization*
3. *The utilization of the unique potential of rhythm to energize and bring order*

The agreement of theory, practice, and research in music therapy comes into clearer perspective by recalling how often music aids in the establishment or reestablishment of desirable interpersonal relationships. In the evolution of man and his cultures, man gradually, but surely, has been drawn into closer interpersonal relationships. Music, from day to day in nearly all cultures, has been one of his most satisfying group activities, not only because of its unique sensory appeal, but because it was, and is, *non-verbal communication*. It is derived primarily from the tender, or positive, emotions—those that draw individuals together. The greatest potential of music arises in group situations. Sears, in "Processes in Music Therapy," devotes nearly one-third of his discussion to experience in relating to others. Music, alone, serves as a reason for being together—the individual subordinates his own interest to those of the group. His self-expression becomes socially acceptable. Music enhances the social situation.

Statements such as the following are found in nearly all descriptions of clinical practice and case histories: "Music and patient relationships have been generally assessed as two mutually supportive ingredients for successful therapy"; "It has been shown repeatedly that a music group provides the earliest and safest group experience for the most seriously ill mental patients." The efficacy of the music group is referred to in a number of ways and in a large majority of the case histories: "The patient needed to achieve in socially acceptable ways, so she was placed in a music group." "The patient cooperated and helped other patients." "The disciplines of belonging to a group require personal organization, recognition, and acceptance of reality goals." "It is believed that this patient was helped greatly by the subtle pressures of the group." "Not all the children cared for every song, but each child learned to respect the rights of the others." These few quotations are representative of literally scores of very similar or identical expressions.

Of the most immediate and pragmatic importance to the music therapist are the prescriptions, recommendations, treatment aims, and suggestions of the psychiatrist or therapeutic team: "Group participation is essential to the life adjustment of retarded persons." "Patients [are] sent to music therapy for social interaction." "The referrals often indicate one or more of five areas [of which] *socialization* is number one." "Music therapy goals were . . . to utilize the socializing effects of musical group efforts." "One of the particular problems of the child with cerebral palsy is participating in meaningful group activities." "Music therapy works to develop skills that will help patients avocationally . . . when they return to the community." It functions "to direct the patient in his relationships with other people."

The basic argument of Braswell in Chapter 30, "Social Facility and Mental Illness," is that "there is more than a chance relationship between social isolation and behavior disorders." Man is a social being. Interpersonal relationships are important to him and necessary for him, because it is from social and personal involvements that there develop systems of shared expectations, patterns of emotional relatedness, and modes of social adjustment, all of which are part of the concept of healthy humanness, of humanity, and of that which most differentiates man from lower animals. From this, it follows that man must have a place and a function with his fellows. He must be paid some attention, have status, and respond accordingly. He must attain greater significance in group functions.

The other side of the coin of good interpersonal relationships is *self-*

esteem. Bringing about self-esteem is the second basic function of music therapy. The frequency of statement, from many sources, of the need for self-esteem is equal to that for social adequacy or adjustment. One cannot exist without the other. Remembering the definition of "interpersonal," we may say that *self-esteem* is a confidence and a satisfaction in one's self; it is self-respect and one's good opinion of himself. A partial list of the synonyms of "self-esteem" is sufficient to point up its importance and acceptance—self-actualization, self-confidence, gratification, pride of accomplishment, competency, self-sufficiency, self-satisfaction, self-security. It is noteworthy that music therapists very rarely, if ever, use competition as a means of motivation. Competency through self-actualization is a need of young and old alike. This need is openly manifested in the young child and often only thinly veiled in the adult. All must have some competency if they are to have self-esteem. If there is no self-esteem, there is usually anxiety. The attestations of psychiatrists, psychologists, and clinicians leave small doubt as to the excellence of music as a means for developing or bringing about self-esteem.

The third music therapy principle is the utilization of the unique potential of rhythm to energize and bring order. Rhythm is the most potent, the most dynamic element in music. It is rhythm that "makes the wheels move." Without it, there is no periodicity; there is little order and, nearly always, only chaos. It is rhythm that most easily passes over from one culture to another and from one subculture to another. Although it has not been referred to as frequently as interpersonal relationships or self-esteem, it has been named the most important element of music for the retardate and the handicapped. Only the most sophisticated enjoy music to which they cannot beat time, and even they yield muscularly, at times, to the takt. Much has been made of rhythm in Chapters 1 and 2, "Man and Music" and "Processes in Music Therapy," and rightly so. Too often we take the nature of rhythm, its functions, and its effects for granted. A second reading of the descriptions and reports with particular attention directed toward the effects of rhythm will bring an awareness and acceptance of its potency and its necessity, even in those instances in which rhythm is not the center of attention of the various writers.

Thus music therapy is a gently insistent but dynamic persuasion of man to change his behavior, to share with and to expect fearlessly from his fellowman, and in so doing to achieve a happy confidence and satisfaction in himself. In the words of the poet Sidney Lanier, "Music is love in search of a word."

E. T. G.

PREFACE

A conference of music therapists was held at Lawrence, Kansas, in June, 1964, to plan a résumé of research and clinical practice in music therapy. The conference and the subsequent preparation and distribution of the résumé were made possible by a grant from the United States Office of Education, Department of Health, Education, and Welfare (Cooperative Research Project No. F–044).

The eleven conference participants were teachers of music therapy in colleges and universities.

RUTH BOXBERGER, Ohio University, Athens, Ohio
CHARLES BRASWELL, Loyola University, New Orleans, Louisiana
VANCE W. COTTER, University of Kansas, Lawrence, Kansas
E. THAYER GASTON, University of Kansas, Lawrence, Kansas
RICHARD M. GRAHAM, Lincoln University, Jefferson City, Missouri
BETTY ISERN HOWERY, University of the Pacific, Stockton, California
SISTER M. JOSEPHA, O.S.F., Alverno College, Milwaukee, Wisconsin
DONALD E. MICHEL, Florida State University, Tallahassee, Florida
ERWIN H. SCHNEIDER, Ohio State University, Columbus, Ohio
WILLIAM W. SEARS, Indiana University, Bloomington, Indiana
ROBERT F. UNKEFER, Michigan State University, East Lansing, Michigan

Some months prior to the meeting, they had been apprised of the nature and intent of the conference. Each had been asked to propose an agenda for the conference and an outline for the résumé, with particular attention to the areas of music therapy in which he was most expert. During the conference, agreement was achieved concerning the important principles and constructs of music therapy. The conferees identified and delineated areas of clinical practice and research pertinent to these areas and discussed in some detail the organization of personnel for the development of the résumé.

During the months following the June meeting, each participant selected research studies appropriate to his area and chose clinicians to prepare clinical descriptions and case studies. Each participant then assembled and organized the material for which he was responsible and forwarded it to the project director, who compiled the résumé. The final step of the project was the distribution of a copy of the four-hundred page résumé, *An Analysis, Evaluation, and Selection of Clinical Uses of Music in Therapy*, to each active member of the National Association for Music Therapy.

The résumé was foundational to this book. Each of the eleven conference participants named here accepted responsibilities in the new volume. Most of them gathered more material and revised and rewrote their original assignments. However, new authors and new areas of information have been included to make this book more representative of the scope of music therapy.

The names of those who wrote particularly for this book have been identified with their writing. In addition, there are those to whom I am indebted for their assistance in the preparation of the manuscript. I depended on Warren E. George for many kinds of help. George L. Duerksen read and corrected the manuscript. Jo Ann Euper read and rewrote when necessary. Charles T. Eagle helped. Mary Jo Johnston typed the edited material. Linda Vonder Bruegge assisted with the typing and checked the bibliographical citations. I am especially grateful to Doris Robison who read the entire work and ably assisted in the editing of the book.

E. T. G.

CONTRIBUTORS

JULIETTE ALVIN, R.M.T., Director of the British Society for Music Therapy, London, England.

SALLY HENNEMAN BAIRD, R.M.T., Wichita Public Schools, Wichita, Kansas

CAROL H. BITCON, R.M.T., Fairview State Hospital, Costa Mesa, California

JOHN W. BIXLER, R.M.T., Hospital School, University of Iowa, Iowa City

RUTH BOXBERGER, R.M.T., Assistant Professor of Music Education and Music Therapy, School of Music, Ohio University, Athens

CHARLES E. BRASWELL, R.M.T., Associate Professor of Piano and Chairman, Department of Music Therapy, Loyola University, New Orleans, Louisiana

HERMINA EISELE BROWNE, R.M.T., deceased (New Jersey Neuro-Psychiatric Institute, Princeton)

BARBARA J. CAVALLIN, Topeka, Kansas

H. W. CAVALLIN, Staff Psychiatrist, Topeka State Hospital, Topeka, Kansas

RONALD CHEN, Staff Psychiatrist, Topeka State Hospital, Topeka, Kansas

BETTY C. CLEMETSON, R.M.T., Topeka State Hospital, Topeka, Kansas

CAROL M. COLLINS, R.M.T., Instructor of Music Therapy, Western Michigan University, Kalamazoo

VANCE W. COTTER, R.M.T., Research Associate, Department of Music Education, University of Kansas, Lawrence

CAROL A. CRIGLER, R.M.T., Willowbrook State School, Staten Island, New York

DOROTHY BRIN CROCKER, R.M.T., Director of Music Therapy, Shady Brook Schools, Dallas, Texas

GEORGE L. DUERKSEN, Instructor, Department of Music, Michigan State University, East Lansing

JO ANN EUPER, R.M.T., Instructor, Peace Corps, University of Honduras

GENEVA SCHEIHING FOLSOM, R.M.T., Assistant Professor, University of Alabama, Tuscaloosa

LOUISE WHITBECK FRASER, R.M.T., Director of Louise Whitbeck Fraser School, Inc., Minneapolis, Minnesota

E. THAYER GASTON, R.M.T., Professor of Music Education and Director of Music Therapy, Department of Music Education, University of Kansas, Lawrence

[XI]

WARREN E. GEORGE, Teaching Assistant and Research Assistant, Department of Music Education, University of Kansas, Lawrence

RAY G. GLOVER, R.M.T., Director of Music Therapy, Larned State Hospital, Larned, Kansas

HERBERT R. GOLDSMITH, R.M.T., Director of Music Therapy, Milledgeville State Hospital, Milledgeville, Georgia

RICHARD M. GRAHAM, R.M.T., Associate Professor of Music Therapy, Department of Music, Lincoln University, Jefferson City, Missouri

RICHARD M. GRAY, R.M.T., Music Therapy Supervisor, Veterans' Administration Hospital, Topeka, Kansas

NEAL HELMUS, R.M.T., Mary Free Bed Hospital and Rehabilitation Complex, Grand Rapids, Michigan

FRANCES KORSON HERMAN, R.M.T., Hospital for Incurable Children, Toronto, Ontario, Canada

BETTY ISERN HOWERY, R.M.T., Associate Professor and Chairman, Music Therapy Department, University of the Pacific, Stockton, California

SISTER M. JOSEPHA, O.S.F., R.M.T., Associate Professor of Music Therapy, Alverno College, Milwaukee, Wisconsin

YOLANDA A. KOZAK, R.M.T., Mary Free Bed Hospital and Rehabilitation Complex, Grand Rapids, Michigan

WANDA B. LATHOM, R.M.T., Director of Music Therapy, Parsons State Hospital and Training Center, Parsons, Kansas

SISTER CLAIRE MARIE, O.S.F., R.M.T., Sacred Heart Hospital, Eau Claire, Wisconsin

CAROL W. MARSH, R.M.T., Central Louisiana State Hospital, Pineville

DONALD E. MICHEL, R.M.T., Associate Professor and Director of Music Therapy, School of Music, Florida State University, Tallahassee

PAUL NORDOFF, Assistant Instructor, Department of Psychiatry, University of Pennsylvania, Philadelphia

PETER F. OSTWALD, Associate Professor of Psychiatry, University of California School of Medicine, and Attending Psychiatrist, Langley Porter Institute, San Francisco

CLIVE ROBBINS, Assistant Instructor, Department of Psychiatry, University of Pennsylvania, Philadelphia

DORIS E. ROBISON, R.M.T., Chicago, Illinois

LUCRETIA ROGERS, R.M.T., Gillette State Hospital for Crippled Children, St. Paul, Minnesota

BARBARA J. ROMERHAUS, R.M.T., Larue Carter Hospital, Indianapolis, Indiana

WAYNE RUPPENTHAL, R.M.T., Director of Music Therapy, Topeka State Hospital, Topeka, Kansas

ERWIN H. SCHNEIDER, R.M.T., Professor and Head, Division of Music Education, Ohio State University, Columbus

WILLIAM W. SEARS, R.M.T., Associate Professor of Music, School of Music, Indiana University, Bloomington

NORMA SHARPE, R.M.T., Ontario Hospital, St. Thomas, Ontario, Canada

FORREST SLAUGHTER, R.M.T., Director of Rehabilitation Therapy and Special Education, Minnesota Residential Treatment Center, Circle Pine

MICKIE M. SNIVELY, R.M.T., Mendocino State Hospital, Talmage, California

DOROTHY TWENTE SOMMER, R.M.T., Davis, California

HARROLD W. SPICKNALL, Lansing Public Schools, Lansing, Michigan

GERALD K. SPRY, R.M.T., Director of Music Therapy, Northville State Hospital, Northville, Michigan

EMILY A. STEVENS, R.M.T., Director of Music Therapy, Georgia Mental Health Institute, Atlanta

MYRTLE FISH THOMPSON, R.M.T., Director of Music Therapy, Essex County Overbrook Hospital, Cedar Grove, New Jersey

MARY RYDER TOOMBS, R.M.T., San Jacinto School, Galveston, Texas

SAM TOOMBS, Psychologist, University of Texas at Galveston

FLORENCE TYSON, R.M.T., Music Therapy Center, New York, New York

ROBERT F. UNKEFER, R.M.T., Associate Professor of Music and Director of Music Therapy, Michigan State University, East Lansing

KAY EWER WELLS, Lansing, Michigan

NATALIE R. WERBNER, R.M.T., Peninsula Children's Center and Stanford Children's Convalescent Hospital, Palo Alto, California

ANNAMARY E. WILSON, R.M.T., Johnson Park Junior High School, Columbus, Ohio

RICHARD WINKELMAYER, Staff Psychiatrist, Delaware State Hospital, New Castle, Delaware

CONTENTS

INTRODUCTION

E R W I N   H .   S C H N E I D E R
R O B E R T   F .   U N K E F E R
E .   T H A Y E R   G A S T O N

Music and therapy have been close companions, often inseparable, throughout most of man's history. Each culture has determined the nature and use of its music in the treatment of illness. Mystic, therapeutic powers have often been attributed to music, even in cultures that took pride in their rationality. Men have believed that music cured illness by warding off evil spirits, absolving sins, introducing moral and ethical forces into human lives, placating the gods, and bringing into balance the four humors once supposed to determine human temperament.

Within the last century, particularly during the past fifty years, medicine has become increasingly specific in its treatment procedures. Until World War II, however, music in therapy continued to be used as a general treatment, a soporific, "good for the soul," and a morale builder. After World War II, music began to be applied more specifically. Challenged by the hospital situation, questioned by psychiatrists, and uncertain at times of his beliefs and procedures, the music therapist examined more thoroughly the use of music in therapy and made greater efforts to evaluate the results.

The use of music in hospitals and the employment of hospital musicians were stimulated by attempts to help hospitalized veterans of World War II. Much of this music was provided by volunteers. The period dating from the formal beginning of music therapy may be characterized as two decades of rapid change in treatment techniques in psychiatry itself. The rapid shift from rural to urban living in America brought into focus the severe problems of large mental hospitals. Concerned individuals and agencies struggled to turn the custodial asylum into an active treatment center. Often, music teachers and school band and choral directors tried to bring music to patients.

Active treatment had its beginning when sufficient numbers of trained staff personnel were available to progress from helping the patient satisfy only his most basic physical needs to helping him satisfy his psychic needs. This active treatment enabled him to recover and leave the hospital or encouraged him to function at his highest level within a planned and protected living situation.

Examination of practices and accomplishments soon made apparent the need for formal training of music therapists. Thus it was that in 1944 the institution that has since been renamed Michigan State University established the first curriculum designed specifically to train music therapists. The first academic course (didactic and laboratory) was taught in 1946 at the University of Kansas. Soon other colleges and universities established degree courses. In 1950, the National Association for Music Therapy (NAMT) was organized, making possible greater unity and standardization through its constitution and various committees on education, clinical practice, research, and certification and registration.

Providing trained staff for mental hospitals continues to be a serious problem. Frequently, not enough money for salaries is available; but even when money is available, not enough trained personnel are ready. Nevertheless, a great increase in the quantity and quality of staff personnel has taken place. New treatment techniques have been developed and defined. Active treatment procedures that were used widely when trained music therapists started to work in mental hospitals have been discarded and are now only a part of the history of psychiatry. Developments in the use of tranquilizing drugs in the middle 1950s allowed stoppage of some of the drastic therapies such as insulin-coma therapy. These drugs have also made unnecessary the early practices used to control the patient's destructive physical activity: There is little need for the hydrotherapy room; many hospital doors that had to be barred and locked in the past can now be left open.

Whereas the use of activities and the employment of activity therapists in psychiatric hospitals date from the late nineteenth century, the recognition of the activity therapist as a unique contributor to treatment is comparatively recent. The employment of activity therapists in large numbers to accomplish specific treatment goals has come about only in the last twenty-five years. Music activities were first used and found desirable by music volunteers, occupational therapists, and recreation specialists. This led to the employment of full-time hospital musicians. Specialized training for music therapists developed, and they became recognized members of the activity therapy disciplines.

A review of reports of clinical practice in music therapy in adult psychiatric hospitals during the past twenty years shows fairly consistent developments of methods and techniques. In general, changes of practice have paralleled those of psychiatry. In 1954, Gaston stated the principles of music therapy after a comprehensive review of clinical practices and research. Those principles differ little in quality from the set of principles developed for this volume. It is possible, however, to trace some differences in the manner in which music therapy practice has been described. What was truly beneficial music therapy in the past has not changed, but the way clinicians have chosen to describe it has changed.

In the 1940s, the small amount of clinical literature that did appear was concerned chiefly with the imagined healing power of music per se. Reports by laymen of miraculous cures appeared in newspapers and some popular magazines; infrequently, there was a report in a professional journal. Almost all these accounts contained a reference to the fact that music could "reach" the patient when he responded favorably to nothing else. Seldom was there a description of the manner in which the music therapist approached the patient or how he used the music. It seemed there was almost a common societal belief that music had inherent healing power, and thus some early practice that now would be considered inappropriate was accepted and at times even commended.

Most activity therapies have passed through a phase during which a particular activity by itself was credited far too much with direct healing power. In the past, attempts were sometimes made to relate the therapeutic use of a specific craft to the alleviation of a certain illness. During the past twenty-five years, experienced music therapists and their hospital colleagues began questioning the miraculous cures related to the music experiences of patients. In consequence, some therapists were too willing and too quick to shift emphasis when questions were raised about the healing power of music. Because they could not prove that such power existed in music, they began to deemphasize music activities and emphasize the development of interpersonal relationships. For a short period of time, more than a few music workers tried to use too much psychotherapy, for which they were scarcely prepared, and indulged in music activities only as the patient desired. Gradually, this condition changed, and selected media and therapist-patient relationships were assessed as two mutually supportive ingredients for successful therapy. The activities (media) serve to set limits and give focus to the important learning or relearning the patient has to experience.

To summarize, music therapy (as well as other activity therapies) has passed through three periods or stages in the past twenty-five years: First, much emphasis was placed on music without recognizing the important role of the therapist. Second, the therapist tended to disregard music in favor of developing a one-to-one relationship with the patient. Third, a position between these two extremes has been adopted. The therapist uses his specialty to focus the relationship with the patient and moves in the desired direction at the most suitable rate in both the activity and the relationship.

This book is organized around the three essential considerations for any discipline—theory, practice, and research. It approaches the practice of music in therapy by considering the phenomenon of man and his music—the genesis of the meaning of music for man and its influence on him. The book is concerned with delincating, defining, and explaining the processes by which music involves man and his responses to these various involvements. Principles and processes from this approach will be referred to from time to time in order to understand the function of music and to achieve coherence and system.

The greater portion of the writings are devoted to clinical descriptions, pertinent research, and case histories. Of necessity, some descriptions of patients are given in order to make clearer the use of music. Most of the general categories of patients—for example, adults suffering from behavior disorders, emotionally disturbed children, mental retardates, and physically handicapped children—and the music therapy for them are covered. *Rather than explaining music therapy in terms of a particular psychological theory, we have made an effort throughout to show how music therapy can bring about desirable changes in behavior and adaptation.*

Finally, the work devotes itself to the exemplifications of research, measurement, and evaluation. Research is a necessity if music therapy is to progress. Many music therapists believe they can do no research. The closing part of the book encourages them to try. There are, of course, many ideas and directions for those who have had some experience. And this part may have still greater value for those who need to understand better those research reports that come to their attention. The volume is concluded, then, with the third of the three essential considerations for any discipline—research.

Part I
FOUNDATIONS OF MUSIC IN THERAPY
E. Thayer Gaston

An adequate understanding of the nature of man and his behavior is incomplete without some knowledge of his development. To apprehend music as an essential form of human behavior is to make more secure the foundations of music in therapy. Music therapy has long needed such a platform for its theoretical constructs, one that would be in accord with biological as well as psychological concepts. It has needed knowledge derived from a multidisciplinary approach. Music therapy is closely related to the behavioral sciences. As is the case in all sciences, music therapy strives to bring about organization, classification, and description until a system emerges, a system that is behavioral, logical, and psychological. To bring more comprehension of man and music and to describe processes in music therapy are the major purposes of this book.

1

MAN AND MUSIC

E . THAYER GASTON

Music Is Human Behavior

Music, a form of human behavior, is unique and powerful in its influence. It can benefit handicapped and ill persons by helping them to change their behavior by acquiring new or better behavior. At times, music itself elicits these behavior changes. However, most often there is the purposeful persuasion, either directly or indirectly, of the therapist. By means of music and persuasion, then, the ultimate goal—to bring about desirable changes in behavior—is attempted.

Human behavior involved with music has been studied by psychologists, anthropologists, and sociologists. These three disciplines—some would also include psychiatry—are known as *behavioral sciences*. They deal with human action (behavior) and aim at the establishment of generalizations about man's behavior. Sometimes, they are quite specific in their applications.

Behavioral sciences are relatively new, and many matters of immediate relationship to man's happiness have been investigated insufficiently. By the admissions of some behavioral scientists, there is a poverty of data on art, particularly on music. As will be seen later, there are few reports of a scientific nature about esthetics. Most of what makes life worth living, the "feelingful" aspects, have been omitted from scientific investigation (Morrison, 1963). Consequently, there is an urgent need for the scientific study of man's musical behavior, and particularly the therapeutic use of music. Because little is known of what happens inside man when he is engaged musically, the only recourse is to observe and study his overt behavior. The best method for such study is the one utilized by the behavioral sciences.

However, to study the overt behavior of man, excluding other sources of knowledge and guidance, is not the best procedure. To set up constructs that bear little relation to physiological function, for example, is to set up guidelines external to the organism. To believe that criminality

[7]

is hereditary when one observes a father and son who are both criminals, is to be misled. There are no criminal genes. To set up a psychological theory that has little or no relationship with organismic states is certain to result in a false theory. "Behavioral science has, up to now, been overly concerned with externally placed guides on behavior" (Pribram, 1964, p. 79).

It is true that, at times, behavioral science has been so pessimistic about ever learning of the inner functions of man that it has made little or no attempt to gain any data except that from observable behavior. This pessimism is, of course, a mistake, because no single scientific approach will explain man or his behavior. Many behavioral scientists are not content with the single approach. Miller accepted the National Medal of Science not only "for sustained and imaginative research on principles of learning and motivation," but also for the analysis of "the effects of direct electrical stimulation of the brain." In the conclusion of his address as president of the American Psychological Association, he said, "A combination of behavioral and physiological techniques is increasing our knowledge of these [brain] processes and their significance to psychology" (Miller, 1965, p. 183).

Bakan (1965), too, protested the purely behavioral approach by saying that keeping the nature of the psyche a mystery and, at the same time, trying to understand human nature are incompatible. Murphy (1963) went into detail to show the potential contributions of genetics, biochemistry, neurology, embryology, and other disciplines to the development of psychology.

There are other reasons why the understanding of human behavior and, specifically, music therapy will profit most from a multidisciplinary approach. "All problems of life ultimately are biological ones, and . . . they should be explored not for themselves alone but for the suggestions they may offer for the complex phenomena of life" (Sinnott, 1955, pp. vii–viii). Scott (1963), speaking of the broadness of the study of animal behavior, which includes human behavior, mentions all branches of zoology and interdisciplinary study involving psychology, sociology, and the physical sciences. Ostwald (1963) cogently makes clear the importance of acoustics for anyone interested in human sounds and the communication of emotions. Such knowledge is essential to the music therapist.

Masserman (1961) postulates "a comprehensive *biodynamic* theory of human behavior" and says that the theory should "be in accord with biologic principles as inferred from the evolution and the structure and physiologic relationships of living organisms" (p. 108). Allport (1961), describing the development of personality, says "that nothing in personality is purely 'social' and nothing purely 'individual.' . . . Both approaches are valid. And for a *complete* account of human action (which no single science yet attempts) we need them both" (p. 193).

Thus far, it seems that music therapy, broadly conceived, follows the path of a behavioral science. However, another emphasis has been to present evidence that some knowledge of other disciplines is essential in order to understand human behavior. The fullness and richness of concept and insight that are necessary in music therapy cannot be achieved unless there is at least background knowledge of other approaches to the nature and meaning of man's production of and participation in music. Music therapy, using a behavioral approach, should be buttressed at every strategic point and in every critical area with whatever will be helpful from other sciences and fields of knowledge. This viewpoint encourages the music therapist to be as steeped as possible in the knowledge essential in music therapy. Such knowledge is best fostered by one's attitude and approach to professional life and bespeaks the maturity that enables the individual to shift to himself the burden of pursuing his own education.

There is a second reason for encouraging attainment of pertinent knowledge. *All music therapists have begun, and future music therapists will begin, their music study long before they consider music therapy as a profession.* Now, music is an extremely jealous and proprietary mistress, particularly in one's youth. This is as it should be, because there is rarely a good music therapist who has not been, or still is, a good musician. It takes years to become a musician. One cannot wait until college to begin. Too often during the years of music study, several unfortunate ideas and influences dominate the attitude and credo of students. One idea, all too prevalent, is that science, mathematics, and the other liberal arts contribute nothing of benefit to a musician. Of course, this belief is not true. A cursory view of ancient Greece or of the Renaissance in Europe will show that broad knowledge is no handicap to artistic endeavor, but, on the contrary, enriches it. The attainments of Michelangelo and da Vinci, universal scholars, attest to this fact. Frequently, the music student believes he cannot be successful in science and, consequently, does not try. There is no conflict between music and science. All truth is compatible, not conflictual.

Because music is an art, the explanation of its meaning and function has been, until recently, in the province of philosophical esthetics, the center of which was speculative theory. But no longer is esthetics found exclusively within the domain of philosophy. *Webster's Third New International Dictionary* describes well the modern situation: "Aesthetics, the science whose subject matter is the description and explanation of the arts, artistic phenomena, and aesthetic experience and includes psychology, sociology, ethnology . . . and essentially related aspects." Music therapy will be much better informed if it looks first to the behavioral and other sciences and then, perhaps, to philosophy. By so doing, a systematic and appropriate approach to the phenomena of music in therapy will develop.

Unlike religious and philosophical explanations, however, a scientific explanation does not pretend to be all-embracing, universal, and eternal. . . . Rather, in each and every detail, scientific explanation remains permanently open to question, to reassessment, revaluation, or reversal in the light of later discoveries of data or better research methods (Hulse, 1963, p. 5).

The Development of Man

"Man is the most mysterious of all experiences. This is why art and science strive to make him comprehensible" (Dobzhansky, 1962, p. xi). "Man has both a nature and a 'history'" (Dobzhansky, 1962, p. 18). Perhaps there is no better way to have a fresh viewpoint of man than to consider his development. It is certain that we cannot understand man well unless we know how he became what he is. In order to understand the nature and function of any living organism—animal (including man) or vegetable—the organism's history, that is, its evolution, must be studied (Simpson, 1963). Man is not only a creature of this earth, but of the universe. He came into being and evolved to his present state in full accord with, and subject to, the laws and principles of this universe. There is only one species of man and we all belong to it. We not only have evolved, we are still evolving and being evolved. "By changing what he knows about the world, man changes the world that he knows; and by changing the world in which he lives, man changes himself" (Dobzhansky, 1962, p. 347). Even though man is the most complex biological organism, he is a biological unit, and he operates and functions always in agreement with the principles of biology. Human nature (modern man) is the result of the interaction of what is in man—in all its complex functioning—and what is outside him—his environment (Gaston, 1964).

We live in a universe, not a *diverse* (situation). The earth, seas, plants, animals, and man all share the same kind of building materials: the elements, molecules, and atoms. Thus, *all that lives is our kin*. The basic mechanisms of reproduction and transmission of heredity are the common property of all plants and animals. Genes and chromosomes exist in sunflowers, roses, cacti, fish, reptiles, birds, and mammals.

Some pains have been taken to show the physical basis of all living things so that we do not slip through the side door of mysticism. *Music is not mystical; it is mysterious*. We do not yet know fully why music is beautiful. But this is no reason to consider music otherworldly. To do so is as erroneous as to ascribe behavior disorders to the infiltration of evil spirits.

Although life has been on this earth a few billion years, we are concerned with the beginnings of man, the immediate prehuman primates of several million years ago. Crude tools have been found, and evidence indicates that Zinjanthropus (an early progenitor of man) used them in Eastern Africa about 1.7 million years ago (Leakey, 1961). How did this progenitor of man develop the characteristics of humanness that eventually set man apart from all other animals? To begin to answer this question, *it is not necessary to separate the biology from the culture of man.* They go hand in hand. "The fact which must be stressed, because it has frequently been missed or misrepresented, is that the biological and cultural evolutions are parts of the same process" (Dobzhansky, 1962, p. 22). This means that the part of man's culture we call music has a biological as well as a cultural basis. The evolvement of cultural capacity is not less than the evolution of mankind (Hulse, 1963, p. 221).

One of the essential conditions for the organization of men into cooperative societies is the suppression of rage and hostility. This could not come about until the cortex of the cerebrum had developed sufficiently so it could exert some control over more primitive parts of the nervous system. Even today, one has to stop and think in order to control anger and destructive rage. The development of the cortex as a control of the autonomic nervous system was recounted by Washburn (1962) and Etkin (1962).

Only in the primate family, that family of mammals to which man belongs, is the female receptive to the male in significantly longer periods between one estrus and the next. This is a vital necessity for the beginning of the family, because the female not only can attract the male, but she can hold the same male. This is the biological basis for the formation of more lasting family relationships. Thus, a long step is taken beyond other animals. The female no longer is forced periodically into the blind, instinctive behavior that would cause her to accept a different male at each period of estrus. The cortical, so to speak, becomes dominant over the endocrine factor. Sexual dimorphism (difference in size between male and female) becomes more apparent. Division of labor occurs. The relationship between male and female modifies aggressive behavior and results in increased communication. All this leads to a uniqueness in humans, among all animals, of the mother-child relationship, without which there would be no culture as we know it.

In apes and monkeys, the central nervous system is developed better at birth than is that of the human baby. Infant apes and monkeys are able to cling to the mother. The human baby, in spite of his larger brain size, is far more helpless at birth than any other neonate. He is highly dependent on the mother for a long period of time. Because the father provides the necessary protection and food, the mother can devote her time to care of the baby. She has time and freedom to teach her child, and the child has time to learn. From this come the early stages of cultural development, because "it is this helplessness and prolonged dependence on the ministrations of the parents and other persons that favors in man the socialization and learning process on which the transmission of culture wholly depends" (Dobzhansky, 1962, p. 196).

Another important genetic factor adds to the time the mother may spend with her individual young: primate mothers rarely have litters (Hulse, 1963, p. 132). There is usually one baby, although there may be twins in a few species. Each child, therefore, receives far more attention from the mother.

From these few important conditions that contributed in part to the evolution of man, it is clear that the trend has been toward greater interdependence of individuals, more communication, and those closer relationships that are characteristic of culture.

In all that has been said of the beginnings of culture, it should not be forgotten that genetic change has been occurring. This change produced the most distinguishing characteristic of man, his brain, and in particular, the newest and largest part, the cerebrum. "Progressive evolution of behavior in the animal world has led to the interposing of more and more nervous processes between the stimuli arriving from the environment and the organism's responses to them" (Dobzhansky, 1962, p. 203). To simplify this statement of important fact, it may be said that stimuli coming to the human brain must penetrate and ramify a brain far more complex and of vastly greater potential than that of any other animal. This is why a baby seems to learn so much more slowly than other animals. Yet he is being affected by the incoming stimuli, and is developing the potentiality for a far greater sensitivity to his environment. It is this great sensitivity to his environment that in the long run enables him to achieve humanness (Becker, 1962, p. 15). It is the basic necessity not only for his "socialness," but for the organization of further stimuli into patterns of deep meaning and influence. Music is one of these areas of organization that stands at or very near the apex of man's humanness.

The two most distinguishing characteristics, then, of man's development are his society and the immense complexity of his brain. They are highly interactive and each is dependent on the other. In the society of man, he has constantly drawn closer together and become more interdependent. His brain makes possible speech, communication, abstract thinking, and, as will be shown, significant nonverbal communication in the form of music.

Man and His Senses—Music

"Einstein said something that needed to be said and that has been said better by no one else: 'The most incomprehensible thing about the world is that it is comprehensible'" (Dobzhansky, 1962, p. xi). This observation of wisdom means, in part, that the most difficult thing to understand about man is how he comes to know the world about him. Without this comprehensibility of the outside world, there would be no music, because from this outside world—the world that man senses —comes the raw data of all that man will ever do, think, or feel (von Buddenbrock, 1958, p. 12). Basically and completely, it is man's sensory experience of hearing that makes possible his music. In spite of all the genetic equipment and all the potentiality of the newborn, it is doomed to an isolated nothingness without the senses. And yet, the sensory operations and perceptions of the baby are part of body perception. They are biological functions (Deutsch, 1962, p. 2).

We are totally dependent on our senses for even the most primary information from our environment, and the brain, so to speak, is the only organ that can accept instruction from the environment (Medawar, 1959, p. 90). This matter of sensory inflow has been emphasized because the greater the sensory development of an organism, the richer the outside world of that particular organism (von Buddenbrock, 1958, p. 33). This is quite precisely the function of music in the life of man: to enrich his life. It is also one of the major functions of music in therapy, because so many recipients of music therapy, particularly children, lack the enrichment of music.

The end organs of our senses—of hearing, seeing (in part), touching, smelling, and tasting—are all differentiated skin. They develop from the ectoderm of the embryo, and although each sense brings its own particular quality of reality to us, no one can say that auditory stimuli are less real than other sensory stimuli. Our senses provide us with the basic material of what is to be our intelligence, but just as certainly of what is to be our esthetic sense. The full fruition of our potential for humanness can never be attained unless we grow and develop within a rich musical environment.

Thus it is evident that monotony of stimuli or isolation from sensory stimuli is not conducive to intellectual development. Any animal reared in an environment that is sensorially restricted will not develop normally, and his intellectual development will correlate with his impoverished sensory stimuli. Furthermore, such animals are likely to show marked disturbances of motivation or of personality (Hebb, 1958; Hebb, 1961). The effect of the breakup of the mother-child relationship, even in monkeys, was shown by Harlow (1958). The effects on the young monkey were disastrous and lasted a lifetime.

A number of experiments that deprived young animals of adequate sensory stimuli permanently stunted the growth of their intelligence. Not only is there behavioral evidence of damage, but anatomical and chemical evidence as well. Weiskrantz (1958) found damage to sight, and Liberman (1962) found alterations in ribonucleic acid (RNA). Deprivation of sensory stimuli not only can damage the young but can make the human adult behave abnormally—losing his sense of self and even having hallucinations (Bexton, Heron, and Scott, 1954). Prolonged immobilization of the body dramatically alters the electroencephalogram (Zubek and Wilgosh, 1963). An adequate amount of sensory stimuli, with some novelty, is essential for health and normality.

As one follows the development of man and sees the many organizations of his experience, the place of music, as a necessity in all cultures, becomes clear.

All mankind must organize, must seek causes and endings. In a multitude of religions and philosophies, man explains how things came to be and how they will be. There are no races, tribes, or peoples who cannot do this. And each individual of every race, tribe, and people began this process of abstraction by receiving sensory stimuli (Gaston, 1964, p. 4).

Pribram (1964), speaking of the consequences of action becoming orderly, suggests that orderliness is a prime factor of reinforcement and that satisfaction results from such orderliness. "Status and role assume a central place in sociology because they describe what is most necessary for behavior; namely, *an ordered simplification of the human environment*" (Becker, 1962, p. 11). There can be little understanding without orderliness and organization. The key to the process of life is organization. Personality, whatever else it may be, is the result of expanding organization (Allport, 1961).

Great emphasis is placed on this universal demand for organization, because it provides a necessary insight into the propensity and demand of human beings for music. There are sense hungers for sights, sounds, shapes, textures, and rhythms. These needs are particularly evident in children, and their satisfaction is essential to normal growth and development. The impulses to see, to hear, to touch, to taste are as natural and demanding as the desire to understand.

Man, with his cerebrum of billions of cells, must not only organize the incoming stimuli that inform him of his environment, but must also create new designs and new forms for his use. From this process comes his esthetic sense. No culture, no tribe has ever been satisfied with only the sounds of nature. Man has made new sounds and has placed them in orderly fashion in some system or organization that is *generally and predominantly rhythmical*, but only sometimes melodic and/or harmonic. Each child born into a culture learns the music of that culture if he learns any music. His music is one of his folkways. Murphy (1958) has said this about the elaboration of the sensory:

There is, however, no group of human beings which has not cultivated devices for enriching contact with the sensory world. . . . The word ordinarily used to describe this class of satisfactions . . . is *esthetic*. . . . The *potentials for becoming a human being*, as compared with a less complex kind of animal, *lie largely in this enrichment and elaboration of the sensory and motor ranges of experience* . . . (p. 34).

Man cannot escape the formation of esthetic constructs. The great potential of his nervous system takes him beyond bare animal adaptation. Furthermore, *esthetic experience may be one of the best devices to help him adjust and adapt to his environment.* The chief significance of esthetic experience, however, is that a man would be less complete as a human being without it. It is toward this humanness that our discourse moves, because, "What matters most for understanding him (man) is that 'humanness' which sets him apart from the rest of creation" (DuBos, 1965, p. 3). To understand "humanness" is to understand more profoundly what is necessary for the health and happiness of man. Music is the essence of humanness, not only because man creates it, but because he creates his relationship to it.

Growing plasticity of response is a characteristic of the development of man from lower vertebrates. The ability to communicate meaning through language is found in all cultures and is a positive necessity for the normality of individuals because of their interdependence—that is, their dependence on each other. Each people develops its own language, and no language is better for communication than any other language as long as its culture is considered (Hulse, 1963, p. 380). In just such fashion is music a folkway. There are many different musics, but each fulfills its proper function in its own culture. Music came into being because of man's interdependence, his need for expression and communication.

Although this discussion will say more about the ubiquity of music and the various ways in which the human potential is accomplished, the main purpose thus far has been to lay a foundation for understanding man and music and, consequently, music therapy. Such an understanding is basic to a knowledge of man's humanness and the relation of music to it, to research and clinical practice in music therapy. Music is an essential and necessary function of man. It influences his behavior and condition and has done so for thousands of years.

In the beginning of this chapter, consideration was given to the benefits of a multidisciplined background for the study of music therapy. The more opportunity there is for checking and verifying concepts and findings with other areas of knowledge, the less chance there is for error in decisions achieved pragmatically or theoretically. To illustrate this and to present basic information, attention is drawn to human and animal responses elicited by a particular sound, unvarying in its qualities. The data from this and similar experiments have, perhaps indirectly, to do with rhythm; but more surely with monotony, familiarity, excessive novelty, organization, and, of course, attention. Mature musicians, from experience, would arrive at much the same judgments as these, but not always. The following report supports these subjective judgments.

Pribram recounts the responses of human subjects to the temporally irregular beeping of a tone. At first, there is full evidence of the alerting or arousal of the subject: turning of the head and eyes to locate the tones, galvanic skin response, and increased flow of blood to the head. Electrical activity of the parts of the brain connected to the internal ear show a choppy pattern characteristic of alerting. Other parts of the brain provide records of altered electrical activity. After five or ten minutes, this pattern of response changes because of the repetitious auditory environment. The individuals apparently no longer react to the situation. However, if the beeped tone is altered, all the previous indications of alerting reappear. "Any slight departure from prior conformations—any nuances —produce the orienting (alerting) reaction. . . . Reaction to novelty appears to be one built-in feature of the central nervous system" (Pribram, 1964, pp. 80–81).

In this same account, Pribram indicates that the most effective attention is that wherein novelty comes from variations on the familiar, from dependence to some extent on what has already been programed in the memory system. Extreme repetitiousness leads to internal inhibition, to drowsiness. If too much novelty is present (in which there is not enough of the familiar), the result will be the same—inhibition and lack of attention. Although these findings are concerned chiefly with learning and habituation, they are applicable to the use of music in therapy. This neurological evidence points to the dulling effect of sensory deprivation or monotony and also to the similar effect of so much novelty that it cannot be organized.

A more elaborate account of the beeping-tone experiment was reported by Pribram (1963). Here he was concerned with the biochemical as well as the neurological aspects of memory. The same point is made: The correct proportion of variation on the familiar is necessary for the best attention. To be at his liveliest, man needs the influence of the right proportion of novelty. It is a necessary ingredient of creative living.

Dember (1960, pp. 341–375) suggests that close study of changes (novelty) may help us understand esthetics.

Rhythm: The Organizer and Energizer

When the musics from all the cultures of the world are considered, it is rhythm that stands out as most fundamental. *Rhythm is the organizer and the energizer.* Without rhythm, there would be no music, whereas there is much music that has neither melody nor harmony. Combinations of rhythm, melody, harmony, and counterpoint have been in existence less than one thousand years, but rhythm has been the music of millions for many thousands of years. It is rhythm alone that makes possible the temporal order of music. For most people it is rhythm that provides the energy of music, be it small or great. Throughout succeeding chapters, the unique potential of rhythm to energize and bring order will be seen as the most influential factor of music.

The statement may be ventured that any normal mother can easily put to sleep the young infant of any other mother. This is true, in part, because lullabies are strikingly alike the world over. Nearly always, there is metronomic regularity. The chief characteristic of lullabies is this regular, monotonous, rocking rhythm. Perhaps this regularity derives from the sound and movement in the environment of prenatal life or if in postnatal life, from the parsimony of physical movement of the mother. However one explains it, the rhythm is metronomic and universal although the tempo may vary.

It would be an ill-founded hope to maintain that the explanation of music is as simple as the lullaby—it is not. It is notable, nevertheless, that most music of adolescents is strikingly similar in regularity to the rhythms of prenatal and infant life. In fact, most individuals in Western culture must study music for some time before they really enjoy music with a nonmetronomic pulse. Most people will disregard music to which they cannot beat time. If rhythmic order cannot be established, then melody and harmony lose their potency.

It is rhythm that makes possible the dance, and *most music is dance music.* This is an important consideration—the union of the dance with music. Dance would be unimportant if man were not the best athlete of all animals (Hulse, 1963, p. 176). It is rhythm that allows two or more people to dance together. The coming together of people in specific conjoint activity such as the dance is extremely important because it brings about a unity of purpose and activity, a joining together that is typical of the healthy humanness of man. This coming together to work in a unity is very difficult for many ill and handicapped children and adults. Rhythmic activities make working together easier because no words are needed; rhythm is the common bond. Somehow, it encourages a freedom with others. During a dance, a man and woman who have just met put their arms around each other in an intimacy that would never be tolerated by the two or the public but is acceptable in the dance as long as the music continues.

Not only is rhythm the chief factor in the organization of music, it is, generally speaking, the chief energizer—the primitive, driving factor in music (Gaston, 1951). When rhythm is enunciated by detached, percussive sounds, it stimulates muscular action, particularly if there is some variation in the rhythmic pattern. When we think of the music of preliterate people, it is percussive in nature; it calls up visions of strenuous physical action. The drum is the best instrument for such dances, just as it is the best instrument for marching. But percussive music may also be the product of other instruments, the piano for example. Whenever the dance is unrestrained and uninhibited, the accompaniment is percussive and highly rhythmical. The basic dynamic factor of dance bands is the rhythm section.

The opposite reaction is found to melodic passages in which rhythm is at a minimum and the sounds are nonpercussive and legato. There is far less physical movement. A typical adagio movement such as that in the *Divertimento* by Mozart actually curtails physical movement. It seems to induce a contemplative response. Sustained, nonrhythmical music makes no demand for physical activity, but rather induces esthetic fantasy.

Although all music exists on a continuum, striking contrasts in response to the two extremes can be observed in our everyday life. The behavior of adolescent dancers could not be what it is if nonpercussive music were used. Church congregations respond differently to the organ from the way they do to the piano. At concerts the most rhythmical music is played last (sometimes it is the most familiar) so the applause will be greater. Generally, the finest legato music receives less applause than, for example, *Bolero* by Ravel.

A number of small studies using these two types of music have been made, and nearly always there were significant differences in the subjects' responses: differences in pictures drawn by children (Zack, 1951), pictures drawn by adults (Cater, 1949), gastric motility (Wilson, 1957), galvanic skin response (Shrift, 1957), pupillary dilatation (Slaughter, 1954), and electromyograms (Sears, 1958). The "startle response" occurs only to percussive sound.

The effect of the lullaby and hypnogenetic music derives from a monotonously regular and mildly accented type of rhythm in which there is little or no variation. All functional lullabies are unrelenting in rhythm;

even the well-known "Berceuse" of Chopin has not the slightest variation in the basic rhythm supporting the melody.

The behavior of groups of people as well as that of individuals can
often be controlled by the type of music used. The music in supermar-
kets at checkout counters, the music and yells (chants) at athletic events,
church music, dance music, and music in crowded elevators are examples
of attempts to control behavior by music. The bugle call "Taps," as it is
usually sounded, is the least rhythmic but the most melodic of bugle
calls, and it demands no action. It is the amount of rhythm and the
manner in which the rhythm is indicated that determine, in large part,
the amount of energy invested in the physical response to music.

It is rhythm that controls the activities of large groups. The music of
a marching band is really a dance in which the dancers make their own
music. A cheering section can do little or nothing without rhythm. For
music therapy, it is not only the doing but the *doing together* that is
important and brings so much satisfaction. Rhythm furnishes a nonverbal persuasion not only to act but to act together. Acceptable social
behavior (acting together) is the ultimate goal for most patients in
mental hospitals and institutions for handicapped children.

Man's Behavior with His Music

Knowledge of other cultures helps us know our own culture better.
And *we shall know our own music best by knowing the music of other
cultures* (Merriam, 1964, p. 27). We shall also be able to understand
music in therapy better. Furthermore, we can understand more distinctly
the function of music if we observe its effect on the healthy as well as
on the ill (Bruner, 1963, p. 15). In the several cultures mentioned will
be seen the close relationship of music and religion, the greater importance
of group music over individual musical effort, the powerful help of music
to memory, and the similarity of some functions of music in all societies.

The first chapter of Hulse's *The Human Species* (1963) contains a description of the grave of a Neanderthal boy. Hulse tells how the body was
arranged in a grave lined by wild goat horns and then, in proper and significant commentary, says, "Perhaps the people sang or wept or recited
charms while they were disposing of the body. We cannot know. But it
is clear that they felt the need to do something special" (p. 3). Hulse is
assuring us of the humanness of the Neanderthal mourners. Today we
sing and weep and say prayers over our dead.

Von Hagen (1961) provided probably the best descriptions of the cultures of the Aztec, Mayan, and Incan Indians when their respective cultures were at their peak development. All Aztec music was indissolubly

bound with dancing. Pure music did not exist. All Aztec instruments were percussive in type, with the exception of the conch shell. Consequently, the music was rhythmic, not melodic, and at times hypnotic. The dance was an important part of religious ceremony in the Aztec culture, and its chief function was to enable the dancers and the watchers to obtain mystic communion with the proper god. Rhythm not only enables conjoint movement but is distinctly an aid in remembering chants and songs.

In such cultures as the Aztec, the priority of the dance over song was clear because there were so many dances that had no words, but were self-sufficient and self-explanatory (Bowra, 1963, p. 241). Rhythm, repetitive and monotonous, was accompanied by repetitive dance movements. One is reminded of the lullaby, the beeping tone that resulted in inattention, and the rock 'n' roll of monotonous beat and movement. When all cultures are considered, it is not difficult to understand why rhythm crosses most easily from one culture to another.

In our culture, percussion instruments are generally the most stimulative of all musical instruments. They mark more precisely the rhythm. The drum is the best instrument for marching. Notice what happens when the drummer of a dance band "takes off" in a solo. Even the piano, as played in a dance band, is a percussive instrument.

Graham (1958) found that if tempo and rhythmic pattern were kept constant, anxious and fearful patients would be much more likely to join in group rhythms, whereas they would not if the rhythm and tempo were changed often. It would seem that the monotony of music in such situations soothes the individual and reduces anxiety. A similar effect can be observed in normal people at a dance. Large numbers will leave the dance floor if tempos of consecutive sets are radically changed.

Both music and dance in Aztec culture were group, not solo, activities. This is usually true in our own society. One of the most important functions of group music is to bring the individual to full membership in the group, to make him feel accepted. This is the basic purpose of congregational singing, singing in service clubs, and singing in convocations. When a person takes part in group music, he is taking an active part on his own behalf as well as on behalf of the group.

The union of music with ritual is nearly universal. In his description of healing ceremonies conducted by a shaman, Frank (1963, pp. 52–53) spoke of the strong esthetic appeal of ritual, particularly when accompanied by rhythmic music, chanting, or dancing. The one time in America when more group music occurs than at any other time is on a Sunday morning during church services. The function of such music is cohesion and integration of the group. Rhythmic music gives a feeling of "oneness."

Group rhythms, group dances, group singing, and other group musical activities provide communications of a special sort among participants and between participants and onlookers. In short, *music is nonverbal communication*. This is fundamental to understanding the influence of music on behavior. It is a communication of such special quality that for thousands of years people have thought music to be mystical or even supernatural. As far as science can know with its present devices, music is not mystical nor supernatural—it is only mysterious.

Music is shaped by culture but in turn influences that culture of which it is a part. It is human behavior—always rhythmically patterned, sometimes melodically and harmonically. It must be agreed on by the members of its society. "Music is a uniquely human phenomenon which exists only in terms of social interaction . . ." (Merriam, 1964, p. 27). Social interaction and social behavior of the right kind are characteristic deficiencies of the behaviorally disordered and the handicapped. It is precisely with such people that music, because of its true nature, is beneficially influential in persuading toward better patterns of behavior.

Thus far, this chapter has dealt with the background of music therapy, a discipline that is concerned with the behavior of man. Scientifically, music therapy aspires to the methods of the behavioral sciences. The development of man and his esthetic sensitivity were reviewed briefly to show that music is an essential of humanness. Descriptions of music from several cultures showed the social nature of music and the primary importance of rhythm. Certain fundamental considerations of man in relation to music can now be made. These fundamental considerations stem from our knowledge of man and the necessities of his development and health. They are essential to understanding the nature of music in therapy and the processes in music therapy described in the next chapter.

All Mankind Has Need for Esthetic Expression and Experience

Masserman (1955) has said that "*all organisms are actuated by their physiologic needs,* including those leading to esthetic expression" (p. 431). This is true, because the young of humans and lower animals will not develop unless they have adequate sensory stimuli and experience. Most handicapped children are primarily in need of more and different sensory stimulation. After early sensory stimulations, the young human will never be satisfied with only the sounds of nature. For his own needs, he must make other sounds. As his esthetic sensitivity develops, he must elaborate and make more intricate and complex his sensory and motor behavior. Of importance is the fact that as he matures, he will formalize his sound, making it into distinct and recognizable patterns. This is music. The expression and experience of music in all cultures and races is an essential of man's health, because his healthy life is one of interdependence. Those individuals who would not be interdependent were dropped from the stream of life long ago.

Sensitivity to beauty and the making of beauty comprise one of man's most distinguishing characteristics (Dobzhansky, 1962, p. 214). Without beauty, man is less than Homo sapiens; and when this is so, he is sick or handicapped. The use of music for man's health, happiness, and comfort is universal. This universal need is not ephemeral—it is a physiological component of man's well-being. Each of the seven major considerations of music therapy that follow adds substance to the fact that *all mankind has a need for esthetic expression and experience.*

The Cultural Matrix Determines the Mode of Expression

Linton (1955, p. vii) indicated clearly that each cultural group develops its own mode of expression. Just as each culture or ethnic group evolves its own language, so each develops its own music; each individual within the group must learn the music of his culture. Man must learn to be human, and he does so in terms of his own tribe or culture. Consequently, music from one culture often makes little sense and has little meaning for an individual or a group from another culture. Morey (1940) submitted music of Schubert, Davies, Handel, and Wagner to the Loma tribe in order to learn the reactions of native West Africans. They said such music expressed no emotions and aroused none in themselves. Their training was different—they had learned a different music.

In our own culture many persons neither understand nor tolerate current dance music, and millions more neither understand nor tolerate classical music. In times past classical music was sometimes thought best for patients because the therapist, as well as music experts, considered it to be "good" music. However, it was only good if the patients understood it. Many times they did not, and music therapy was considered impotent as treatment when in reality it was not impotent at all—strange music had been used instead of familiar music. If patients are to be reached, the music employed must be that which they understand, at least to some extent.

Music and Religion Are Integrally Related

One of the clearest and most evident uses of music is with religion. The coincidence of music and religion is strikingly widespread. This is true because some of the purposes of religious services and music performances are very similar. The great valence both music and religion possess is to draw people together. Music and religion are often at their peak function when they are group activities. DuBos (1965) says that "When *Homo sapiens* first becomes identifiable on the archeological scene, he is already found in fairly large social groups. . . . Man is a social animal, dependent on other human beings for his physiological needs and his emotional satisfactions" (p. 8).

In nearly all cultures, music and religion go hand in hand as a defense against fear and aloneness (Masserman, 1955, pp. 616–620). However, drawing individuals together is not the only function of music. Its peculiar quality also seems to make it a fit means to reach or influence that which is thought to be supernatural. Nevertheless, "The individual in society at once feels very close to and very far from other human beings, but always there remains the strongest of desires, to be related to one's fellowman. Human beings have devised no more successful means of achieving this relatedness than religion" (Montagu, 1958, p. 141). And group music is frequently a successful means.

Music Is Communication

Music is communication, as has been indicated, but more often than not it is, or functions as, *nonverbal* communication. It is the *wordless* meaning of music that provides its potency and value. There would be no music and no need for it if it were possible to communicate verbally that which is easily communicated musically (Gaston, 1958). Even though the experiencing and observation of the potential of music to communicate profoundly in our own culture is an everyday event, we know far less about its exact communicative qualities in other cultures (Merriam, 1964, p. 10). As late as 1952, European musicians of excellent training said there was no pattern or form in native African drumming (Herskovits, 1962, p. 441). We know now that there is pattern and form in African drumming; it was simply too foreign to Europeans—they could not organize the rhythms, much less understand the communications.

There is so much nonverbal communication in our everyday life that we are often unaware of it or its importance. We are unaware that some of our most valued and functional communications are, and will continue to be, carried on without words, because they cannot be verbalized. How do you communicate verbally a kiss, a smile, a frown, a gesture of farewell, or a condescending stare? How can you say in words the feelings elicited by the national anthem, a marching band, a Strauss waltz, the Brahms

Fourth Symphony, a Bach prelude? The best verbal substitute for non-verbal music is poverty stricken. Music is a most intimate type of non-verbal communication deeply cherished and nurtured by mankind.

Music Is Structured Reality

Even though music is nonverbal communication, only to the unknowing and the uninitiated does music seem to be unstructured. From a Mayan Indian who was severely punished when he broke rhythm (von Hagen, 1961, p. 281) to a school band musician who must, and can, distinguish discrepancies in accuracy of time as small as an eighth of a second, we observe that there is little question of structure in music. Melodic pattern, pitch, tempo, rhythm, and dynamics all demand a preciseness that is astounding when carefully considered. All the senses bring to us aspects of reality. To hear a chord of music is no less real than to smell a rose, to see a sunset, to taste an apple, or to feel the impact of striking a wall. Perhaps, because of the "message" of music, we are prone to forget its structure, a structure so real that it can, in part, be represented by a figured bass. In addition to the enticing aspects of music, its reality and structure make it a valuable therapeutic medium.

Music Is Derived from the Tender Emotions

Earlier in this chapter, it was seen that man's genetic and cultural development brought him into more and more interpersonal relationships until these relationships became second to no other influence in his life. So important are his fellows to man that he can never know himself until he knows his fellowman. He cannot understand his relationships except as they emanate from the group. A person cannot become human without the group (Montagu, 1962, p. 28). The vast majority of all music is concerned with the positive relationships that draw man closer to his fellowmen—love, loyalty, patriotism, and religion, to name a few. Consider popular music, folk songs, religious music, art songs, opera, and other types of music. Nearly all of them have to do with love in one form or another. Musical activity is a source of social cohesion, a coming together. The value of the adaptation of the individual to the group can hardly be overestimated in a society (Dobzhansky, 1962, p. 217). Group music brings a feeling of belonging.

Music involves the individual so totally and in such unique fashion that closeness is felt, and painful aloneness may be alleviated. Music is non-punitive and, in nearly all cases, nonthreatening. The desire for closeness furnishes much of the motivation for the group singing done in service clubs, convocations, and church services in our own culture. It is not the beauty of the singing that matters in most of these cases, although the pleasure of singing may be a motivational factor also. In our culture, as well as in others, *music is nearly always an expression of good will, a reaching out to others*, and is so interpreted. Music, then, is a powerful expression of the interdependence of mankind, and, from the lullaby to the funeral dirge, an expression of the tender emotions. Because of this and the guidance of the therapist, *music persuades with honesty, feeling, and power toward better individual and group behavior*.

The last two considerations are concerned with music as a source of gratification and the necessity of the group for the individual's final fulfillment. Broadly conceived, the essential progress of one's life consists in the development of self so that participation in more significant groups is possible, or more significant participation in the same groups is possible.* Such phenomena are verified by observation of man's behavior. Thus far, much evidence shows man to be a *social* animal. Without enculturation, he remains only animal and devoid of his most distinguishing behavioral feature, humanness. In brief, we are nothing in ourselves. We must be acknowledged by someone or some group.

Life is a process of self-expansion embracing both man and his environment (Angyal, 1965, p. 5). According to his culture, man strives to improve himself, to self-actualize himself. The process of his development leads from infancy to very early childhood, at which time his strivings for acceptance become more noticeable. Constantly, he must check with his parents or with others of the family to see how he is getting along. The family guides, helps, and encourages the child. At times, the parents must restrain him when his actions are unwise. But always, in some manner or other, the child's chief gratification comes from approval and acceptance, necessities for becoming enculturated.

The time will come, *through the interplay of himself and his environment*, when the child is ready for kindergarten. He has learned to talk, to behave more appropriately, to handle his toilet requirements, and to get along reasonably well with others. He is now ready to join a larger, and in some important ways, a more significant group. Throughout his life, he will work to develop his potential toward certain ends so that he may join more significant groups. The groups, for him, will be more significant or his participation will be more significant. Thus, he goes through grade school, junior high school, senior high school, and college.

In grade school, the child may join the boy scouts and a few years later go through the rigors of becoming an eagle scout. He may get a trumpet

* This statement is not meant to support any particular, or exclusive, psychological theory. Nor do certain words, *self-actualization*, for example, have an esoteric meaning.

—not primarily to play the trumpet, but to play in the band. A girl in high school may decide to become a nurse, so she joins the candy stripers. A boy resolves to become a chemical engineer or a professional baseball player. He may want to become a mechanic or a salesman. The girl may choose to become a secretary or a dancer. Whatever the case may be, there will have to be self-development—by himself or herself at times, in a group at other times—but always the eventual success will be in terms of the group. In each instance, it is the circumstance of environment that persuades the individual to change poor or inappropriate behavior for better behavior. And *behavior* used in this sense means anything that an organism does that involves action and response to internal or external stimulation. *This process of inducing appropriate behavioral changes is precisely what the music therapist brings about—and not just musical behaviors, but many other sorts of behaviors. The therapist helps the patient to a healthier adaptation to society.*

There is another facet of "becoming" that is important to healthy development and a happy life. The course of life is somewhat similar to shaping a work of art, because both are creative and expressive. When life is creative, new vistas come into view, and new horizons are explored. Perceptions widen, and life, to its very end, does not become dull. The process of such a life is self-actualization in greater degree and more meaningful participation in more significant groups. Thus, one's life becomes broad and rich. Man does more than just cope with his environment—he lives expressively in his self and in his groups.

Music Is a Source of Gratification

The performance of music generally brings an intimate sense of gratification. Such gratification springs from feelings of accomplishment and mastery. It is a matter of achievement, in most cases, *in noncompetitive situations.* Music has order and predictability, and both are essential for competence. Allport (1961) has written of the child seeking competence in a number of areas and continues, "*When we come to adulthood we need the concept of competence as much as in childhood*" (p. 214).

Becker (1962, p. 79) believes that anxiety is the prime mover of human behavior. However, self-esteem is the best protection against undue anxiety. Whatever terms are used, one remembers the feelings of worth, of competence, and of gratification that have followed mastery in performance. The part one plays may be large or small, easy or difficult; music provides an ecstasy uniquely its own. *Music permits and encourages each person to participate dynamically in his own growth and change.*

The Potency of Music Is Greatest in the Group

The chief aim of therapy is to enable the individual to function at his best in society. The handicapped child needs to learn to behave in such a manner that his full participation in society is assured. Those whose behavior has become disordered are in want of help to establish once again proper relationships and demeanor. The history and nature of man point toward these goals of music therapy. The evidence and argument of this chapter has been toward these ends.

Music, by its very nature, draws people together for the purpose of intimate, yet ordered, function. Group morale and the distinctive valence of music are dominant factors. Music provides a gestalt of sensory, motor, emotional, and social components in which, for the most part, the participants concur. It unifies the group for common action, and it is this setting that elicits or changes many extramusical behaviors. Group music leads toward desired ends with a minimum of verbal commands.

Thus it is that the individual may be subtly but compellingly moved toward improvement and change in self that will make it possible for him to rejoin society on a more significant level. Music and the therapist are important parts of the process and the environment that persuade the individual to participate actively in beneficial changes of behavior.

In all the uses of music, no laws of nature are abrogated. Music and its influences can be studied scientifically, using the methods of the behavioral sciences. To study music therapy by such means requires adequate multidisciplinary knowledge, without which our vision is restricted to the one old construct of greatest familiarity. "There is much yet to be discovered in us, in our behavior towards one another, and in our group activities" (Ostwald, 1963, p. 158). The two best hopes for personal growth and happiness are the strengths of our positive interpersonal relationships and our love for, and increase of, knowledge.

References

ALLPORT, G. W. *Pattern and growth in personality*. New York: Holt, 1961.
ANGYAL, A. *Neurosis and treatment*. New York: Wiley, 1965.
BAKAN, D. The mystery-mastery complex in contemporary psychology. *Amer. Psychologist*, 1965, 20, 186–191.
BECKER, E. *The birth and death of meaning*. New York: Free Press, 1962.
BEXTON, W. H., HERON, W., and SCOTT, T. H. Effects of decreased variation in the sensory environment. *Canad. J. Psychol.*, 1954, 8, 70–76.
BOWRA, C. M. *Primitive song*. New York: Mentor Books, 1963.
BRUNER, J. S. *On knowing*. Cambridge, Mass.: Harvard, 1963.

CATER, M. L. The effect of music on painting. Unpublished master's thesis, Univer. of Kansas, 1949.

DEMBER, W. N. *The psychology of perception.* New York: Holt, 1960.

DEUTSCH, F. *Body, mind and the sensory gateways.* New York: Basic Books, 1962.

DOBZHANSKY, T. *Mankind evolving.* New Haven, Conn.: Yale, 1962.

DuBos, R. *Man adapting.* New Haven, Conn.: Yale, 1965.

ETKIN, W. Social behavior and the evolution of man's mental faculties. In M. F. A. Montagu (Ed.), *Culture and the evolution of man.* Fair Lawn, N.J.: Oxford University Press, 1962. Pp. 131–147.

FRANK, J. *Persuasion and healing.* New York: Schocken Books, 1963.

GASTON, E. T. Dynamic music factors in mood change. *Mus. Educ. J.,* 1951, 37, 42–44.

GASTON, E. T. Music in therapy. In J. H. Masserman and J. L. Moreno (Eds.), *Progress in psychotherapy.* New York: Grune & Stratton, 1958. Pp. 142–148.

GASTON, E. T. The aesthetic experience and biological man. *J. Mus. Ther.,* 1964, 1–7.

GRAHAM, R. Suggested procedures for conducting rhythm activities on wards of chronic and regressed mental patients. Unpublished master's thesis, Univer. of Kansas, 1958.

HARLOW, H. F. The nature of love. *Amer. Psychologist,* 1958, 13, 673–685.

HEBB, D. O. *A textbook of psychology.* Philadelphia: Saunders, 1958.

HEBB, D. O. The mind and its integration. In S. M. Farber and R. H. L. Wilson (Eds.), *Control of the mind.* New York: McGraw-Hill, 1961. Pp. 42–53.

HERSKOVITS, M. J. *The human factor in changing Africa.* New York: Knopf, 1962.

HULSE, F. S. *The human species.* New York: Random House, 1963.

LEAKEY, L. S. B. *The progress and evolution of man in Africa.* Fair Lawn, N.J.: Oxford University Press, 1961.

LIBERMAN, R. Retinal cholinesterase and glycolysis in rats raised in darkness. *Science,* 1962, 135, 372–373.

LINTON, R. *The tree of culture.* New York: Knopf, 1955.

MASSERMAN, J. H. *The practice of dynamic psychiatry.* Philadelphia: Saunders, 1955.

MASSERMAN, J. H. *Principles of dynamic psychiatry.* Philadelphia: Saunders, 1961.

MEDAWAR, P. B. *The future of man.* New York: New American Library, 1959.

MERRIAM, A. P. *The anthropology of music.* Evanston, Ill.: Northwestern University Press, 1964.

MONTAGU, A. *Man: his first million years.* New York: Mentor Books, 1958.

MONTAGU, A. *The humanization of man.* Cleveland: World Publishing, 1962.

MOREY, R. Upset in emotions. *J. Soc. Psychol.,* 1940, 12, 333–356.

MORRISON, R. S. Toward a redefinition of culture. Paper read at Amer. Acad. Arts and Sci., May, 1963.

MURPHY, G. *Human potentialities.* New York: Basic Books, 1958.

MURPHY, G. The psychology of 1975: an extrapolation. *Amer. Psychologist,* 1963, 18, 689–695.

NEAL ELGAR MILLER. *Amer. Psychologist,* 1965, 20, 183.

OSTWALD, P. *Soundmaking.* Springfield, Ill.: Charles C Thomas, 1963.

PRIBRAM, K. The new neurology: memory, novelty, thought, and choice. In

G. H. Glaser (Ed.), *EEG and behavior*. New York: Basic Books, 1963. Pp. 149–173.

PRIBRAM, K. Neurological notes on the art of educating. In E. R. Hilgard (Ed.), *Theories of learning and instruction*. Chicago: National Soc. for the Stud. of Educ., 1964. Pp. 78–110.

SCOTT, G. P. *Animal behavior*. Garden City, N.Y.: Doubleday, 1963.

SEARS, W. W. The effect of music on muscle tonus. In E. T. Gaston (Ed.), *Music therapy 1957*. Lawrence, Kan.: Allen Press, 1958. Pp. 199–205.

SHRIFT, D. C. The galvanic skin response to two contrasting types of music. In E. T. Gaston (Ed.), *Music therapy 1956*. Lawrence, Kan.: Allen Press, 1957. Pp. 235–239.

SIMPSON, G. G. Biology and the nature of science. *Science*, 1963, *139*, 87.

SINNOTT, E. W. *The biology of the spirit*. New York: Viking, 1955.

SLAUGHTER, F. The effect of stimulative and sedative types of music on normal and abnormal subjects as indicated by pupillary reflexes. Unpublished master's thesis, Univer. of Kansas, 1954.

VON BUDDENBROCK, W. *The senses*. Ann Arbor, Mich.: The University of Michigan Press, 1958.

VON HAGEN, V. W. *The ancient sun kingdoms of the Americas*. Cleveland: World Publishing, 1961.

WASHBURN, S. L. Tools and human evolution. In M. F. A. Montagu (Ed.), *Culture and the evolution of man*. Fair Lawn, N.J.: Oxford University Press, 1962. Pp. 13–19.

WEISKRANTZ, L. Sensory deprivation and the cat's optic nervous system. *Nature*, 1958, *181*, 1047–1050.

WILSON, VIRGINIA M. Variations in gastric motility due to musical stimuli. In E. T. Gaston (Ed.), *Music therapy 1956*. Lawrence, Kan.: Allen Press, 1957. Pp. 235–239.

ZACK, M. The effect of music on drawing. Unpublished manuscript, Univer. of Kansas, 1951.

ZUBECK, G. P., and WILGOSH, L. Prolonged immobilization of the body: changes in performance and in the electroencephalogram. *Science*, 1963, *140*, 3564.

2

PROCESSES IN MUSIC THERAPY

WILLIAM W. SEARS

Music therapy is closely related to the behavioral sciences because it often concerns musically elicited behavior in therapeutic situations. Because music therapy is a very young discipline, much of its data and knowledge have been obtained through empirical observation, and sometimes the data are not as factual and well organized as they should be. Nevertheless, modern music therapy seeks to establish itself on acceptable scientific observation.

To describe music therapy as being closely related to behavioral science should not be thought presumptuous. Such a relationship implies an orientation and method of approach to verified knowledge; it does not declare that all, or even most, is known. (The scientific approach does not negate the presently mysterious beauty of music.) When this beauty is gone, these is no reason for music. It seems the nature of man to seek organization, classification, and description until a system emerges. This is the case in all sciences, and music therapy is no exception. To present such a system, even if incomplete, is the purpose of this writing. It will classify and describe processes in music therapy. The system can be characterized as behavioral, logical, and psychological.

Specific discussion of the music therapist has been omitted, although his presence is implied. This omission does not mean that his role is unimportant. Because a therapist is a common factor in most therapeutic situations, his adequacy as a therapist in the broad sense is, of course, related to successful therapy. The intent here, however, is to help him be more proficient as a *music* therapist by giving him a better theoretical understanding of the function of music in therapy. Furthermore, this discussion of processes in music therapy does not intend to tell the music therapist what to do. "What to do" is left to the therapist and should be based on his understanding of the theory and practice necessary to achieve the goals of treatment.

No attempt is made here to describe how music or music therapists can be used in combination with other therapeutic approaches. This does not imply that music therapy is considered a cure-all or that it cannot be used with other media. It signifies only that consideration of combined therapeutic approaches is beyond the scope of this discussion.

Of most importance in any therapeutic situation is the person receiving therapy. Only through the individual's behavior, and changes therein, can the success of a therapeutic endeavor be seen. Thus, behavioral descriptions, insofar as possible, receive major consideration. The terms are defined and used in a logical and consistent manner. This should permit better communication among the individuals concerned. Finally, the classifications and descriptions are consistent with pertinent and accepted psychological principles and theories. No attempt is made, however, to express the classifications and descriptions in the terminology of any particular psychiatric or psychotherapeutic school of thought. Rather, a definite attempt is made to express them free of such connections, to express them as specifics, properly a part of music therapy. This is done not to create the impression of a new school of thought nor to claim any special status for music therapy, but to permit the fitting of what music therapy has to offer into various orientations.

Classification, as used here, signifies a general idea, a broad concept or category, concerning the use of music in therapy. In a sense, the several classifications are broad answers to the question: What does music therapy offer the individual? A *construct* attempts to propose formally, to define and to limit, an explicit relationship between music and the behavior of an individual. The *process* then attempts to describe the manner in which the construct affects the behavior of the individual.

The various classifications and constructs with their processes are not mutually exclusive. In any given therapeutic situation, several, or all, may be operating; however, the various exemplifications were deemed both significant and necessary to permit their delineation and to identify bases for specific therapeutic action.

In most cases, only the word "music" has been used in reference to musical situations, although it may have any of four designations: (1) the music itself; (2) listening to music; (3) having music in the environment; and (4) the making of music. The processes should permit the reader to determine which of the four is meant. Furthermore, the use of the single term, music, may lead some readers to think more deeply about the application of a given construct to situations other than the obvious, thus expanding the function of the construct. The three classifications that underlie the constructs and processes of music therapy are (1) experience within structure, (2) experience in self-organization, and (3) experience in relating to others.*

* At first, five classifications were formulated: (1) gratification, (2) structured experience, (3) environment conducive to recovery, (4) relationships, and (5) diagnosis

The words used to phrase the classifications were chosen purposely and carefully. Each classification is defined later; however, at this point, the word *experience* should be made clear. For most persons, this word signifies events through which one has lived. Experience, however, may also designate the actual living through, or undergoing, of events in the present. Furthermore, it can be used either as a noun or a transitive verb—the gerund and the present participle being "experiencing." In a basic sense, *music therapy offers the individual the experiencing of events in certain ways; the processes attempt to define those ways of experiencing.*

Although past experiences of the individual may serve as a basis (often a very important one) for organizing the therapeutic situation, that situation always begins in the present and goes into the future. No therapist can change the past experiences of the individual, but he can organize a *present* situation so that the *effect of the past* is altered for a more adequate *future.* It is in this sense—that of the present going into the future —that the word experience has been selected for use.

Even though all the classifications might be considered equally well as experience within structure, the term *structure* has been reserved for the first classification in order to emphasize the uniqueness of music—the structure demanding experiencing is inherent in the music. The order of terms in the adopted classifications is important and indicative. A natural order is evident in the progression—an individual must be aware of or have some structure before an experience can become his or become organized. Also, the individual must have organization (possibly in his own version, when viewed by another individual) before he will use the experience externally or overtly. Assuming this order, are there similar orders by which to express the constructs under each classification? If so, on what bases? Three such bases seemed appropriate.

One possible order was founded on the continuum from how much of an individual's behavior is required *by the music itself* to how much is required *by the situation* in which music is used. Phrased in another way, how much control of behavior is demanded by the music and how much

---

and evaluation. After further analysis of the classifications, only three were considered necessary. In all phases of the use of music in therapy, "diagnosis and evaluation" should be constant activities. The principles originally placed under that classification would also logically fall under "structured experience." Somewhat similarly, "environment conducive to recovery" implies a definite structure, and "relationships," although not strictly equivalent to, might be considered as, socializing experience. Temporarily, the three classifications became structured experience, gratifying experience, and socializing experience. Gratifying and socializing, however, are commonly used terms and, in part, are associated with certain psychiatric and psychotherapeutic schools of thought. To avoid misinterpretations that might arise from the use of the more common terms and because their meanings were not strictly what was desired, the terms *self-organizing experience* and *other-relating experience,* to be defined later, were selected.

by the therapist's manipulation of the environment? (This was thought to apply to the major classifications, also.) A second basis was the consideration of the directness with which the behavior might be observed —again a kind of continuum, directly observable behavior to inferred behavior, for example, "He played his note on time" to "He looks like the music made him sad." One further basis seemed logical: Could the behavior be graded on a continuum from simple (almost reflex or conditioned response) to complex (involving integration of several or many simple responses), for example, from just beating a drum to beating it *appropriately* so that others might play or dance with the beat?

The classifications and constructs are presented in outline form, both for convenience and to show the influence on their development of the three orders or bases described.

A. Experience within structure
    1. Music demands time-ordered behavior.
        a. Music demands reality-ordered behavior.
        b. Music demands immediately and continuously objectified behavior.
    2. Music permits ability-ordered behavior.
        a. Music permits ordering of behavior according to physical response levels.
        b. Music permits ordering of behavior according to psychological response levels.
    3. Music evokes affectively ordered behavior.
    4. Music provokes sensory-elaborated behavior.
        a. Music demands increased sensory usage and discrimination.
        b. Music may elicit extramusical ideas and associations.

B. Experience in self-organization
    1. Music provides for self-expression.
    2. Music provides compensatory endeavors for the handicapped individual.
    3. Music provides opportunities for socially acceptable reward and nonreward.
    4. Music provides for the enhancement of pride in self.
        a. Music provides for successful experiences.
        b. Music provides for feeling needed by others.
        c. Music provides for enhancement of esteem by others.

C. Experience in relating to others
    1. Music provides means by which self-expression is socially acceptable.
    2. Music provides opportunity for individual choice of response in groups.

3. Music provides opportunities for acceptance of responsibility to self and others.
   a. Music provides for developing self-directed behavior.
   b. Music provides for developing other-directed behavior.
4. Music enhances verbal and nonverbal social interaction and communication.
5. Music provides for experiencing cooperation and competition in socially acceptable forms.
6. Music provides entertainment and recreation necessary to the general therapeutic environment.
7. Music provides for learning realistic social skills and personal behavior patterns acceptable in institutional and community peer groups.

Experience Within Structure

Experience within structure refers to those behaviors of an individual that are required by and are inherent in musical experience. Even though a therapist must prepare the experience for the individual, the mere commitment to the experience places the individual in a situation where his (future) behavior is determined primarily by musical factors and not by other factors or persons in his environment. The commitment to the structured experience may be only temporary, for the duration of the music or some part of it. This, however, does not negate the possible continued influence of the music on the individual; it refers mainly to the immediately observable behavior of the individual. Furthermore, music is not considered impersonal. (The meaning, or importance, of music to the individual belongs in the next classification, experience in self-organization.) The focus of concern, here, is on the musically structured experience and on the behavior required by that structure. The motivation for this experience tends to be an intrinsic quality of the music, which carries its own persuasion for behavior.

At this level, the individual is involved in coming to terms and getting along with a part of his environment, a musical part in this case. He may be led to understand and respect certain laws of the environment, the gaining of such understanding and respect possibly made easier because the demands come from the music. His awareness of structures as useful and necessary may take on an elaboration through the meaningful and objective connecting of symbols and referents. Along with this elaboration, the individual is required to expand his self, to discover some of his own potentialities, and to govern himself—facets of development leading to the next level, experience in self-organization.

Major goals in therapy are to lengthen the temporal commitment (objectively measurable), to vary the commitment (objectively describable), and to stimulate an awareness (inferred from behavior and directly related to the next level) of the benefits derived thereby.

Music Demands Time-ordered Behavior

The unique structure of music—it exists only through time—requires the individual to commit himself to the experience moment by moment. Except for relatively minute deviations, music (whether an entire piece or merely a measure or phrase in repeated practice) cannot be interrupted without losing its intent. Participation in music is not ordinarily achieved by a note a day. Once begun, music must be continued without interruption in order that a completed idea or expression may result; regardless of its length or complexity or the type and degree of skill it requires, the music must be carried through in its time order.

The necessity for moment-to-moment commitment by the individual rests in the music itself and does not derive from any other part of his environment. The extent and rapidity of the commitment can be adjusted to the individual by an appropriate selection of the level of skill required, the length and complexity of the music, and the specific responses required, including the number of responses per unit of time.

Time order, as conceived here, is a broader concept than rhythm. On the most elementary level, it involves the sequence of sounds and no sounds. On other levels, it concerns not only the making of sounds at the correct times (rhythm), but also the correct sounds (pitches), the correct emphases or stresses of those sounds (dynamics), the accuracy in making several sounds together (harmony and ensemble), and the organization of other kinds of sounds (timbre). Regardless of the organizations in music, the underlying factor is time order.

This construct is considered fundamental to all the other constructs. It might be called the working principle. Building on the time-ordered structure inherent in music, the skillful therapist can involve the individual in any of the relationships defined by the other constructs. An individual develops through time; music develops through time—uniquely, the tempos of life and music are quite comparable, possibly even congruent.

This construct also emphasizes the uniqueness of music when contrasted with other approaches used in therapy. Even though all experiences have beginnings and go into the future, the time order of music requires the individual to structure his behavior in, relatively, the most minute and continuous manner. No other form of human behavior both demands and depends so completely on strict adherence to time-ordered structure.

MUSIC DEMANDS REALITY-ORDERED BEHAVIOR

Once the individual is committed to music, his behavior becomes reality ordered. Music involves reality orientations in many forms and on such levels as the situation requires—responses to, for example, aural stimuli, musical and verbal; instruments; musical notation; conductor's or therapist's directions; and the individual's own body and its parts. The individual's responses can be judged for their appropriateness to the "real" stimuli, stimuli built on the time-ordered necessities of a given musical situation and established in the individual's environment by the therapist.

A question concerning the place of free improvisation and the possibility that it would not necessarily be reality ordered might be raised here. (Improvisation is included in the next classification, experience in self-organization.) Concern is for the individual's evidenced behavior and not for what the music means to him. Improvising implies doing something that is meaningful to the person doing the improvising. The pursuit of meaning in music is personal and internal. The ability to improvise, at least meaningfully for others, demands a background of structured experiences that permits the improvisation to take place. Thus, at this level and within the meaning and intent here, the question is premature.

MUSIC DEMANDS IMMEDIATELY AND CONTINUOUSLY OBJECTIFIED BEHAVIOR

Once committed to the music, the individual's behavior is no longer subjective, but becomes immediately observable or "objectified." The musical appropriateness of the behavior must always be judged with reference to the ability of the individual. Furthermore, his behavior is continuously objectified and observable, requiring attention to the music through the duration of the musical experience, even if attention fluctuates.

Because the time order of music is continuous, the individual's responses must be continuous; and because the individual's responses are continuous, the appropriateness of his responses are immediately observable, moment by moment.

Music Permits Ability-ordered Behavior

The behavioral requirements in music are uniquely adaptable to the individual's operational levels and capacities. Musical behaviors, the specific functionings of the individual in specific musical situations, range from the simple to the complex, from the awareness or performance of a simple rhythmic beat to the awareness or performance of a highly complex musical structure. Behaviors ranging from simple to complex may coexist among several individuals, as in group performance where the behavioral require- ments of one musical part are of a more simple nature, such as beating the bass drum, than those of another part, such as playing the melody on a trumpet. Also, especially desired musical experiences, such as playing a certain piece, can be modified or adapted (rearranged) to fit the capabil- ities of each individual.

Music Permits Ordering of Behavior According to Physical Response Levels

Required musical behavior can be adapted to the physical capacities and operational levels of the individual. The physically handicapped can be helped to make music by the use of special devices, such as especially de- signed mouthpieces or prostheses. Modifications of the traditional positions for playing certain instruments, such as placing a bass drum on its side, or preparing a special stand for an instrument can be made to permit the use of the individual's movement capabilities. The variety of physical move- ments used in playing musical instruments or in singing offers a wide range for structuring needed muscular movements. The attainment of gratifying musical ends usually makes such exercises more acceptable to the in- dividual.

Music Permits Ordering of Behavior According to Psychological Response Levels

Required musical behavior can be adapted to psychological capacities and operational levels. The psychological levels may have several bases: (1) mood—such as sad to happy, depressed to manic; (2) motivation— low to high desire to achieve; (3) intellect—mentally retarded to gifted; or (4) levels of musical knowledge. Partly through the motivation intrin- sic to music and partly through the appropriate structure provided by the therapist, the individual can either be moved from a less desirable to a more desirable psychological level or have the requirements of the activity suited and paced appropriately to his capabilities, as the case may be.

Music Evokes Affectively Ordered Behavior

The general behavior of groups can be controlled, or at least influenced, by appropriately chosen music. Slow tempos, smooth (legato) lines, simple harmonies, and little dynamic change are characteristic of music that tends to reduce or sedate physical activity and, possibly, to enhance the contemplative activity of individuals; fast tempos, detached (staccato) lines, complex and dissonant harmonies, and abrupt dynamic changes tend to increase or stimulate physical activity and, possibly, to reduce mental activity. Given a knowledgeable use of music, the desired result is usually achieved with groups; prediction is less sure when dealing with an individual because of the possible unique associations he may have with the particular music or with music in general. These associations in themselves can be significant.

Music Provokes Sensory-elaborated Behavior

Sensory stimulation and resulting awareness have been shown to be human needs. Participation in music offers unique sensory experiences ranging from just perceptible responses on the neuromuscular level to the highest level of human behavior—intellectual mediation and contemplation—all of which are essential to esthetic experience. Furthermore, both initiation and recall of experiences involving sight, sound, odors, tactile sensations, and so on, can be evoked by music. Experiences such as the smell of rosin on the bow; the tactile sensation of vibration; and the auditory and visual awareness of concerted efforts, such as identical phrasing, bowing by stringed-instrument players, and breathing by wind-instrument players, offer an elaborate world of sensations.

Music Demands Increased Sensory Usage and Discrimination

Involvement in music requires the individual both to become more aware of and to refine his use of sensory data in a great variety of forms. Not only must he increase his auditory discrimination of pitch, volume, rhythmic, and quality differences, he also must bring into use and refine all other sensory modalities: sight, for reading symbols, responding to visual instructions, and seeing where different sounds come from; touch, for contacting the instrument in what are sometimes very delicate ways and for receiving temperature sensations from different instruments and their parts; proprioception, for learning to breathe correctly, producing correct vocal sounds, and controlling body parts; and smell and taste, which, although less describable, are nonetheless involved. Music significantly demands the integrated use of several or all of these sensory modalities at any given time within the musical experience.

Music May Elicit Extramusical Ideas and Associations

Music may often bring about certain pictures or ideas. When the individual's ideas fall outside the "normal," his differences may reveal significant insights into his particular structuring of his world. Such insights have been used as the basis of several projective tests and also in psychotherapy. In certain cases, the association-provoking quality of music can be used to reinstate or remind the individual of healthy forms of behavior, including ideas.

Experience in Self-Organization

Experience in self-organization concerns inner responses that may only be inferred from behavior, and has to do with a person's attitudes, interests, values, and appreciations, with his meaning to himself. It includes most, if not all, of what has been commonly termed gratification and also the strictly personal factors in the esthetic experience. (Of concern here is not only gratification, but also the fact that nearly all people like some kind of music very much.)

At this level, the individual may come to discover what he really is— to find his own ways of living, of valuing and appreciating himself as an individual with potentialities. He may come to discover that these potentialities have sufficient meaning to himself to be used for experience in relating to others.

A common goal in therapy is to structure experiences (objectively describable) so that the individual receives the satisfactions (inferred) necessary for him to seek more such experiences (objectively measurable), and to see that such experiences lend themselves to the maintenance of better adjustment (objectively describable) with his environment.

Music Provides for Self-Expression

Whenever choice by an individual is involved, his behavior is a reflection of his self-expressive needs. These needs, although not in themselves directly observable, may give rise to consistent patterns of behavior. Such patterns of behavior can become the bases for structuring activities in which the person will be involved, in making possible or impossible (or at least limiting) the continuance of certain behaviors. The adaptability of music provides many avenues for self-expression in performance and listening; they range from random to complex and highly organized. Such a wide range also offers many socially acceptable ways of expressing negative feelings, energetic behavior, and closeness, any of which may reduce the need for expression in more overt, unacceptable forms. The movement from random expression to organized, meaningful expression is the goal.

Music Provides Compensatory Endeavors for the Handicapped Individual

By being helped to accomplish in music some of the same things that his "normal" counterpart does, the handicapped individual may be led to a healthy acceptance of his limitations. He may come to place his handicap in perspective, as a limitation only of his means, as only one aspect of himself, rather than his whole person.

Music Provides Opportunities for Socially Acceptable Reward and Nonreward

When appropriately structured, musical activities may carry an inherent pleasure found in the performance itself. The individual may, realistically, receive commendation where indicated for musical and/or treatment purposes; or commendation may be withheld. The adaptability of music provides many opportunities for rewards, ranging from immediate to long term. In music, it is generally the performance that receives negative criticism, not the individual. In this way, the criticism *need not* become rejection.

Music Provides for the Enhancement of Pride in Self

Positive learning experiences usually enhance an individual's feelings of worth. A foreseeable product or result often serves as its own stimulus to learning. The adaptability of music to learning, on many levels of required ability, makes it uniquely versatile for structuring situations leading to feelings of pride. The individual is confronted with objective evidence concerning the relationship of effort spent and goal achieved.

Music Provides for Successful Experiences

The individual may choose, or have arranged for him, a level of musical participation almost certain to ensure success. Careful guidance of the activity and the wide range of experiences offered by music make this possible. The permissive atmosphere of most musical group activities provides a continuum of opportunities for successful experience, ranging from mere presence within a group to a position of prominence.

Music Provides for Feeling Needed by Others

Successful performance normally leads to enhancement of self-esteem. The feeling of being needed by others, of giving the self to an important pursuit, and of achievement, may be gained through especially structured musical situations. Situations specifically structured toward this end (and under the next construct) provide necessary support for the individual to commit himself voluntarily to experiences in relating to others.

MUSIC PROVIDES FOR ENHANCEMENT OF ESTEEM BY OTHERS

A person who shares successful musical experiences with others or contributes to the success of others through a supporting role normally receives the esteem of others. Due commendation can be given and positions of leadership can be arranged in structured musical situations.

Experience in Relating to Others

Experience in relating to others deals with the behavior of the individual in relation to other individuals, singly or in groups. Music provides experiences for persons as group members. The music is the reason for being together; the individual need not participate in the group except as a musician, and he is usually accepted when doing so. Ensemble music, however, requires the individual to subordinate his own interests to those of the group if music is to result; this demand, although possibly enforced by another person, objectively derives from the music and not from the other person. Such experiences, considerately arranged, may support the individual in his feeling of being needed by others—to gain identity in a whole (group) larger than himself.

Also at this level, and possibly of greatest importance, the individual is enabled to assess his identity. *Only by self-comparison with the group can the individual become aware of his identity and his accomplishments.* This comparison, if appropriately provided, may stimulate the individual to further accomplishment; if inappropriately provided, the experience may lead to a rejection of, or at least reduced desire for, similar experiences. Thus, caution must be exercised by the therapist.

The goal is to increase the size of the group in which the individual can successfully interact (objectively measurable and describable); to increase the range and flexibility of his behavior in those interactions (objectively describable); and to provide experiences that will help him relate to noninstitutional life (objectively describable).

Music Provides Means by Which Self-Expression Is Socially Acceptable

Music provides a wide range of emotional expression. Positive, as well as negative, feelings for others can be expressed through music, and social acceptance is usually forthcoming or at least permitted. Ways to achieve and excel through superior performance are abundantly provided and accepted in music. Expressions not otherwise permitted may be acceptable in music. Dance activities permit a closeness to other individuals not normally possible in a different situation. Both transitory and continuing feelings are expressible in music.

Music Provides Opportunity for Individual Choice of Response in Groups

Optimum performance of each individual in a musical group is desirable. However, the individual may wish to choose his own level of response. Because it is desirable for the patient to *wish* to make choices, opportunity to do so must be provided. Freedom to choose is sometimes more important than the choice.

Music Provides Opportunities for Acceptance of Responsibility to Self and Others

Music provides many opportunities for the individual to accept responsibility. His arrival on time for lessons or other activities or his participation as an important member of a group requires him to be responsible to others. Music may be his reason, at first, for accepting responsibility, but extension to acceptance in general is the goal.

Music Provides for Developing Self-directed Behavior

The wide range of experiences and levels of achievement offered in music permits the individual a variety of choice in personal goals. Once a choice has been made, the individual must initiate and maintain the practice required to reach the goal. Although the situation may be structured to assist the individual in attaining his goal—for example, helping him to establish realistic expectations or arranging steps in his program that assure success—he must increasingly assume more responsibility for directing himself. Musical progress can, in the end, be made only through his own efforts; it cannot be achieved for him.

Music Provides for Developing Other-directed Behavior

In group settings, the individual must learn to subordinate his performance to that of the group. An awareness of the performance of others, and of his own in relation to theirs, is constantly required in the process of achieving appropriate musical expression and interpretation. Control of the self in relation to behavioral patterns of the group is necessary.

Music Enhances Verbal and Nonverbal Social Interaction and Communication

Most social occasions are accompanied by music, which generally increases sociability. With music in the background, many individuals find it easier to talk with others. In psychotherapy, patients often talk more freely in the presence of music. They may express in music or through musical preferences feelings not otherwise expressible. *Music may speak where words fail.*

Music Provides for Experiencing Cooperation and Competition in Socially Acceptable Forms

The very nature of music makes possible the experiencing of socially acceptable forms of cooperation and competition, singly or in combination. Musical groups not only require the individual to cooperate, but also offer him the opportunity to compete musically. Also, he may compete with himself, striving always to improve his performance; no degree of excellence of which he is capable and to which he might aspire is denied him.

Music Provides Entertainment and Recreation Necessary to the General Therapeutic Environment

Diversional and recreational activities are a necessary part of institutional routine. Performances by community musical organizations, individuals, and stage groups can assist the patient in maintaining a general morale that may make specific therapeutic goals easier to attain. Such activities also permit him many experiences common to the world outside the institution. Although these activities are desirable, they should not be confused with formal music therapy procedures specifically designed with therapeutic intent.

Music Provides for Learning Realistic Social Skills and Personal Behavior Patterns Acceptable in Institutional and Community Peer Groups

Music skills usually enable individuals to interact more successfully in community groups. Dancing and other musical skills may help the patient participate with more poise and less need for defense. Musical groups in the community are becoming more available and usually require minimal financial and social prerequisites.

Some individuals possess asocial characteristics of which they are unaware. Others know very little about personal hygiene and acceptable modes of dress. Musical situations can be especially structured and in many cases provide the necessary motivation to bring about an improvement in these areas of behavior; such matters often greatly influence the individual's success or failure in his environment.

Music therapy uses the methods of a behavioral science and, as such, requires a theoretical formulation of its processes. To construct such a formulation has been the purpose of this chapter. The formulation is not proposed as a set of "true" laws and relationships. It is, rather, an attempt to integrate into one system the best knowledge and thought *presently available* concerning the function of music in therapy. Its orientation or integrating focus is the behavior of the individual when involved in a musical experience.

A theoretical formulation such as this may suffer one of several fates: It may pass into history having received little consideration. It may be examined and found wanting, but because of the study it required, result in a different, more adequate formulation of theory. Finally, it may prove of enough interest and worth to be put to the test in practice and research—to be modified, improved, and expanded. Hopefully, the latter fate will come to pass. In any case, processes in music therapy take place *by uniquely involving* the individual in experience within structure, experience in self-organization, and experience in relating to others.

Part II

MUSIC THERAPY
FOR MENTALLY RETARDED
CHILDREN AND ADULTS

Betty Isern Howery

Slowly but quite perceptibly, the young child learns the rhythm of life. With each sunrise and sunset he adapts himself more intimately to the enduring and to the changing aspects of his environment. As the seasons pass he begins his lifelong search for personal identity . . . " (From the introduction of Voices in Time by J. T. Fraser) The key words in this perceptive statement are "learn" and "adapt." They are key words in most clinical situations, but particularly with the mentally retarded. The use of music with the mentally retarded has grown more than any other therapeutic use of music. Perhaps this is because it has a greater variety of uses. This section will bring added meaning to the principles and processes of music therapy discussed in Part I.

3

OVERVIEW

BETTY ISERN HOWERY

Introduction

Those who have used music in working with mentally retarded children soon become aware of its value for these children and of the fact that the retardate often responds more readily to music activities than to most other activities. The literature on the subject reveals that prior to 1940 music was generally used with these children for its educational value. Teachers were concerned mostly with what the child was capable of learning through music. With the introduction of music therapy, there has been an increasing concern with adaptive behavior during the music activity. Greater effort has been made to understand how and why such children respond to music as they do.

Since 1940, the use of music therapy for those who are mentally retarded has grown more rapidly than any other use of music in therapy. One reason for this remarkable growth is increased emphasis on the care and treatment of the mentally retarded by state and national agencies. A second and equally important reason is the deepening realization of the unique applicability of music as a therapeutic and educational instrument.

As one reads the available literature, one finds that the use of music for the mentally retarded appears generally in one of three different settings: (1) special education, (2) therapy, or (3) a deliberate combination of education and therapy. However, the emphasis of an institution or any setting may be, quite clearly, education or therapy. In this present discussion, the concern is primarily with music therapy, although it is fully realized that there is education in therapy and that educational goals are a constant motif in the pattern of treatment. The orientation is toward that situation wherein the retardate undergoes testing, evaluation by the medical staff, and observation by other staff members; on the basis of these combined evaluations, a treatment plan is determined. The goal of the treatment plan is to bring about changes of behavior in the retardate so that he will be better able to adapt to and function in his environment. The music therapist uses music to assist in achieving a therapeutic relationship with the retardate, and the therapeutic potentials of music are used to realize predetermined treatment goals. The music therapist is always, directly or indirectly, a dynamic and important part of the therapeutic situation.

In not all places is the ideal function of the music therapist achieved. It is not always possible to have the necessary ingredients and concepts for an ideal therapeutic situation. However, a therapist working in a situation that is less than ideal can use music therapeutically. This can be accomplished if he is aware of the therapeutic potentials of music and of himself, understands the behavioral problems of the retardate, and knows how to use music and music activities to accomplish the desired change in behavior so that the retardate can function more adequately in his environment.

Definitions

Many terms and definitions have been used in descriptions of mental retardation. Professional people in the various disciplines have attempted to define and classify it, but these definitions usually reflect variations in orientation and training. Thus, one is confronted with confusing terminology and definitions of such terms as "feebleminded," "ament," "mental defective," "moron," "idiot," and "imbecile." The definition of *mental retardation* used in this discussion is as follows: "Mental retardation refers to subaverage general intellectual functioning which originates during the developmental period and is associated with impairment in adaptive behavior" (Heber, 1961, p. 3). This definition is generally accepted by most persons in the field (Dybwad, 1961). It is useful and pragmatic because it includes reduced intellectual function *and* impaired social adaptation. Other definitions, for the most part, are concerned with either intellectual function or social function as their sole criterion. Heber (1962), in justifying the use of the two-dimensional definition, says,

All abnormalities of human behavior represent impairments in social competency and, consequently, this as the sole defining characteristic does not serve to distinguish mental retardation from other disorders of behavior. Subaverage psychometric intelligence is inadequate as the sole criterion of mental retardation since our tests of intelligence are only predictors of certain aspects of behavior and are, as predictors, subject to a degree of error. Regardless of what test score was used as a criterion we would find individuals below the cut-off score whose social adaptation was adequate and individuals above the cut-off score whose adaptation was inadequate (p. 71).

This concept of mental retardation provides two rich and comple-mentary dimensions—measured intelligence and adaptive behavior. These two dimensions should not be considered independent of each other; they are correlated positively. However, the dual nature of the classification allows for the frequent discrepancies found in the level of performance in one or the other of the two dimensions (Heber, 1962, p. 74). Table 1 provides the names and levels of measured intelligence.

TABLE 1

Levels of Measured Intelligence

	Level	IQ
Borderline	1	83–68
Mild	2	67–52
Moderate	3	51–36
Severe	4	35–20
Profound	5	<20

Adaptive behavior is best explained as "a composite of many aspects of behavior and a function of a wide range of specific abilities and dis-abilities. Intellectual, affective, motivational, social, sensory, and motor factors all contribute to, and are a part of, total adaptation to the envi-ronment" (Heber, 1962, p. 76). The names and levels of adaptive behavior are shown in Table 2 (Heber, 1962, p. 75). Levels of adaptive behavior are derived from a composite of several sources—tests, such as the Vineland Social Maturity Scale; clinical observations; and evalua-tions of the individual's everyday behavior.

TABLE 2

Levels of Adaptive Behavior

	Level
Mild	1
Moderate	2
Severe	3
Profound	4

There are good reasons for the use of behavioral and measured intelli-gence classifications. First and foremost, the adaptive behavior approach stresses quite clearly the fact that the mentally retarded person would benefit from therapy. Second, this concept places emphasis on all aspects of his present level of functioning and removes undue emphasis from intelligence test scores, which all too often are misleading and only a part of the total picture. Also, this approach is oriented more objectively to therapy. Consequently, the therapist will be concerned with the individual's adaptation to his total environment, particularly the way he copes with problems that arise. *The music therapist will be concerned not only with how the child responds to the music activity, but with how he relates and adapts to the therapist and to others in the group. The therapist's attention will center on the changes that occur in the retardate's behavior as he functions in the music activity and on the individuals involved rather than on the musical outcome.*

Values of Music for the Retarded

Whether one is a music therapist or a music teacher in special education, it is important to know well the potentials of music, to know how retardates respond to music, and to understand why music is an effective tool with retardates. Only with this knowledge and understanding can the best results be achieved. It is not magic that causes the retardate to respond so well to music. He responds to the same basic features of music as the normal child. Music has certain unique characteristics that make it an ideal means to help achieve appropriate behavioral changes.

One of the greatest problems of the retarded is communication. Either they have limited use of words or, particularly in the case of the severely retarded, they are nonverbal. This makes it most difficult for others to use words to establish contact with them, and thus creates problems in interpersonal relationships. According to Michael-Smith (1962), "Contact is the first step in the amelioration of the problems in interpersonal relationships" (p. 38). Music, because it is nonverbal communication, is a natural medium for establishing this desired contact.

Many persons believe it impossible to carry on any type of therapy with the mentally retarded because of the verbal communication problem. This is not true. Interaction can be achieved in nonverbal as well as verbal situations (Hutt and Gibby, 1958, p. 293). Traditional approaches are not always effective, and new approaches are needed (Hutt and Gibby, 1958, p. 297). Music, because it is nonverbal, may be the opening wedge with the mentally retarded. The lack of communicative ability in the retarded necessitates satisfactory, socially acceptable means of communicating feelings, which music can provide. Although the degree and emphasis may be different, music functions with the retarded just as it does with the normal.

Group participation is essential to the life adjustment of retarded persons. They have few social contacts, and many of them function at an extremely inadequate level in interpersonal activities. Music is an excellent medium for group experiences because it affords interaction at a nonverbal level and allows acceptable and successful nonthreatening participation at different levels of ability. Hutt and Gibby (1958, p. 298) stated that music provides the retarded with an opportunity for growth in a group situation. Michael-Smith and colleagues (1962) found musical activities to be most effective in group therapy with retardates. Their purposes were

. . . psychic reintegration based on the overcoming of severe ego defect, due not only to basic retardation, but to years of overprotection and unconscious rejection by the parents. We attempted to utilize non-verbal body awareness with the purpose of making the child more sensitive, using activities involving sight, smell, and touch . . . we attempted to encourage group relatedness through games and activities related to music, such as hand-clapping, stamping of feet and singing (p. 40).

The retardates in this study made successful "progress in the degree of self-expression, both verbal and kinesthetic; group relatedness developed, and parents reported increased initiative and self-expression in the home" (Michael-Smith, 1962, p. 41). Gaston (1958) has stated, "Music offers an excellent milieu for the operation of group dynamics. Thus . . . music operates as an integrating and socializing agency by providing a situation for the adaptation of suitable behavior to group function" (p. 302).

The mentally retarded child needs to feel secure; music provides this security through its inherent inner order and structure. The same music activity can be repeated happily many times, and thus, for the child, predictability becomes certain. The continuous basic beat and the repetition of the melodic structure provide an expectancy that will help alleviate the retardate's fear of the unknown. Security also may be achieved by providing some structure to the music period itself, including repetition of familiar activities. When presenting a new activity, it should contain some elements of familiarity. If this is not done, the retardates may refuse to participate. Security can be enhanced through the musical experience because of the positive feelings engendered. Gaston (1958) has written that music is related closely to the tender feelings and therefore "may effectively arouse that which is often at low ebb in patients. . . . This arousal of 'love' is vitally important and essential because it helps provide feelings of security . . ." (p. 299).

Gratification, and consequent self-esteem, is another basic need of the mentally retarded. Often they are aware of their deficiency and lack of accomplishment, and this awareness affects their sense of personal worth. They experience insufficient development of self-esteem because of their to cope with the demands of society. Music can provide experi- at bring about greater development of self-esteem. The music allows for different levels and different kinds of participation; therefore, the mentally retarded child is able to participate regardless of the severity of his retardation. The response may be quite simple, but he is participating. He is a contributing member of the group, and thus he can feel successful. This feeling of success brings about gratification and self-esteem. Music provides for the enhancement of pride in self, self-actualization, successful experiences, and more significant participation at whatever level of ability the child possesses.

Probably most important of all the values of music for the retarded is the esthetic sensory experience. Gaston (1964) has said, "The significance of the aesthetic experience of music for the individual is, that without it, *he would be less complete as a human being.* Children, not only of our own culture, but of other cultures need music for their healthy and normal development" (p. 5). He also said, "the richer the sensory environment, the greater the development of the brain. Therefore, we understand why the sensory environment of the child must be rich" (p. 4). If this is a need for the average child, it is certainly a necessity for the retarded child.

Planning Music Activities

In planning music activities, the therapist must know the developmental level of the retardate. A retardate may have a chronological age of fourteen, but his developmental level may be around four years. Research in the area of motor ability seems to indicate that the degree of motor retardation may be greater than often supposed (Francis and Rarick, 1959). In other words, the fact that motor development of a retardate might be considerably lower than his development in other areas emphasizes the need to consider each individual separately. Because intelligence quotients and mental ages alone do not furnish sufficient information, the best procedure is to base the method of approach and the music activity on his developmental level, taking into account specific learning disabilities. Hunt (1963), in testing the responses of various types of retardates to meaningful auditory material, found that the particular learning disability rather than the type of retardation is an indication of the retardates' responses.

It is difficult to select activities and songs that allow the retarded to participate and that are suited to their social development. This difficulty is not so much in rhythm and listening activities, but in the selection of appropriate materials for singing. The song must have a simple melody and text with a certain amount of repetition and, at the same time, meet the retardate's interest and social level. Songs containing repetitious syllables are generally an excellent choice, particularly for the severely retarded. Folk songs and many traditional songs often meet these requirements and qualifications. The Los Angeles County (1960) manual for special training classes of the severely retarded suggests that "children's familiarity with current music or songs that are part of our culture improves their chance for fitting into the community and environment in which they live" (p. 17).

When introducing new music activities to retardates, each step should be subdivided into logical, simple tasks. Hudson (1955) explains that

. . . below any level in I.Q. there is much that is, or can be made, concrete and simple enough to be within the individual's grasp . . . the difference between the average child and the mentally deficient is that the former can pick up much of what he learns informally, while the latter must be taught formally at every step of the way.

Given time, with learning broken down into logical steps and simple and related parts, the severely retarded child is capable of grasping much . . . (p. 585).

Kodman (1963) believes that the sensory income may arrive at such a rapid rate that the retardate is unable to assimilate or decode the input. Thus, a type of sensory deprivation prevails. Spivack (1963), in summarizing the findings in research of the perception of the mentally retarded child, reported that "as a group [they] are less efficient than those with normal intelligence in the ability to make fine discriminations between different points along a single stimulus dimension and less able to recognize or identify complex stimuli when exposed for brief intervals" (p. 500). This indicates the course that must be taken in presenting music activities. The procedure must be simple and in logical steps with frequent repetition and a large number of supportive clues.

The mentally retarded are capable of participating in many musical experiences, including movement to music, rhythm activities, singing, listening, simple instrumental playing, and creativity. The responses probably will be vague at first, but gradually structure and concepts may be developed, depending on abilities and needs. There must be successful experiences, because this convinces the child of his worth and acceptance. Each concept learned, no matter how small, is a significant gain for the retardate and helps to effect a change in his behavior.

Providing for Leisure Time and Posttherapy Activities

Another important aspect of therapy is to help the mentally retarded use their leisure time properly. This is often neglected, the therapist being concerned mainly with immediate behavior problems. All is lost if the retarded are not shown how to use adequately what they have learned in therapy, either outside the institution or in school. Too often, the retarded are rehabilitated for the particular setting in which their therapy occurred. When they leave the school or institution, they are prone either to sit around or to pursue undesirable problem-causing activities. Social workers find that many of the families of the retarded, particularly the severely retarded, are deteriorating because of the problems caused by the retarded individual. This suggests that in providing music experiences for the mentally retarded, care must be taken to help them see how they might utilize music in their leisure time. It cannot be assumed they will use music in this way just because they have been exposed to it. *This will have to be taught.* The therapist or teacher must not only discuss with them how they might use music in their homes, but carefully show them. This course of action needs to be repeated again and again. Interest will be created by experiences such as field trips, demonstration of instruments, and discussions about certain music events occurring in the community. Before retarded individuals are taken to a concert in the community, they should have the opportunity to hear some of the music. They then will be familiar with the program, and their attention and response will be enhanced. A selection of some of the music activities must be made with the idea that the retarded will be able to use them in the community or at home. Such activities may be simple forms of square dancing and listening.

Those who have learned to play instruments must be encouraged to continue. The music therapist should discuss with parents the value to the children of continuing this activity and, if possible, assist in finding understanding teachers. If the retarded child is going into a special education program in junior or senior high school, parents should be cautious about placing him in an instrumental organization. This can be dangerous because he may not have the ability to perform at the level of the available instrumental organization. This may lead to frustration and feelings of inadequacy, so that all the gains made through the successful experience of learning to play the instrument are lost. There is not so much danger for those who are interested in vocal groups.

Because of the short attention span and limited range of interest of a retardate, a listening program is difficult, particularly for the severely retarded. However, an interest in listening can be developed through the use of short, simple, melodic pieces.

Music has much value for the retarded. It can benefit them in many ways. Music fulfills a number of their needs in a subtle, nonthreatening way. Perhaps most important for many retarded children, music activities can minimize the differences between the mentally retarded, those with different types of handicaps, and normal children.

References

DYBWAD, G. Mental retardation. In J. Rothstein (Ed.), *Mental retardation.* New York: Holt, 1961. Pp. 5–7.

FRANCIS, R. H., and RARICK, G. L. Motor characteristics of the mentally retarded. *Amer. J. ment. Defic.*, 1959, 63, 792–811.

GASTON, E. T. Functional music. In N. Henry (Ed.), *Basic concepts in music education.* Chicago: The University of Chicago Press, 1958. Pp. 292–309.

GASTON, E. T. The aesthetic experience and biological man. *J. Mus. Ther.*, 1964, 1, 1–7.

HEBER, R. A manual on terminology and classification in mental retardation. *Monogr. Suppl. Amer. J. ment Defic.* (2d ed.), 1961.

HEBER, R. Mental retardation: concept and classification. In E. P. Trapp and P. Himelstein (Eds.), *Readings on the exceptional child.* New York: Appleton-Century-Crofts, 1962. Pp. 69–81.

HUDSON, MARGARET. The severely retarded child: educable vs. trainable. *Amer. J. ment. Defic.*, 1955, 59, 583–586.

HUNT, B. M. Differential responses of mentally deficient brain-injured children and mentally deficient familial children to meaningful auditory material. *Amer. J. ment. Defic.*, 1960, 64, 747–753.

HUTT, M. L., and GIBBY, R. G. *The mentally retarded child.* Boston: Allyn and Bacon, 1958.

KODMAN, F. Sensory processes and mental deficiency. In N. Ellis (Ed.), *Handbook of mental deficiency.* New York: McGraw-Hill, 1963. Pp. 463–479.

Los Angeles County. *The education in special training classes for children who are severely mentally retarded.* (rev. ed.) Los Angeles: County Superintendent of Schools Office, 1960.

MICHAEL-SMITH, H. Psychotherapy for the mentally retarded. In H. Michael-Smith and S. Kastein (Eds.), *The special child.* Seattle, Wash.: New School for the Special Child, Inc., 1962. Pp. 27–43.

SPIVACK, G. Perceptual processes. In N. Ellis (Ed.), *Handbook of mental deficiency.* New York: McGraw-Hill, 1963. Pp. 480–511.

4

MUSIC THERAPY FOR THE
SEVERELY RETARDED

BETTY ISERN HOWERY

The severely retarded are identified as having intelligence quotients (IQs) between 30 and 50 and are rated at levels 3 and 4 according to the behavioral classification scale described in Tables 1 and 2 in Chapter 3, p. 49. These retardates usually require some type of continued custodial care. Baumgarten (1955) said,

> . . . that most of them have some form of physical handicap, and that their mental development and speech and language abilities are distinctly limited. Although they are usually incapable of learning academic skills beyond a rote memorization basis, they do have capacity to learn to live cooperatively and to develop good personal habits, and under supervision, they have the potential to make a marginal adjustment socially and economically in a sheltered environment (p. 13).

This description is particularly applicable because of its positive approach; it is not limiting, and it recognizes that many times severely retarded individuals are capable of making some social and economic adjustment.

Historically, the severely retarded were confined in institutions or restricted to their homes. Today, although many are still in institutions, more and more community services are being provided for them. Many schools are establishing special classes, and a number of communities are offering day-care centers and sheltered workshops. Furthermore, modern medicine has lowered significantly the mortality rate of severely retarded individuals (Dybwad, 1964). Because of the various services devoted to their care and training, many severely retarded children grow to the age of young adults, and some may return to the care and protection of their homes. As a consequence, the home and community now face the major problem of supplying adequate facilities for severely retarded adults. Today, the emphasis is on home care and community treatment, not institutionalization.

The music therapist must keep in mind that the severely retarded child, after some years of training, may be able to return to his home and live there after he has reached adulthood. This will place added pressure and responsibility on the family. Too often, family members lack the necessary knowledge and are not psychologically ready to accept essential responsibilities. They may fail to allow the retardate to operate on his own, insofar as feasible. Improper behavior by the family may nullify to a great degree the gains made in the special classroom, the day-care center, or wherever previous training occurred. It is apparent that the family, in many instances, will need considerable attention, education, and help in dealing with the young adult. Certainly they need to know what he has learned and how he can continue to learn or to use what he has learned. This continuance of development includes not only activities but the furtherance of adaptive behavior. The music therapist can lend real assistance to parents by explaining in detail what the retardate can do in music, what he likes in music, and what the parents can do to nurture an ongoing attitude and productive behavior.

The main goal in working with the severely retarded is to help them adjust to their environment by teaching and guiding them to utilize more adequately the capacities they have; thus, the process of their full self-actualization is encouraged (Hutt and Gibby, 1958, p. 264). This suggests a program that provides basic skills in living, such as self-help, social awareness, simple work tasks, and appropriate use of leisure time. Most severely retarded persons are prone to develop emotional problems in varying degrees, which in turn adversely affect their adjustment to society. If these individuals are to utilize in full their capacities, programs should be provided to alleviate their emotional problems. Thus, treatment for the severely retarded has two distinct goals: (1) to stimulate growth, and (2) to alleviate emotional disturbances (Hutt and Gibby, 1958, p. 265). These two goals make necessary an integrated team approach to help the retardate in his process of full self-actualization.

The basic goals of music therapy for the severely retarded are to help them adapt to their environment, develop interpersonal relationships, and learn certain basic skills. This is accomplished by establishing a therapeutic relationship through the music activity. The retarded learn to relate to the therapist and others in the group; they adjust to the demands of the situations and, at the same time, learn other basic skills in living.

Review of Research and Related Literature

Severely retarded children often are confused about their physical body image; they have difficulty discriminating themselves from their environment. Lathom (1963) attempted to discover the effect of action songs on body concept.

The study was based on the hypothesis that a child must have some organization of his physical appearance before he can begin to relate, in a very meaningful manner, to the people and objects around him; and that as his body-concept increased, he would begin to incorporate the concept of self in relation to space, time, and physical objects and a growing social awareness would also occur (p. 116).

She believed that patients sent to music therapy for social interaction obviously needed therapy for reality orientation to their environment. Sixteen subjects, from levels I, II, and III of the adaptive behavior scale (Table 2, p. 49), were assigned to control and experimental groups of eight members each. In the experimental group, songs were used that required the subjects to move or point to certain parts of their bodies. The test results were not statistically significant. However, it seemed that several uncontrolled variables may have affected the results. Lathom (1963) said,

Many social changes seemed to occur as the Ss [subjects] in the training groups seemed to get improved orientation to self in relation to objects and other people. These children would usually be prescribed to music therapy for increased social interaction. It might, therefore, seem that songs that deal with body orientation would be a useful place to start socialization for young patients, and music therapy can contribute to the milieu that is working for increased body orientation (p. 121).

Stockbine (1951) also found music to be a socializing device, particularly for the severely retarded. Ludwig (1957), in a rehabilitation program with hyperactive mentally retarded children, discovered music to be an effective device in the socialization process. She believed that their awareness and contact with other children improved through the music activities.

The severely retarded respond with greatest success to the rhythmic element of music. Certain aspects of the rhythmic responses do not demand as much intellectualization as some other responses to music. Verbalization, for example, need not be involved. Murphy (1957) studied rhythmic responses of sixty-four subjects divided into two groups. The average mental age of one group was three years and of the other group, eleven months. The group with the lower mental age engaged in rocking movements and

. . . appeared to represent a solitary, self-absorbed infantile level of social-emotional development as well as . . . a primitive gross motor and maturational level.

. . . [The older group clapped and] appeared to be capable of engaging in socialized group activity, specialized motor responses and in general represented an early childhood level of development in the intellectual area (Murphy, 1957, pp. 363–364).

This experiment reveals that there are varying levels of motor responses, but even those children with the lowest level of mental age respond in some way.

Tapping the beat is appropriate and needed in rhythmic activities, and this repetitive structure provides security. Rhythm also allows many different acceptable responses, at all levels of difficulty, at the same time. That music provides means for successful experiences is illustrated in the following description of the use of rhythm. Weigl (1963) found rhythm to be an excellent medium, because it is expression on the nonverbal level. She used the rhythmic approach extensively with the severely retarded, starting with the simplest movements, such as handclapping or the mere nodding of the head, and slowly progressing to more complicated responses such as marching. This same process, simple to complex, was followed when rhythm instruments were used. Progress was made because the children were able to respond to rhythm in some acceptable fashion, and this became an incentive for further endeavor. Weigl (1963) wrote that the rhythmic approach was valuable because

. . . (3) it facilitates coordination with others through the organizing, stimulative force of rhythm; (4) it gives them a chance for early success by eliminating tedious drill, finger exercises, and complicated harmonies; (5) it teaches them organization through the structure and genuine discipline inherent in musical form and rhythm, while still giving opportunity for "nonconformity" through individual improvisation and listening to others within the group; thereby, (6) increasing their self-esteem, feeling of security, and the courage to go on trying and exploring (p. 80).

Many therapists have found music an excellent tool in helping the retarded with speech problems, particularly delayed speech. Because there is a developmental scheme for the learning of speech, certain stages must be mastered before the next stage can be attained. In the first stage, the sounds are discrete and are made initially for kinesthetic enjoyment. Later, they are combined with consonants; this is the auditory stage. The next stage is imitating the sounds of others, which is the scholastic stage. The final stage is true speech, in which the child uses words independently and meaningfully. Goda (1960) states that "this same sequence should be expected before a retarded child develops speech. But with the retarded child each stage should be expected later [in the child's development]" (p. 269). Music offers the mentally retarded an opportunity to go through these developmental stages in a nonthreatening, socially acceptable way. They can become acquainted with musical sounds and imitation of these sounds; later they sing songs with non-sensical syllables; and finally, if possible, they sing isolated words, and then sentences. Music is a motivating factor in this type of therapy. Somerville (1958) believes that "one of the more effective ways to teach mentally retarded children to talk, children that have only expressed themselves by making murmuring noises, by lip movement and by pointing . . . is to introduce your words through music and rhythmical activities" (p. 286).

Flanders (1961) approached the problem through rhythmic activities and imitation of familiar sounds. Studying phonics in this way was believed to be unobtrusive and painless. She was successful in introducing songs with motions and repetitive words and songs that included the retardate's own name. Loven (1957) described the case of a seven-year-old boy who was diagnosed as mentally retarded and who had developed no speech. The boy, after one year of therapy, gradually began communicating, using one word and then adding more. This was achieved through the repeated singing of songs with nonsensical words and vowels accompanied with motions. Jordan (1961, p. 52), in discussing programing for the severely retarded, suggested listening to musical records and singing to encourage skills in communication.

Music is used successfully as an aid to learning in other nonmusical areas. Isern (1961) used 104 mentally retarded subjects with an average IQ of 47 to determine whether music might enhance learning and affect retention. The experiment was devised so that two learning situations were structured, one with and one without music. The identical material to be learned was presented in story and in song. Statistical results showed that a significantly larger number of items were recalled from the song situation than from the story situation. It was concluded:

Perhaps music improved the memory of mentally retarded children because it created or positively influenced the psychological conditions necessary at the time of original learning. Music being an added factor during the original learning period might have increased the vividness of the material, helped to organize and pattern the material through its rhythm, added to the emotional experience and enhanced the meaningfulness by helping to interpret the content of the material to be presented . . . (Isern, 1961, pp. 151–152).

Fraser (1961) found music most helpful in teaching the severely retarded to write. Music caught their attention and helped them accept organization. By starting with gross body movements, the subjects could progress gradually to refined movements, such as finger motion. This activity helped the children learn orderly patterns. Listening span increased, and some discipline developed. After these preliminary activities, music was used when the children began their first writing exercises on the board. Music used in this setting permits the ordering of behavior according to physical response levels.

The severely retarded often have physical problems. Their gait may be shuffling, coordination is usually inferior, and their posture is poor. In conditions of poor coordination, the learning experiences should include activities that help improve the use of extremities, not only for better physical facility, but because poor use of extremities often calls unwanted attention to the retarded. Rothstein (1961, p. 345) believes that muscular development can be improved, and movement to music and rhythm instruments should play an important role in this. Because their movements are slow, appropriate activities can be provided that demand slow responses and are, at the same time, socially acceptable.

Music therapy for the retarded is used with groups and with individuals. Often a retardate is incapable of tolerating a group experience and needs individual therapy prior to group participation. Denenholz (1954) worked individually with ten severely retarded children. She used music as a tool to help alleviate certain emotional disturbances and to overcome particular learning problems. Her goal was also to help develop better speech through music. The speech of eight children improved. She also found that many of the emotional and learning problems were abated.

Wilson (1958) saw a mongoloid girl daily for four weeks and found that, therapeutically, there were some slight gains. The pediatrician involved agreed with this. No doubt the gains might have been greater if the time spent in therapy had been longer. Music commanded attention, increased the attention span, evoked a mood change, and increased vocabulary to some extent. Instrumental music appeared more effective than vocal music.

Griffin (1963), in describing a music therapy program at a state school, saw that "the role of music in the institution [was] a varied one" (p. 13). Music was used therapeutically, purely recreationally, or as an adjunct to specific activities and projects. He suggested that more structure is required when working with mentally retarded patients than with neuropsychiatric patients. He also found the listening classes, the most passive activity, to be excellent for those who could not tolerate or function in other groups. "The nature of this activity allows the patient the security of passivity with the opportunity for more active participation when he becomes psychologically able and motivated to do so" (Griffin, 1963, p. 15).

A psychiatrically oriented program with a team approach for the treatment of the mentally retarded was described by Loven (1957). The primary goal was to help the children adapt appropriately so that they could assume a useful role in proportion to their ability. The children were prescribed to individual and/or group therapy on the basis of their specific needs. "Prescriptions include specific attitudes and roles to be assumed [by the therapist] in the treatment of each child . . ." (Loven, 1957, p. 166). The usual music activities successfully met, in many instances, the predetermined goals because

. . . the value of music for these cases depends on *how* it is used. For, as big a contribution as it makes, it is not music alone, nor any other tool alone working a magic phenomenon, but rather the predetermined goals set with it; the carefully planned and executed use of it by qualified persons, and the follow-up and support of its effect in the total child (Loven, 1957, p. 170).

Murphy (1958) reported a somewhat different use of music in the hospital setting. She believed that a music therapy program might be a partial solution for emotional problems of the severely retarded. Music was provided for 74 percent of the population that was not participating in a formal training program. The average intelligence quotient was about 20, and the average mental age was two years and two months. Music was provided on the wards once a week for seven months. The instruments were a saxophone and an amplified guitar. No attempt was made toward directed group activities. According to Murphy (1958), these musical presentations on a ward for emotionally disturbed and hyperactive adolescent boys resulted in these changes:

. . . self-initiated group participation, voluntary self-discipline, development of desirable interpersonal attitudes, efforts at pronunciation of the words of the songs by some, improved pronunciation of the words of the songs by others, vocabulary development as more words and phrases of familiar songs are learned, development of gross motor coordination, and enjoyment of music as a source of recreation (p. 271).

Similar music programs were organized in hospital cottages. "The progressive learning observed in the cottages . . . suggests the possibility of rather dramatic hold-over effects . . ." (Murphy, 1958, p. 272). In the cottage with the smaller, hyperactive boys, less bed-wetting and soiling was noted. The observable results obtained from this study indicate the striking influence of music on the mentally retarded. Many severely retarded persons may not be able to participate actively, but behavior changes occur, nevertheless.

Alvin (1959) used somewhat the same technique. Her experiment with severely retarded children utilized the concert approach. She played the cello, explained the instrument, and showed how to play it. Twenty-four children, ages six to sixteen, with IQs from 22 to 50, were the subjects in this experiment. Observational reports were made by the children's teacher and by Alvin. On the basis of these reports, the following conclusions were drawn: Music proved to be a further means of communication with each of the children. Responses to music included increased desirable physical activity; more verbalization; and increased signs of interest, satisfaction, and pleasure. There was some development of sense perception and substantial gain in attention span. Social integration was improved.

The need of a bridge, so to speak, between home and community, or institution and community, is growing rapidly. For this reason, day-care centers are being established in many areas. Music therapy has an important role in these centers. Perhaps the most important role music plays in this type of situation is helping children and adults learn various music activities to use in their leisure time. Harbert (1957) showed the effectiveness of music in a similar way. A music clinic that included many severely retarded children was held once a week in the winter and three days a week in the summer. She found this type of situation particularly beneficial in achieving socialization, causing feelings of well-being and joy, and providing experiences in self-expression.

The author has observed music activities in an adult center for the severely retarded. These people either had not attended classes in special education, or had attended and failed to benefit from them. They were not capable of working in a sheltered workshop. It was believed, however, that some skills could be learned, and that behavior changes might occur through music activities. Many of these severely retarded adults had poor use of their extremities. Music was provided twice a week for nine months. The goals for the music experiences were to stimulate communication, participation, socialization, and interest in music activities that might carry over to home and community. Particular emphasis was placed on listening, simple square dancing, adult rhythm instruments, and singing. The listening program consisted at first of live performance. The (student) music therapist played short melodic pieces on the piano and cello. Occasionally, other performers were brought in. It was thought that live performances would be more effective in holding the attention of the patients. During the first listening experiences, the therapist pointed out certain aspects of the music that were important, such as melody or rhythm. Listening to recorded music was introduced later, using music that had been heard previously in live performance. It was noted that attention span increased when listening to recorded music after listening to live performances.

Square dancing was successful, although the process of teaching the patterns was slow and tedious. After nine months, the patients could do simple squares. There were some who would participate only in this activity. One patient was observed who spent most of his time hallucinating. However, during the square dancing, he appeared to be in contact because he participated and executed all the necessary movements. It was observed that his hallucinations did not start immediately after dancing, and the longer he danced, the longer the period before the hallucinations returned. Other personnel at the center believed that the music activity met the desired goals and considered it a desirable and needed facet of their program.

This review of literature and practice does not contain reports of the use of music in special education. The goals of music in special education are similar to those described. However, books on training the severely retarded and curriculum outlines of various schools indicate a wide use of music in programs for the retarded. Many of the programs use music not only for socialization and communication, but also to teach other concepts needed for daily living.

The music therapist has much to offer special education and should be included on the staff of such a department. One cannot expect the teacher in special education to be skilled in all the activities needed in a classroom. Perhaps, in view of this, it would be beneficial to use the services of a music therapist in classes for the retarded. Music therapists have been trained for this work and know how to use music to achieve most of the desired goals of such training classes.

References

ALVIN, JULIETTE. The response of severely retarded children to music. *Amer. J. ment. Defic.*, 1959, 63, 988–996.

BAUMGARTEN, BERNICE B. *A curriculum guide for teachers of trainable mentally handicapped children.* Chicago: Illinois Council for Mentally Retarded Children, 1955.

DENENHOLZ, BARBARA. The use of music with mentally retarded children. In Mariana Bing (Ed.), *Music therapy 1953.* Lawrence, Kan.: Allen Press, 1954. Pp. 99–107.

DYBWAD, G. Mental retardation. In J. H. Rothstein (Ed.), *Mental retardation.* New York: Holt, 1964. Pp. 5–7.

FLANDERS, FLORENCE R. A music program for the mentally retarded child. *Bull. NAMT*, 1961, 10, 7–8.

FRASER, LOUISE W. The use of music in teaching writing to the retarded child. In E. H. Schneider (Ed.), *Music therapy 1960.* Lawrence, Kan.: Allen Press, 1961. Pp. 86–89.

GODA, S. Vocal utterances of young moderately and severely retarded nonspeaking children. *Amer. J. ment. Defic.*, 1960, 65, 269–273.

GRIFFIN, J. E. Music as an activity in a state institution for the mentally retarded. *Bull. NAMT*, 1963, 12, 13–16.

HARBERT, WILHELMINA K. Treatment of emotionally disturbed children in a music therapy clinic. In E. T. Gaston (Ed.), *Music therapy 1956.* Lawrence, Kan.: Allen Press, 1957. Pp. 156–164.

HUTT, M. L., and GIBBY, R. G. *The mentally retarded child.* Boston: Allyn and Bacon, 1958.

ISERN, BETTY. Summary, conclusions, and implications: the influence of music upon the memory of mentally retarded children. In E. H. Schneider (Ed.), *Music therapy 1960.* Lawrence, Kan.: Allen Press, 1961. Pp. 149–153.

JORDAN, T. E. *The mentally retarded.* Columbus, Ohio: Charles E. Merrill Books, Inc., 1961.

LATHOM, WANDA. The effect of certain action songs on body concept. In E. H. Schneider (Ed.), *Music therapy 1962.* Lawrence, Kan.: Allen Press, 1963. Pp. 115–121.

LOVEN, MARTHA A. Value of music therapy for mentally retarded children. In E. T. Gaston (Ed.), *Music therapy 1956.* Lawrence, Kan.: Allen Press, 1957. Pp. 165–171.

LUDWIG, ALICE J. The role of varied therapies in the rehabilitation of the retarded child—music therapy. *Amer. J. ment. Defic.,* 1957, *61,* 508–515.

MURPHY, MARY M. Rhythmical responses of low grade and middle grade mental defectives to music therapy. *J. clin. Psychol.,* 1957, *13,* 361–364.

MURPHY, MARY M. A large scale music therapy program for institutionalized low grade and middle grade defectives. *Amer. J. ment. Defic.,* 1958, *63,* 268–273.

ROTHSTEIN, J. H. (Ed.) *Mental retardation.* New York: Holt, 1961.

SOMERVILLE, MARGARET. Learning to talk through singing. *Except. Child.,* 1958, *24,* 286.

STOCKBINE, F. Music for retarded children. *Educ. Mus. Mag.,* 1951, *30,* 21, 48–52.

WEIGL, VALLY. The rhythmic approach in music therapy. In E. H. Schneider (Ed.), *Music therapy 1962.* Lawrence, Kan.: Allen Press, 1963. Pp. 71–80.

WILSON, BEVERLY JANE. A case study giving the results of the applications of music therapy with a mongoloid child. Unpublished master's thesis, Texas Coll. of Arts and Industries, 1958.

5

THE USE OF MUSIC THERAPY
WITH RETARDED PATIENTS

WANDA B. LATHOM

The Entering Child

When a child first enters an institution for the retarded, he may be confused by many factors in his new environment—the change from family living to an institutional schedule, the number of unfamiliar people, and the need for orientation to the physical setting. In this early stage of the child's development, music therapy can be a supportive and relatively nonthreatening facet of the hospital environment. To the new patient, a guitar, Autoharp, or some other instrument on which he can focus his attention may be less threatening than a verbal relationship. As he observes the therapist at work with other children, he may find that the persons who sing and play with his group are not frightening. Thus, the music therapist may be among the first of the staff with whom the patient can initiate a relationship.

It is important that the therapist be skilled in observing the patient and in reporting his observations objectively. If the child is scheduled for regular periods of therapy, the therapist will be able to observe him in a variety of situations. As the child performs on a number of instruments, the therapist may note his use of abstract symbols. For example, is he able to play the chord organ by matching the letters on the organ with those in the book? Does he do this in a logical, orderly manner that indicates an understanding of the relationships of letters, or does he have to search for each letter? If he sees a group of identical letters, does he perceive them as a group, or does he consider each one separately? Does he use fingering logically, or does he search for the notes with one finger? Is he matching the shapes of letters, or does he associate a word with a symbol? The answers to questions such as these are indications of the patient's use of abstract symbols and of his level of functioning. The same procedure of identifying abstract symbols may be repeated with numbers on the melodica, colored bells, or other musical instruments to which symbols can be attached. The information obtained from the procedure can be used later, for it will indicate whether the patient uses abstract symbols well enough to learn musical notation without excessive frustration.

The child's organization of rhythm patterns also can be tested. If his attention span is very short, he probably will be unable to repeat short cadences or maintain a basic beat for the duration of a song. However, he may be quite attentive and have the ability to organize long, difficult cadences and repeat them accurately. This, too, shows the child's level of functioning and gives some indication of which music activities would benefit him most.

The therapy program can be modified according to the manner in which the patient uses objects. Redl and Wineman (1957) note that some objects indicate certain actions—a chair is perceived as an object on which to sit, a pencil is an object with which to write. The chair and the pencil are used so commonly for these purposes that most children do not need to be told how to use them—they learn by imitation. There may be a number of reasons why a child does not use common objects correctly. If a drum is placed in front of a little boy and he does not strike it, the therapist must try to determine why. The patient may be from a culturally deprived home where he failed to learn that a drum is an object used to make sounds, or he may be afraid the therapist will scold him for being noisy, or he may fear that his peers will laugh at him if his performance is not good. He also may consider the striking of a drum an aggressive act and fear the loss of control of his own aggressive impulses. A skilled therapist, observing the child in similar situations, can often determine the reason for his reaction to a particular object; and this knowledge will be useful when the time comes to decide what treatment the child needs.

Circle games, line games, and action songs are useful for young or regressed patients. During these games, the therapist can determine whether the patient is able to imitate other persons, whether he is comfortable enough with the group to introduce new motions, and whether he has a fund of ideas from which to introduce new motions. Indications of his spatial and body orientations also can be noted as he takes part in forming a circle or a line and as he performs actions that require him to move a particular part of his body. The child who must have someone take his hands and lead him around the circle seems to be on a different adaptive level from one who is able to maintain this formation on his own.

It is important to observe how the patient reacts to frustrating situations and the defenses he uses when he fears he will be unsuccessful.

Many patients project their failures on the therapist, the instrument, or their peers. They say, "You gave me the hardest one to blow," or "This one is broken—I could play if you gave me another one," or "I could play if he would be quiet." Some patients refuse to try if they suspect that the task will not be easy, whereas others become angry and refuse to quit when they have to put the instrument away before they have been able to produce a sound. Some withdraw and return to an activity in which they were successful.

The therapist attempts to determine which interpersonal relationships are least threatening. Is the child more comfortable in a one-to-one relationship with the therapist or in a group? Does he relate differently to a male therapist than to a female therapist? How does he react when with patients who are older or younger than he? In what manner does he try to establish relationships with his peers? All these questions must be considered in designing an effective treatment program.

Continuing Treatment

When the retarded patient is referred to music therapy for further treatment, the referrals often indicate one or more of five general aims. These are (1) socialization, (2) strengthening of defenses, (3) intrusion on fantasy, (4) stimulation, and (5) gratification.

Socialization

In establishing social relationships, there seem to be three levels at which assistance is particularly needed by retarded children.

PREGROUP SOCIALIZATION
Very young and severely regressed patients seem to prefer object relationships to interpersonal relationships. They are willing to play with simple rhythm instruments and anything else small enough to handle with which they can make noise. Most of these patients have very short attention spans, and many are hyperactive. They usually can begin some social interaction in therapy sessions in which they participate with their peers, but their main focus is still on objects. Increased orientation to self, space, and time usually is needed before they are able to interact. Symonds (1951) comments on the importance of a realistic self-concept: "The self is the most real thing in our experience and is the frame of reference with which a person perceives, conceives, and evaluates the world around him and toward which he reacts" (p. 70). If the child is unsure

of the limits of his own body boundaries, he cannot begin anything as complex as social interaction. Fisher and Cleveland (1958) state that "the more definite an individual's body image boundaries, the greater his capacity to enter into intimate expressive relationships" (p. 211). However, as he begins some interaction, the manner in which the child perceives himself is modified. Schilder (1950) notes that "the building up of the body image is based not only upon the individual history of an individual, but also on his relations to others" (p. 138).

Action games that allow everyone to do similar things and that stress imitation can be performed with a minimum amount of interaction in the group. Rhythm band activities and songs that allow the patients to reenact events that have occurred in their immediate environment also can be used. The therapist can structure games, dances, songs, and rhythm band activities that require increased consideration for others in the group and call attention to the physical structure of the body. Machover (1957) seems to agree when she states that "personality does not develop in a vacuum, but through the movement, feeling, and thinking of a specific body" (p. 4). Ayres (1961) notes,

When a child does not learn through the normal course of development to synthesize impulses into a body scheme, training procedures are based on increasing the flow of sensory impulses, developing a conscious knowledge of the construction and basic movements of the body, and associating the sensation and conscious knowledge through simple gross meaningful motor tasks (p. 97).

The hyperactive child with a very short attention span may participate in short action songs or games that provide an outlet for his physical need to move. Because these songs are short, the child may withdraw between songs, but be brought into group activity for increasing lengths of time.

Much of the therapy with preschool children is directed toward preparation for special education classes. If the child is not yet able to interact, he will not be able to tolerate the group activities within the classroom or to pay attention long enough to learn. The child who is still at a preschool level usually lacks the variety of firsthand experiences that are necessary for beginning special education activities.

The classroom teacher carefully notes the child's stages of development in physical condition, social adjustment, emotional stability, fund of ideas, ability to think, command of the English language, work habits, sensory ability, motor habits, and his interest in learning to read. At least nine of these ten areas must be developed satisfactorily before the child can be considered mature enough to learn to read successfully. If two or more areas have not emerged, then the classroom teacher tries to provide an extensive program of first-hand experiences suited to the interests and level of the immature learner (Jorgensen, 1949, p. 5).

GROUP-LEVEL SOCIALIZATION

Another type of therapy for socialization is prescribed for patients who have learned to interact with others, but do so in an antisocial manner. This includes children who are physically and verbally abusive to their peers as well as very shy insecure children who lack a repertoire of ways in which to reach out to other people and establish new relationships. Music activity can be structured to provide a variety of interpersonal relationships and social situations. ". . . music operates as an integrating and socializing agency by providing a situation for the adaptation of suitable behavior to group function. It is a nonthreatening, intimate, enjoyable, and expressive activity blessed with social acceptance" (Gaston, 1958, p. 302). The music activity can be so appealing that patients modify their inappropriate social responses in order to be included and to cooperate in producing the music.

If anyone would question the social value of music, it should be enough to point out that it is invariably used when any gathering or organization desires to create a community of feeling, or harmony and congeniality of spirit (Schauffler and Spaeth, 1927, p. 40).

The aggressive child and the fearful child need a predictable environment. It is often helpful, therefore, to establish a regular routine for the therapy session. For example, the session may always begin with the children entering the room and sitting in chairs around the piano. The first third of the session may be used for singing, the second third for active games or dances, and the last third for playing instruments. Although the music used in each section of the period may be varied, the same predictable structure can be followed in each session.

There may be more emphasis on adjustment within a treatment program. Children, it is held, may be frightened by too much freedom, and lack of patterning in daily living may be confusing. In an orderly environment, the child's anxieties may be lessened and his potentialities for growth and adjustment may be encouraged (Psychiatric Inpatient Treatment of Children, 1959, p. 89).

Although the normal child, who is able to establish limits for himself that are in keeping with his community's mores, can profit from a permissive environment, the aggressive or fearful child seems to need a firmly structured environment with clearly defined limits. Rodman (1964) states,

Insistence on behavior within established limits becomes central in the treatment of a child whose problem is expressed by aggressive behavior. The goal, simply stated, is to provide such a child with an environment in which there is a degree of consistency that will enable him to internalize an orderly atmosphere and approach the problems of his own life in a calm mood, a mood that will enable him to come closer to realizing his capabilities. . . . A treatment program aims to restore to the community a child who is able to utilize his capabilities within certain internalized limits; in other words we hope to help him make his community's judgment of appropriate behavior his own (p. 606).

ADOLESCENT SOCIALIZATION

Retarded adolescents, in many instances, need therapy for social interaction. During adolescence, girls assume more feminine behavior, and boys often need a strong male figure with whom to identify, as well as activities that are obviously masculine. Both the boys and girls may be afraid to initiate relationships with the opposite sex and need a structured setting in which to try a variety of means of establishing these relationships. Retarded adolescents, like normal young people, often have difficulty in handling their emotions. Their reactions are sometimes extreme—they laugh too loudly, cry too easily, and may feel rejected as the result of an unimportant incident.

The ability to gain control of feelings and to initiate and maintain appropriate relationships is an important aspect of the adolescent's adaptive behavior. All adolescents test their more mature roles. Testing frequently involves questioning or challenging the persons whom they perceive as authority figures. Linnell (1960) notes that relationship with authority is one of the adolescent's chief concerns. If this relationship with the therapist can be maintained in a supportive structure in which the patient is not rejected, more mature behavior may be the result. Music groups also can be structured to give the patient an opportunity for more social and individual responsibilities, other aspects of adaptive behavior. Leland (1964), in referring to the American Association of Mental Deficiency (AAMD) definition of retardation, states,

The third aspect of our definition of mental retardation is also associated with "impairment in adaptive behavior." This is described as relating to *independent functioning, personal responsibility, and social responsibility.* Since every child who is able should be given every opportunity to remain in his own home and be aided in learning to live a happy, useful life, the problem of adaptation in children becomes the responsibility of many disciplines (p. 27).

The retarded patient who is not institutionalized until adolescence usually has experienced failure in many situations, and the defenses he has adopted to handle his disappointment and frustration may not be beneficial.

Adolescents are often very self-conscious; therefore, they feel verbal interaction to be a threat. Guthrie, Butler, Gorlow, and White (1964) note,

Since retardates have a very limited ability to say how they feel and what they think, their reports do not give us sufficient material to identify the patterns of attitudes which they have developed toward themselves and toward others. We must infer from other sources of information their characteristic conflict areas and their perceptions of, and solutions for, these difficulties (p. 42).

Music can fill the void in conversational lapses. If two people are listening to music, it is appropriate for them to stop talking and listen to the song. This can relieve some of the psychological stress that the adolescent may feel. Because the musical activity can be structured to focus mainly on the activity rather than the interpersonal relationships, it can be a relatively nonthreatening means of working on more appropriate relationships. It also allows the therapist to observe the patient's nonverbal responses to social situations. Imitation of social roles can be encouraged by rewarding appropriate behavior.

Strengthening of Defenses

Music therapy also is prescribed for patients having difficulty with impulse control. They seem to benefit from tightly structured activities that are gratifying to them. "The fact that adolescents of the acting out type do better in an atmosphere of restrictions rather than of unlimited freedom is an indisputable empirical finding" (Hacker and Geleerd, 1945, p. 624). The retarded patient, who is very impulsive and does not think of the eventual consequences of his actions, may be led easily into delinquent activity by his more intelligent peers. Leventhal (1964) conducted a study of the inner control deficiencies in runaway children. He concluded that "runaways seem to have a generalized experience of little or no control in relation to both internal and environmental events. They give more indications of discharge-type behavior, of deficient regulatory mechanisms, and of a 'helpless' self-image" (p. 176).

One example of a highly structured group is a drum corps. (For a detailed description of such a group, see Bitcon's report in Chapter 7.) Within our society, marching and playing a field drum or a bass drum usually are perceived as masculine activities. They are, therefore, appealing to some adolescent boys who are trying to express their masculine identification. Because a drum corps marches in step and formation and plays a repetitive cadence, the structure is established to the fraction of a second. As it marches on the hospital grounds, other people stop to watch, and soon the members may have pride in their ability as a group. At this point, there may be considerable peer pressure for members to conform in order to give the group a uniform appearance. The therapist has a good opportunity here to stress grooming and posture. Because the activity is tightly structured, close relationships are not necessary; therefore, the patient may be allowed a long time to form a relationship.

It seems beneficial to have two therapists with this group, because they can maintain tighter structure. It is possible for one therapist to remove a disturbed patient from the group to work with him individually.

The patient who is struggling to maintain impulse control may experience considerable anxiety. "The cliché is often repeated that fear is a psychic state produced by a set of objective events that signify danger; anxiety is a similar psychic state, but the precipitating events are absent or 'unconscious'" (Sarbin, 1964, p. 630). A physically active music session may relieve some of the physical tension resulting from anxiety. If, at the end of the session, the patient is physically tired, but relaxed, he will have better control.

A modern-dance group offers many of the same goals. In our culture, dancing often is considered an effeminate activity, even though it requires considerable physical dexterity and control. The activity can be structured as tightly as the drum corps, but it can also be a creative experience, as the patient is free to participate in expressive ways. In Chapter 27, Toombs writes in detail of the benefits of modern dance.

Intrusion on Fantasy

A retarded patient may be severely depressed or schizophrenic. His limited intelligence may make it difficult for him to cope with reality, particularly if he is acutely aware of his limitations. The defenses that he uses to handle his frustration may include acting-out behavior and severe withdrawal. The fact that an individual may be functioning on a retarded level does not always indicate that the problem was initially the result of brain damage. It may be the result of emotional disturbance or lack of sensory stimulation. This is discussed by Leland (1964):

We seem to be dealing with various kinds of combinations of emotionally disturbed, brain damaged, retarded individuals, the emotional disturbance either growing out, or existing alongside, of the retarded condition. There are some instances where the emotional disturbance may directly cause retardation, but in those instances there also seems to be some evidence of brain damage. This latter is related to lack of brain functioning. Thus, if the retardation is caused by emotional disturbance, the brain is kept at a semi-nonfunctioning level, as for an extended period of time, regardless of whether or not it was damaged when the emotional disturbances started. By the time we have been able to correct the situation, the brain will be damaged (p. 27).

Frequently, music therapy is prescribed as an intrusive means of treating the withdrawn retarded patient. In finding reality-oriented activities in which the retardate can succeed, the therapist may be able to establish a relationship with the patient. "Children live in a world of people, and much of their development centers around their relations with people. Since music is largely a social art, it is quite naturally inseparable from social living, its opportunities, its challenge, and its problems" (McMillan, 1959, p. 17). The patient may be able to begin with very concrete reality (for example, matching colors or letters to play a melody, or keeping time to music with simple instruments) and progress to an acceptance of the reality of his feelings and behavior. Because music is an expressive medium, it can lead to discussions of the patient's affective reality. Music that encourages motor participation can be useful because it intrudes on the patient's fantasy life. Music listening, however, depending on the type of music and past experiences of the patient, may not only allow but encourage the patient to escape into his fantasies.

As the therapist intrudes, the entire treatment team should be aware of the patient's need to test new reality functions. In the initial stage of testing, much of his behavior may be antisocial; therefore, the team should be supportive in encouraging the testing. However, inappropriate behavior also should be called to the patient's attention, and more appropriate behavior suggested. However, the acting out may be looked on as progress; it is a beginning of reality testing. Because music is structured, it can lead to more organized behavior.

Stimulation

A large number of retarded children are from culturally deprived homes. These children have not received enough stimulation to provide a basis for future learning.

Of importance, particularly in the etiology of mild mental retardation, are the complex physical and psychological deprivations to which some youngsters are exposed in their families and communities. . . . An unfavorable social environment, disorganized family life, or other stress situations may of course also result in an ego defect with or without mental retardation (Committee on Mental Retardation, 1959, p. 12).

If a child is exposed to a wide range of sensory stimuli, he will have adequate firsthand learning experiences so that he can benefit from more abstract learning. The child from a marginal home often is unable to keep up with peers who are from homes where they have been exposed to educational toys, music, travel, and similar enculturating experiences.

Of the group of retardates who are institutionalized, many have congenital brain malformations. Goldberg, Foster, Segerson, and Baumeister (1963) found that "in a survey of an institutional group of retarded children, 61 percent of the retardates were found to be associated with errors of intrauterine development" (p. 287). But even though the retardation is caused by brain damage, there also may be a direct relationship to an inadequate home situation.

Many patients from marginal homes are referred to music therapy for stimulation of interests and additional sensory experiences. They need the reinforcement of successful participation because their inability to compete with their fellows often causes them to be satisfied with less than they are capable of achieving. Music activities can be structured at the level on which the patient can gain increased confidence in his ability to learn new material. Music activities also may provide a setting for learning social skills and personal behavior patterns.

It is seemingly, though not actually, paradoxical that we demonstrate our understanding of the child's aggressive action by setting firm limits on it. The hospital is a microcosm of the community at large; its tasks are to fulfill the aims of the community for its citizens, to produce in the child a sense of structure and conviction, and to establish limits within which he is free to act (Rodman, 1964, p. 606).

Because the child may not realize that his behavior is inappropriate, the therapist should carefully reward or gratify every effort that the patient makes to conform to new social mores. The child from a culturally deprived home may also need music therapy to stimulate his interests in object relationships as well as expand his social contacts.

Cultural factors play a large role not only in determining which children in a given community will be considered mentally retarded, but also when they will be identified. . . . Children from certain sub-cultures may score low on psychometric tests primarily because these tests are culturally biased. Studies have shown that the children from culturally deprived homes will score progressively higher on successive psychometric tests after exposure to social and educational stimulation (Committee on Mental Retardation, 1959, p. 12).

Gratification

There may be groups that are structured with gratification as the primary goal. Musical achievement may offer considerable gratification in itself. However, if performance is rewarded with praise from the patient's companions or from adults, the gratification may be even greater. Many children seem to enjoy performing in programs if they feel assured of success. These performances also allow emphasis on grooming, appropriate group behavior to attain a musical effect, and both personal and social behavior and responsibility. Some patients may request individual practice. This practice can be gratifying, even though the gratification comes from musical accomplishment rather than praise from others. Practice periods may be among the first experiences that the patient has in structuring a block of time for himself. If the retarded child has been institutionalized for a long period of time, he may be accustomed to having people tell him what to do with each minute. However, if he is to make adequate use of his leisure time, he must learn to work at goal-directed activities without depending on others to structure them for him. Fine and Dawson (1964) discuss the need to structure free time:

Failure to adjust in the community was found to be largely the result of the patient's inability to utilize her own free time. She would have no difficulty on the job, but the long evenings and the weekends would hang heavy on the girl and result in her becoming depressed, restless or getting into difficulty, necessitating her return to the institution (p. 28).

Among the studies now being conducted in the area of retardation, there are many that focus on community change and the problems that the institutionalized patient faces in this adjustment. The use of leisure time is one important area for which music therapy can teach music skills and planning for their use, both of which will assist the patient in preparation for community life.

Music therapy can contribute to the diagnosis and evaluation of retarded patients and is useful in treating the emotional maladjustment that typically occurs with retardation. A further contribution can be made in the area of adaptive behavior, because the music therapy session can be structured to include a wide variety of social situations and opportunities for the patient to assume personal and social responsibility.

References

AYRES, JEAN. Development of the body scheme in children. *Amer. J. occup. Ther.*, 1961, 3, 97–102.

Committee on Mental Retardation. *Basic considerations in mental retardation: a preliminary report.* New York: Author, 1959, 43.

FINE, R. H., and DAWSON, J. C. A therapy program for the mildly retarded adolescent. *Amer. J. ment. Defic.*, 1964, 69, 23–30.

FISHER, S., and CLEVELAND, S. E. Body image boundaries and sexual behavior. *J. Psychol.*, 1958, 45, 207–211.

GASTON, E. T. Functional music. In N. Henry (Ed.), *Basic concepts in music education.* Chicago: The University of Chicago Press, 1958. Pp. 292–309.

GOLDBERG, B., FOSTER, B., SEGERSON, J. A., and BAUMEISTER, JACQUELINE. Congenital brain malformations in the mentally retarded. *Bull. Menninger Clin.* 1963, 6, 275–287.

GUTHRIE, G. M., BUTLER, A., GORLOW, L., and WHITE, G. N. Non-verbal expression of self-attitudes of retardates. *Amer. J. ment. Defic.*, 1964, 69, 42–49.

HACKER, F. J., and GELEERD, E. R. Freedom and authority in adolescence. *Amer. J. Orthopsychiat.*, 1945, *15*, 621–630.

JORGENSEN, ELIN K. Helping the classroom teacher build a more effective music program by relating principles common to child development, reading readiness, and music. *Kans. Mus. Rev.*, 1949, *11*, 5–6.

LELAND, H. What is a mentally retarded child? *J. Psychiat. Nurs.*, 1964, *64*, 26–27.

LEVENTHAL, T. Inner control deficiencies in runaway children. *Arch. gen. Psychiat.*, 1964, *2*, 170–176.

LINNELL, Z. M. Authority as a treatment modality with adolescents in a psychiatric hospital. Unpublished manuscript, Israel Strauss Adolescent Pavilion, Hillside Hospital, Glen Oaks, New York, 1960.

MACHOVER, KAREN. *Personality projection.* Springfield, Ill.: Charles C Thomas, 1957.

McMILLAN, L. EILEEN. *Guiding children's growth through music.* Boston: Ginn, 1959.

Psychiatric inpatient treatment of children. Washington, D.C.: American Psychiatric Association, 1959.

REDL, F., and WINEMAN, D. *The aggressive child.* New York: Free Press, 1957.

RODMAN, F. R. Setting limits for aggressive children. *Ment. Hosp.*, 1964, *15*, 606.

SARBIN, T. R. Anxiety: reification of a metaphor. *Arch. gen. Psychiat.*, 1964, *10*, 630–638.

SCHAUFFLER, R., and SPAETH, S. *Music as a social force in America and the science of practice.* New York: Caxton Institute, 1927.

SCHILDER, P. *The image and appearance of the human body.* New York: International Universities Press, Inc., 1950.

SYMONDS, P. M. *The ego and the self.* New York: Appleton-Century-Crofts, 1951.

6

MUSIC THERAPY FOR THE
MODERATELY RETARDED

RICHARD M. GRAHAM

Many moderately retarded persons are able to live in the community, whereas others, needing more help, reside in institutions. Retarded children who are institutionalized usually have more severe personality disorders than do children who reside in the community, although intellectually they may be much the same. The basic goals of music therapy for the moderately retarded, whether provided for in the community or in special institutions, are basically the same: to help the children to higher adaptive behavior levels; to establish better interpersonal relationships, which some authorities consider a part of adaptation; and to help them develop self-esteem. In accomplishing these goals, music therapy sometimes enables retarded children to function more adequately than individual tasks would indicate.

There is evidence that intelligence and musical ability, when measures of musical ability are based on complex musical tasks, are closely related (Drake, 1940; Fischer and Butsch, 1961; Mursell, 1937; O'Brien, 1961). Nevertheless, low measured intelligence does not preclude effective music therapy for the mentally retarded, because music therapy does not depend on the achievement of professional or even medium levels of performance in order to reach its goals. Frequently, a mentally retarded person has achieved more in music therapy than had been predicted for him in his original diagnosis. In considering such cases of unexpected achievement, Jordan (1961) said, "Different levels of performance exist in children at different times. This applies to all children, normal and retarded. In the case of the retarded we may say that situational factors can produce a better picture than anticipated even when the child is truly functioning below average at diagnosis" (p. 208). Such unanticipated changes should not be regarded as cures. "The change is one of amelioration, of improvement, rather than of restoration to normality (cure)" (Jordan, 1961, p. 208).

Music Therapy in Public School Settings

Moderately retarded children who live in the community often are students in the public schools. There has been some disagreement as to whether these students benefit more when placed in regular school classes or in special classrooms. The results of several studies (Baldwin, 1958; Bennett, 1932; Blatt, 1958; Cassidy and Stanton, 1959; Elenbogen, 1957; Pertsch, 1936; Thurstone, 1959) favor regular class placement of the high-level retardate if the goal is academic achievement. In bringing about social and personal adjustment, areas that concern the music therapist in special education, the same studies indicate that placement in regular classes may be inferior to placement in special classes.

Miller (1954), in a junior high school class for mentally retarded children, developed a music program to provide for individual initiative, leadership, and general improvement in capacity for musical self-expression. The use of familiar songs with repetitive words and folk dances based on simple steps allowed the children to improve speech, gain poise, develop a sense of rhythm, and exercise leadership.

Carey (1958), working with a special class, found that mentally retarded children progressed at the same rate in music as they did in academic subjects. It was found that somber songs tended to result in student disinterest and highly stimulating songs tended to cause nervous reaction. Rhythmic activities proved useful in developing self-expression. Weigl (1959) described procedures used in a school for mentally retarded children. In an evaluation of adjustment and attitude changes effected by these procedures, it was found that 10 percent of the students showed no change, there was some change in 20 percent, and 70 percent evidenced improvement that carried over to home and school.

These examples of music with the mentally retarded reveal the special class philosophy. There was no pressure on the children to improve their skills or behaviors so that they might some day participate with "normals" in performing groups. A mentally retarded child with normal musical performance ability would be exceptional. Stevens and Heber (1962) said, "The information obtained from survey and case-study material indicates that competencies in art and music are related largely to the mental development of the child. The mentally retarded are slower to learn and remain longer at each stage" (p. 91).

Some authorities hold the viewpoint that music therapy for the mentally retarded should be a medium for integration into the total school community. These individuals view the instrumental ensemble, for example, as a democratic, cooperative society in which each person does what he can do best. "In music, do not give him (the exceptional child) a separate program—if possible bring him into the musical experiences of normal children, where the exceptional child can cease to be exceptional . . ." (Cruickshank, 1952, pp. 18–20).

Music Therapy in Residential Settings

The institutionalized mentally retarded child usually has some personality disorder that may be the primary cause of his institutionalization. This is particularly true of high-level retardates. Typically, the institutionalized child with high-level mental retardation can be described as being socially and culturally deprived and as having personality disorders that are complicated by subnormal intellectual functioning. One aspect of cultural deprivation normally suffered by mentally retarded children is music deprivation. The harsh circumstances frequently present in the preinstitutional life of the high-level retardate often preclude a normal introduction to and growth in the areas of music. Such a child has only limited opportunities to learn to express himself on a musical instrument. The direct expression of sheer joy through singing—in which normal preschool-age children generally participate—may not be encouraged or tolerated in a home characterized by "poor health, improper diet, frequent moving, and noisy TV . . ." (Riessman, 1962, p. 5). Except for those exposures to TV and radio, the early musical life of the institutionalized mentally retarded child is as much characterized by deprivation as are the other aspects of his life.

The child's previous musical background influences the way he reacts in an institutional music setting. Thus, the music therapist takes this background into consideration when planning and carrying out treatment. A study by Graham (1965) revealed a significant relationship between amount of music deprivation experienced by institutionalized mentally retarded children and their need to perform or express themselves musically. (A discussion of this study will be found in Chapter 39, p. 454.) The evidence from this study revealed that the greater their music deprivation, the greater the children's desire to pursue a musical task designed for their abilities.

A study by Murphy (1957) suggested that social and emotional levels of development can be indicated by the rhythmic responses that middle- and low-grade defectives are capable of making. An attempt was made to elicit active participation from two groups of mentally retarded children. Murphy reported that one group of subjects who responded to musical rhythms with handclapping also would engage in socialized group activity and socialized motor responses. The other group responded on a lower level.

Sheerenberger (1953) described an institutional music program that not only would meet current needs, but would orient the children toward community living. This program was developed around singing and rhythm activities. Songs were selected on the basis of interest, enjoyment, and curriculum correlation. Younger children concentrated on rhythm activities that were used to assist in developing finer coordination between the visual, auditory, and motor processes. The older children participated in folk dancing and other rhythmic activities.

For those retardates who live in an institution, there is a practical problem of adjusting to the norms of musical behavior peculiar to that institution. To be a "good" music therapy patient in an institution requires that the retarded child derive satisfaction from his institutional music experiences and see the "outside" community music activities as relatively less urgent and rewarding. On occasions, a local church choir or similar community music group can be used as an integral social group or part of the "half-way" program for newly released patients. *Far too often on these occasions, the institutions find they have taught the newly released outpatient to function well only in supportive, structured, institutional music ensembles.* In relation to this issue, Sarason's (1952) statement regarding institutional living may be paraphrased to state that there seems to be a choice of goals—either the welfare of the child or the smooth-running institutional music program.

Case Histories

The following case histories demonstrate how some of the problems of moderate mental retardation can be alleviated through therapeutic situations that use musical performance. Reference to the principles and processes in music therapy in Chapters 1 and 2 will indicate more precisely the function of music therapy with the retarded child.

The first case study demonstrates structured and nonstructured uses of rhythm. The creative abilities of the children are enhanced by encouraging them to invent rhythmic patterns. The study also illustrates how well the retarded work in a group during the music sessions. This is because of individual success in an activity in which their group participation is significant and successful.

Case 1. *Ten children (aged seven to ten) of low measured intelligence were students in a special ungraded room of a public school in a large city. Each one was taught to perform on certain rhythm (percussion) instruments. After each child had developed at least a minimal technique, he was integrated into a group that performed alternately as a rhythm band*

and as a free and unstructured music-making group. The rhythm band was a learning situation in which students were taught to recognize and respond to rhythmic accents that were in groups of twos and threes. The therapist would play the piano, and the group, on command, would imitate the beat or rhythmic pattern. During the free period, the students were encouraged to make up rhythmic patterns. These patterns were used as rhythmic backgrounds for piano improvisations by the therapist. Improvisations on the rhythmic idea of a particular student were given a title that included the student's name.

The music therapy session was the only purposely designed group activity experienced by these students. The remainder of the day was devoted to a special class curriculum that consisted of reading, arithmetic, writing, and speech. It was the opinion of the special class teacher, the school principal, and the music supervisor that the students were helped by the music therapy sessions, because *the students accepted each other better while taking part in the music therapy activities than at any other time during the day.*

The next study indicates how music is used to develop skills other than music. In the case of this boy it was used for language development. Also, because of his success in music, the boy's relationships with his peers and teacher improved.

Case 2. T, a ten-year-old boy whose revised Stanford-Binet test IQ score was 68, was assigned to the special class of a public school. T had started kindergarten at the age of six and had been promoted regularly until he reached the fourth grade. His language skills were underdeveloped, and his motor skills appeared to be restricted. When inquiry was made as to his major interests, he mentioned music. Discussions with his former teachers, however, indicated that T would not and did not, or could not, sing. He did not participate in daily rhythm activities. Welfare reports indicated that the home was characterized by considerable cultural deprivation.

The teacher's first concern with T was in the area of language development. Because T had spoken of an interest in music, she asked him to sing a song. T was very reluctant to sing and would only tell her the names of his favorite songs. He was induced to sing after his second day in the special class. His style of singing was country-western. The singing voice was nasal; the diction, enunciation, and pronunciation were patterned after a commercial hillbilly performer; and the intonation was poor.

The teacher realized that for T, singing offered the best way to begin the development of receptive and expressive language skills. The problems of his hillbilly style of singing were discussed with a local music teacher. His teacher had to decide whether to encourage what was considered poor singing in order to foster language development or to develop the singing and leave language development to some means less attractive to T. Because T tended to be withdrawn and hostile in activities except when he was singing for the group, the teacher decided to use his interest in singing for language-development activities.

Most of the songs T knew had lyrics unsuitable for classroom use. He was permitted to sing these songs on occasion, however, simply to allow self-expression. One song, "Detour, There's a Muddy Road Ahead," was used to develop receptive language skills. When he sang the words to the class, all students were required to pay close attention. Afterward, there was a general discussion of the meaning of the word "detour." Later, "detour sign" was considered, and this led to a general discussion of traffic signs. The class and teacher altered the lyrics of some of T's songs, or wrote new verses for them. These songs were used in rhythm games and to help all students learn to follow simple directions presented in musical context.

The skills developed during three weeks of this activity were essentially receptive in nature. Receptive language skills can provide a basis for developing expressive language skills. The gradual development of these receptive skills, coupled with T's desire and apparent need to sing, resulted in a greater ability to express himself. After eight weeks, he was able to participate in formal articulation drills and new games and could recite simple poems. His attitude toward his peers and toward his teacher was much more acceptable to those around him. After sixteen weeks, a retest on an equivalent form of the Stanford-Binet test of intelligence showed a definitely higher performance than the original test. It was the teacher's opinion that T's singing had improved to some degree. She had noticed no detrimental effect of his singing style on the singing of the remainder of the class.

The following is an excellent example of the use of music in therapy. A definite treatment plan was based on a psychiatric evaluation. This study shows the importance not only of the music activity, but also of the relationship between the patient and the music therapist. Here, one is able to follow the behavior of a patient who had difficulties in changing from a one-to-one relationship to that of a group, but who improved sufficiently to assume leadership. This example also demonstrates that the music therapist deals only with behavioral problems exhibited during the music activity, and it emphasizes the importance of the music therapist, without whom progress would not have been achieved.

Case 3. M was institutionalized in a state school for delinquent girls. She had a medical diagnosis of hypothalamic epilepsy and a moderately low level of intelligence. When committed, M was thirteen years of age and had been attending the fifth grade where the teacher described her as "clumsy, unsociable, undisciplined, and having a poor background." Several sexual incidents led to her institutionalization. Her psychiatrist mentioned that organic factors were of less importance than her overall adjustment problem.

Therapy consisted of individual sessions with a psychiatrist and three sessions a week with a music therapist. The goals were better social and personal development and an enriched experiential background. Because M had shown interest in the piano and proved to have some facility, the treatment plan was to allow her isolated activity in the form of piano playing or practice—whichever she desired. Later, parallel musical experiences, directly or indirectly involving the music therapist, might replace the isolated activities.

The first five meetings with the music therapist were devoted to making M comfortable in the music therapy area, and she was allowed to play the piano as much as she desired. After these five sessions, the music therapist introduced duets, assuring M that she was not going to give her lessons but only wanted to have a little fun at the piano. The four-hand piano performances constituted the parallel musical experiences, and only a few suggestions were made to the patient. The music therapist was becoming more and more a highly regarded person in M's life, and on one occasion M told the psychiatrist that she would like to become a music therapist someday.

The psychiatrist then suggested more direct measures toward changing the patient's behavior. M was assigned to the music therapy department as a patient assistant. She accompanied the music therapist to certain cottages where she passed out song materials and collected them, and assisted the therapist in other ways. Because she did not now object to piano lessons, she was put on a regular practice routine. Certain aspects of her conversation regarding boys and sex were no longer tolerated in the music therapy sessions. Other negative aspects of her behavior were discouraged, whereas her progress in piano playing was praised. After six months of increasing proficiency, she was appointed assistant conductor of the church choir. It was her assignment to see that all choir girls were in their seats for rehearsals and to conduct them in one or two familiar hymns. She was readily accepted by the choir, which was very gratifying to her.

The assignment as assistant choir conductor began the period of structured group music activities. M demonstrated considerable improvement in her social and personal development, in her work habits, and in her ability to enjoy herself in certain group recreation activities. A refinement in motor activity was observed in her increased proficiency at the piano and during the conducting sessions.

A psychiatric reevaluation, after seven months of commitment, resulted in reclassifying her level of mental retardation and adaptive behavior from a moderate to a mild level of retardation. Future therapy included plans for some exposure to heterosexual groups and singing in a community church choir. It was believed she had learned much in music therapy that would help her not only in the choir, but in a gradual return to community life.

References

BALDWIN, W. K. The social position of mentally handicapped children in the regular classes in the public schools. *Except. Child.*, 1958, 25, 106–112.

BENNETT, ANNETTE. *A comparative study of sub-normal children in the elementary grades.* New York: Columbia, 1932.

BLATT, R. The physical, personality and academic status of children who are mentally retarded attending special classes as compared with children who are mentally retarded attending regular classes. *Amer. J. ment. Defic.*, 1958, 62, 810–818.

CAREY, MARGARETTA. Music for the educable mentally retarded. Unpublished doctoral dissertation, Pennsylvania State Univer., 1958.

CASSIDY, VIOLA M., and STANTON, J. E. *An investigation of factors involved in the educational placement of mentally retarded children.* Columbus, Ohio: Ohio State University Press, 1959.

CRUICKSHANK, W. Challenge of the exceptional child. *Mus. Educ. J.*, 1952, 38, 18–20.

DRAKE, R. M. The relation of musical talent to intelligence and success in school. *J. Musicol.*, 1940, 2, 42.

ELENBOGEN, M. L. A comparative study of some aspects of academic and social adjustment of two groups of mentally retarded children in special classes and regular classes. *Dissert. Abstr.*, 1957, 17, 2496.

FISCHER, H., and BUTSCH, C. Musikalische begabung und intelligenz. *Z. exp. angew. Psychol.*, 1961, 8, 508–518.

GRAHAM, R. The effect of early music deprivation on the musical performance of institutionalized mentally retarded children. Unpublished doctoral dissertation, Univer. of Kansas, 1965.

JORDAN, T. E. *The mentally retarded.* Columbus, Ohio: Charles E. Merrill Books, Inc., 1961.

MILLER, ANN. Growing with music. *Except. Child.*, 1954, 20, 305–307, 310–311.

MURPHY, MARY M. Rhythmical responses of low grade and middle grade mental defectives to music therapy. *J. clin. Psychol.*, 1957, 13, 361–364.

MURSELL, J. L. *The psychology of music.* New York: Norton, 1937.

O'BRIEN, C. C. Exceptional tonal memory and intelligence. *Percept. mot. Skills*, 1961, 12, 282.

PERTSCH, C. F. A comparative study of the progress of sub-normal pupils in the grades and in special classes. Unpublished doctoral dissertation, Columbia Univer., 1936.

RIESSMAN, F. *The culturally deprived child.* New York: Harper & Row, 1962.

SARASON, S. B. Individual psychotherapy with mentally deficient individuals. *Amer. J. ment. Defic.,* 1952, 56, 803–805.

SHEERENBERGER, R. Description of a music program at a residential school for the mentally handicapped. *Amer. J. ment. Defic.,* 1953, 57, 573–579.

STEVENS, H. A., and HEBER, R. *Research in mental retardation.* Chicago: The University of Chicago Press, 1962.

THURSTONE, THELMA G. *An evaluation of educating mentally handicapped children in special classes and regular classes.* Chapel Hill, N.C.: The School of Education, University of North Carolina Press, 1959.

WEIGL, VALLY. Functional music, a therapeutic tool in working with the mentally retarded. *Amer. J. ment. Defic.,* 1959, 63, 672–678.

7

CLINICAL PRACTICES

Music Therapy As a Basic Program for the Handicapped Child

L O U I S E   W H I T B E C K   F R A S E R

The following clinical procedures were developed in a home-study school for retarded children. The program of this school is based on educational rhythms and eurhythmics to the fullest possible extent. This approach is used to establish a program in which each handicapped child can develop his potentials to the best of his ability.

The students range in age from three to twenty years. Some of them are not able to succeed in public schools; others are severely retarded. The classes contain mongoloid and brain-injured children, also those with multiple handicaps, including the blind and the deaf.

Described here are techniques for the use of music to increase feelings of security, to instruct, to improve muscular coordination, to develop speech, and to encourage socialization. These techniques have been found successful in work with students at the home-study school.

Methods for Establishing Security and Introducing Attention and Listening

These children seem to find security when they enter the music activity with a good attitude and perform under an appropriate amount of pressure. Therefore, the method of entering the music room is important. The children, guided by a music therapist, form a single line outside their classroom and sing as they walk to the music room, "_____ is our leader, our leader, our leader. _____ is our leader, he will lead us to our room." (In the blanks, insert the name of the child who has been chosen leader.) Each child, on entering the room, finds his place as indicated by his teacher, on a sit-upon on the floor, and waits quietly for further directions. Then recorded music with an emphasized walking rhythm is

[87]

played. The teacher takes each child by the hand and walks with him in a circle, returning him to his place on the floor. To encourage the child's awareness of himself and of what he is doing, the teacher tries to help him associate the action with the word by saying, "Walk, walk, walk," until the walking is completed. Soon, the group as a whole can get up and walk independently to the music of the record. Progress is accelerated by the feeling of achievement that the children derive from this independence. This same method is used in teaching running, walking on tiptoes, and clapping when walking.

Success is measured by the children's enjoyment and the pleasure they find in working with music. Nearly every desirable capacity they have will be brought into use through music. It is the *unity of music and movement that is valuable*. Much time must be allowed for this instruction, because these children assimilate the various reactions to music very slowly. In this unhurried response, they keep their feelings of security. That is why lessons based on individual experience with balls, hula hoops, rhythm sticks, and musical instruments always must be flexible, clearly explained, and given only at the tempo accepted by the individual child.

In working with balls, 10-inch balls of bright colors are used. The children try out new skills, such as learning to bounce the ball and catch it with both hands, until finally they can bounce the ball while saying, "Bounce, catch, bounce, catch," to the rhythm of the walking music. Later, to help coordination of movement, the child can try walking and bouncing the ball at the same time. This activity becomes group experience guided by music.

The children delight in using a tambourine or Indian drum to signal group activities. This is done by choosing one child to be the "teacher" and giving him a drum. This child may beat a rhythm for the other children to follow by walking, running, or skipping, as the music indicates. The child acting as teacher is shown how to tap out a slow, even beat contrasted with a fast, even beat, and how to change from one pattern to another after each one has been mastered separately.

Another useful aid is a brightly colored hula hoop that can be rolled, spun, or swung. The hoops can be scattered all over the floor and each child allowed to choose his own hoop, which becomes home base. The children start walking or running freely around as the music directs; when the music stops, they are told to hurry to home base. This introduces color into their experience and is useful as a way to start teaching color recognition.

There is also a period of relaxation during the lesson. At that time, all sit quietly on their sit-upons listening to a lullaby or doing simple finger plays to words sung by the music therapist. It is during a quiet period of listening that the children may assimilate the activities they have tried.

Aids for Developing Ability to Listen and Presentation of Printed Words

The procedure for entering into a music room is always the same. The children come in swinging their arms and singing softly as they take places on the sit-upons in front of their teacher and wait for instructions. Music up to this point has been very simple and direct. *In responding to it, the children have learned to listen to music rather than simply to hear it.* Now, instructions are given for better listening. These instructions are nonverbal and are given by means of a piano or a percussion instrument. The names of the children, having been previously printed in large and clear letters on separate cardboards, are introduced. The children must watch as each cardboard is held up and listen to the name called. The child having that name stands and is told to follow the directions from the instrument played. If it says "march, march, march" and the child responds quickly and correctly, he is recognized by the clapping of his listeners and proudly takes his seat. Each child is asked to perform in a like manner as his name is shown and called. This type of training can be carried on by having two or three patterns played, such as "march—run—march." The ability to listen and a growing awareness of what is being done have developed together.

Introduction of Action Words

The words, "run," "walk," "jump," "hop," and "skip," are printed in large letters on individual cards that are placed on the chalkboard ledge. A child is requested to locate the card that tells the name of the action being played. If the child can find the correct word, he may pick up the card and perform the act. This type of training can be made more complicated by combining a child's name with a certain action. By listening to the music, the child can find out what he is told to do.

Another approach to good listening can be obtained by having the group stand in a straight line with their arms extended in front of them. A chord is struck on the piano. They are told that if the tones played go higher on the piano, they must move their arms up, and if the tones go down, their arms go down. The piano can make rapid changes that delight the children who will try to follow the scale correctly. This can be done individually, calling for quick thinking and muscular coordination. Each child builds self-esteem by trying to follow directions correctly.

Children should never feel they are being subjected to sounds that never cease, particularly to loud music. Music then becomes a noise to which they really do not listen, and that influences them adversely. They either recoil from it or try to compete with it by making more noise themselves. Therefore, there should be frequent physical rest periods in which all may sit and listen to a record of quiet music.

Development of Muscular Coordination

Isolation exercises offer much that the child needs. Seated in front of their teacher, the children are shown a series of simple finger plays. A song is sung that can be illustrated by use of the fingers and thumbs. Each child must be considered individually and helped to gain independent movement of his fingers. A circular movement of the thumb alone can show that "Thumbkin" can dance. Next, the whole hand is exercised by opening and shutting actions accompanying an improvised song. The wrist is now located and named by each one in readiness for a wrist exercise. Each child holds one wrist with his other hand as he sings in rhythm, "I turn my wrist round and round." The children change from right to left wrist.

For arm exercises, the children stand and space themselves. Spacing is done by having them stretch their arms at full length directly in front of themselves and then turn a complete circle in this position, taking care they do not touch anyone. After spacing, they are ready for exercises. When each one has learned what and where his elbow is, a record, such as RCA Rhythm Activities, volume II, is played. Each child makes a shelf with one hand, places the opposite elbow on this shelf, and makes circular turns with his hand, using his elbow as a pivot in time with the music. At the same time, he says, "I am turning my elbow around, I am turning my elbow around." Then the process is repeated using the opposite elbow.

In the next step, each child finds his right shoulder and places his left hand on it. He then swings his whole right arm in complete circles to the music while he repeats, "I am turning my arm on my shoulder." The procedure is reversed for the left arm. Similar exercises, with slightly different procedures, can be used for the legs. When the right leg is swung from the hip, the child supports himself by placing his left hand on the back of a chair for balance. He always repeats what he is doing, such as "I am swinging my leg from my hip." In this way, he can learn the names of the joints of his legs and arms.

Better posture can be promoted by having the children march around the room to music with objects balanced on their heads. The music starts slowly, and the tempo increases as the children's posture improves.

Introducing and Improving Speech

Nursery rhymes are played on the piano and sung by the teacher. Children who have speech join in, gradually learning the words. Those without speech mouth the words without sounds. The same familiar songs are sung to syllables, such as "la-la-la," thus encouraging and enabling a speechless child to try for audible sounds. Eventually, children without apparent speech often participate audibly through complete songs.

Songs can be used to strengthen different speech muscles. Relaxation must be acquired in training for speech. First, a stretching exercise is directed. After spacing themselves, the children stand straight with their hands stretched as far above their heads as possible. A chord is sounded on the piano and a command given to the children. "Push up-up-up-up." As each "up" is pronounced, the chord goes up the scale, and the children are urged to push harder and harder. Finally, a low, loud chord tells them to relax. They are to relax by bending their bodies down from the waist with their arms dangling. This relaxation exercise is needed for a short time each day along with each of the speech-assisting exercises described here.

Socialization Through Music

The children form a circle. This is done in the following way: Each child takes his place on the floor and is shown how to offer his hand to another. Thus, everyone helps to construct the circle. The children are divided, and two small circles are made. This can be shown on the board by drawing a large circle and then drawing two smaller circles. From these experiences with circles can come the learning of games in which a circle is the center of action. Such training produces an awareness of other children and the realization that others are needed in order to have fun in circle games. An acceptance of one another and a desire to help each other in joining hands may be the beginning of social behavior. These games, *accompanied always by music*, can develop into more advanced activities that require acceptable social behavior and cooperation with partners.

Rhythmic Movement

In the beginning, simple movement to music is introduced by having the child walk in circles with his arms stretched out like wings. This is a difficult combination of motions for these boys and girls. The tension felt by most children of limited experiences tends to cause them to keep their arms close to their bodies at an angle similar to the prenatal position. It takes many patient and repeated attempts to develop a free movement in space with arms extended. A child who has fewer handicaps sometimes can move very easily to the rhythm and can be a great help to the others by letting them see how it is done.

Greater movement can be encouraged by the use of a flimsy silk scarf a yard or less square. The child first learns to hold one corner of the scarf and run with it as he watches it float behind him. He may try holding it high as a flag or turning in circles as he watches it follow him. Later, as he holds a corner with each hand, he learns to float it high like a cloud. He can float it at his waist, high as grain or grass, or he can float it low as a stream of water. He learns to enjoy movement with the scarf, and when the record, "My Playful Scarf" (Children's Record Guild, number 1019), is played, he can use the scarf as the record directs him— as a cowboy with a tie around his neck, or as a pirate with a sash around his waist. He also can float it as Batman's mantle. All these imaginative games develop rhythm in movement.

The chalkboard can be used as an aid. Children draw circles on the board to the song, "Little Red Wagon" (Children's Record Guild, number 1004). The circles are large and formed awkwardly in the beginning, but with practice they become more uniform in size and shape. This establishes use of the smaller hand muscles later used in painting, writing, or craft work.

Music is a direct help in reducing feelings of insecurity that stand in the way of future progress. Music, with appropriate action to its rhythm, calls for and maintains attention. Rhythm closely cements the movement of children with the sound of music and thus integrates and socializes. Music can be used as a signal or as a symbol, and often more effectively than the spoken word. It motivates so subtly that it brings added effort toward muscular coordination. Music in song is a stimulation toward speech. Thus, music therapy can be basic and effective in developing better skills in severely handicapped children.

The Drum Corps As a Treatment Medium

CAROL H. BITCON

In the music therapy program of a large state hospital, a drum corps was chosen as a major activity for retarded patients. It was composed of patients whose unit physicians had specified treatment goals for which the drum corps seemed appropriate, those who asked to be included, and others for whom the program seemed likely to be helpful. The average membership of the corps was fifteen. Twenty-one male patients were programed during the period included in this report. Each of the twenty-one members was in the program for at least three months.

The mean intelligence quotient (IQ) of the twenty-one patients was 55, with a range of 30 to 82. The mean age of the patients was twenty-one years, with a range extending from seventeen to thirty-nine years. Table 3 lists the disabilities that were present in the group.

TABLE 3

Disabilities of Patient Group

Disability	Number
Cerebral palsied	1
Severely hard of hearing (IQ 62)	1
Mongoloid speech	3
Oral inaccuracy	7
Industrially blind (glasses worn)	1
Mild stuttering	1
Frontal lisp	1
Epileptic (controlled)	9
Various forms of character disorders	8

The first step in training the corps was to group the patients around two large Masonite tables. Each of them held one drumstick in his left hand. The therapist also held one stick and, together with the patients, counted aloud, "One, two, three, four," while tapping the table with the stick. After this ten-minute exercise, the group practiced drum strokes using the correct hand and stick position. This exercise was used to encourage them to work together. The therapist periodically worked with the patients to enable them to imitate her performance.

The counting eventually turned into "dah, dah, dah, boom" (the boom meaning to drop the stick). The speed was varied. Sometimes, the strokes were extremely slow for a five-minute period and then gradually accelerated to a more rapid beat. This was practiced individually and with the therapist to develop better control and coordination. After the therapist and individual members had worked on the controlled beat, the patients were grouped in units of two and three for additional practice. Eventually, all the members would work together again. In order to control the group, the therapist enforced close adherence to established rules in the drum corps program.

For three weeks, the patients and the therapist spent one-half hour each day working with one drumstick. Then the second drumstick was added. The same procedure was used for training the right hand as with the left, except that the patients held the left drumstick while learning to use the right. Acceptable use of the right stick was achieved in one week. A black circle was painted one-third of the way up the left-hand stick in order to assist the patients in remembering their left hands. This also helped to add emphasis to the left hand.

Each of the daily sessions ended with five minutes or more of marching. Different members were selected to be leaders. The patients formed lines and marched around the room chanting, "Left . . . left, right, left." Some of them could not coordinate the word *left* with the left foot. The therapist occasionally marched with the group, but more frequently stood observing, commenting, encouraging, and assisting individual patients. A whistle signaled the marchers when to start and to stop.

When the patients appeared to be losing interest in the routine drilling with the sticks on the table, a longer time was spent on marching. Chairs and other obstacles formulated a course, and a large mirror was placed along the route so the marchers could observe themselves, thus leading to better posture and motion. Recorded march music was utilized occasionally. Marching helped release undesirable tensions that built up during the period of work with the drumsticks. When a patient marched well, he was asked to march alone so the others could watch and comment. If a patient had problems, a more accomplished member helped him, and the two practiced together. When the patients were first asked to observe each other and to comment, many of the statements were derogatory. However, as each had his turn, many valuable criticisms, which would have been difficult for the therapist to make, were offered readily and accepted by the patients. The members who could not keep a continuous beat on the table with drumsticks were given cymbals to play.

After four weeks of practice, drums were assigned to the patients. As soon as this was done, possessive behavior and insecurity became evident. There were continuous questions regarding the instruments. The therapist believed the patients should be allowed to be possessive because, in an institutional setting, the opportunity to possess is limited.

The group reviewed its earlier experiences of using the table top for a drum pad, practiced marching with the drums, and then the sticks were added. At this point, there was uncontrolled banging and undisciplined participation for four days. Hence, the drums were put away and each step was reviewed. Gradually, after nine weeks of practice, the patients were ready to work on controlling the drums when marching, and a good level of performance developed. Free play with the instruments was allowed for approximately three minutes at the end of each session to permit the patients to bang away, loosen up, and explore. This was found useful because it provided relaxation after the tension of marching, and the members became more familiar with their instruments.

The therapist held weekly meetings with the patients, and various projects were proposed. Members of the corps made suggestions as to where they might perform on the hospital grounds and discussed behavior problems. One successful project emanating from these meetings was a drum corps scrapbook. The patients were asked to look for pictures of bands, marching units, and instrumentalists, and they enthusiastically collected them from ads, magazines, and newspapers. The scrapbook contained pictures, news releases, and especially written comments by each member after participating in special events. During one session, the patients drew pictures of the corps and of themselves. These pictures were placed tenderly in the book.

Gradually, the group developed a "we" rather than an "I" attitude. When one section was assigned to practice, others watched and criticized in a constructive manner. When the sections played together, they worked as a unit rather than as competitive individuals. Discipline at this point was not a problem. Finally, when work was begun on a cadence, it was introduced as a tune. After the corps had chanted the tune, the chant and the drumming were combined. When the cadence became garbled, the group practiced the chant without sticks. These tunes were useful in teaching the three cadences learned.

The first opportunity the patients had to perform, after twenty-four weeks in the drum corps program, was for the regional conference of the National Association for Music Therapy. Following this experience, the corps participated in a local 3-mile parade and finally in a 5-mile Christmas parade. In order to prepare for this latter parade, two Marines from the local air base worked daily with the patients to improve their marching. The military approach was an exciting and refreshing change for the patients. Daily, the members of the corps, volunteers, and auxiliary units marched entirely around the hospital grounds, 2½ miles, to get in condition for the parade.

Many members of the drum corps made progress toward their treatment goals. One patient, who had no tolerance for neatness, progressed in his attempts to improve his appearance. Staff personnel of a unit housing eight of the corps members noticed a change in the appearance of three patients. Two members of the group seemed to become more sociable. During the period of time reported, four members separated from the institution, and additional patients were placed in the corps. Because the group was then performing with self-discipline and control, the new members rapidly adjusted to the program and readily learned the necessary skills. The corps still functions.

Part III

MUSIC THERAPY
FOR PHYSICALLY DISABLED
CHILDREN AND ADULTS

Sister M. Josepha, O.S.F.

*D*iscussion of the use of music with the physically disabled allows description of disablements in great detail, and Sister Josepha provides such descriptions. To the person reading about music in therapy for the first time, and even to the experienced, it may be surprising that the same qualities and potentials of music therapy operate for the physically disabled as for the mentally retarded. However, it should be remembered that all human beings are far more alike than different—all operate under the same laws and are subject in great amount to the same dynamic environmental influences. This becomes clear by reviewing the principles and processes of music in therapy discussed in Part I. In every instance, the purpose is to exchange poor behavior for better behavior.

8

THE PHYSICALLY DISABLED

SISTER M. JOSEPHA, O.S.F.

The physically disabled are persons with physical impairments and defects that are of congenital origin or the result of disease or accident. These impairments may be either single or multiple, ranging in effect from a slight to a total degree of disability (Pomeroy, 1964). The innumerable possibilities of physical impairment indicate the immensity of this group of handicapped persons. Fortunately, the variability of physical impairments permits easy subdivision of the large category of the physically disabled into a number of separate and distinct groups.

Cruickshank (1958), in defining the problems of education for physically handicapped children, classifies these disabled according to their visual, auditory, speech, orthopedic, or neurologic impairments. His classification and description of the various handicaps might be summarized as follows:

1. *Impaired vision* includes partial sight and blindness. Because blindness often is understood to mean total blindness, severe visual impairment sometimes is designated as partial blindness.
2. *Impaired hearing* ranges from a slight to a profound degree of hearing loss. Persons with impaired hearing are divided into two groups, the hard of hearing and the deaf. Further distinction usually is made between congenital and acquired conditions of deafness.
3. *Impaired speech* can result from developmental causes such as delayed speech, from functional causes such as stuttering, or from organic causes such as cleft palate and cerebral palsy.
4. *Crippling conditions* include cerebral palsy, poliomyelitis, clubfoot, osteomyelitis, Perthes' disease, and spina bifida.

Cruickshank makes no mention of aphasia when listing the types of impaired speech that can result from organic causes. Yet, aphasia properly belongs in this category. As defined by Wepman (1951), aphasia is

". . . any language problem resulting from organic disturbance of cortical tissue in which the defect is not due to faulty innervation of the musculature of speech, dysfunction of the peripheral sense organs, or general mental deficiency" (p. 4). This same position is taken by Longerich and Bordeaux (1954), who state, "Aphasia, by definition, implies injury to nerve cells and association fibers" (p. v).

Frequently, aphasic children are described as being brain injured. Kleffner (1960) cautions against synonymous use of the terms "aphasic" and "brain injured." He holds that the term brain injured is very general, whereas aphasia is a specific kind of deficit in language ability. The term brain injured has a connotation of general intellectual defect which, according to him, excludes it from the classification of aphasia. Kleffner, as well as Wepman and Longerich and Bordeaux, seems to justify using a physical approach to the problem of aphasia. In this work, therefore, persons with aphasia will be included in the category of the physically disabled.

In the preceding classification, Cruickshank identifies stuttering as a functional speech disability. Although this definition automatically excludes stuttering from the category of physical disabilities, it has sometimes been explained as being caused by physical or constitutional differences. However, exhaustive studies have not produced definite and positive conclusions of this. Rather, the findings of other studies seem to support the theories that stuttering is a symptom of psychoneurosis or is a learned behavior (Ainsworth, 1958). In light of these findings, stuttering will be excluded from the category of physical disabilities as presented in this book.

In a detailed work on the education of crippled children, Connor (1958) classifies crippling conditions according to their causes, which seem to fall naturally into five categories:

1. *Congenital abnormalities:* cerebral palsy, Erb's palsy, spina bifida, orthopedic deformities, and amputation
2. *Infection:* poliomyelitis, tuberculosis, arthritis, myositis, and epiphysitis
3. *Metabolic disturbances:* muscular dystrophy and myasthenia gravis
4. *Traumatic conditions:* as occur in accidents, and with fractures and burns
5. *Unknown or miscellaneous conditions:* multiple sclerosis and tumors

The remainder of this chapter describes briefly the impairment of, and therapy for, persons with the following conditions: (1) impaired vision; (2) impaired hearing; (3) impaired speech—cleft-palate speech, deaf and hard-of-hearing speech, cerebral palsy, and aphasia; and (4) crippling conditions—congenital abnormalities, infection, metabolic disturbances, traumatic conditions, and miscellaneous crippling conditions.

Therapy for Persons with Impaired Vision

Conditions of blindness can range from complete to slight loss of sight. For practical purposes, a line has been drawn between partially sighted persons and those who are not able to function with the aid of a correction and/or the use of sight-saving devices. Legally, a person is defined as being blind when he has a "visual acuity of 20/200 or less in the better eye after correction, or a visual field restricted to less than 20 degrees in the widest diameter" (Hurlin, 1962, p. 162).

Distinction also is made between the blind and the blinded through the use of terms such as "congenitally blind" and "adventitiously blind." According to Carroll (1961), these distinctions do not clearly define essential differences between the person who has never seen and the person who has seen but has lost his sight. Carroll holds that intelligent efforts toward rehabilitation of the blind are not possible unless there is a realization of a qualitative difference between congenital and adventitious blindness. Yet he feels that it is only by gaining greater insight into the problems of the adventitiously blind that one can come closer to recognizing the problems of the congenitally blind.

In his book on blindness, Carroll deals mainly with problems involved in the rehabilitation of the adventitiously blind. For Carroll, rehabilitation of the blinded person implies the restoration of losses in psychological security, basic skills, communication, appreciation, occupation and financial status, and personality. In their subdivisions, these areas embrace a total of twenty specific losses. Carroll (1961) describes rehabilitation as having four main phases: "training the other senses to take over the role of sight; training in skills and the use of devices; restoring psychological security; and influencing the attitude of his society to him and assisting him to meet the prevailing attitude" (p. 98). They are involved in varying proportion in each of the twenty restorations.

Principles of rehabilitation for the adventitiously blind are mentioned also in some of the music therapy literature. Dauterman (1957) describes three stages of the rehabilitative process for the adventitiously blind: (1) acceptance of blindness as an emotional reality, (2) depression, and (3) subsequent rebuilding of self-concept. He attributes the discovery of these basic concepts to Cholden, who believed that certain definite reactions could be expected from a "normal" person on his loss of sight and that a certain sequence of events and treatment procedures for use in a planned rehabilitation program could be discovered.

In a review of music therapy literature related to the rehabilitation of the blind, Unkefer (1956) recommends as appropriate to all rehabilitation work a short paper by Cholden in which rehabilitation efforts are divided into three classifications: (1) the physical restoration class, (2) the educative rehabilitation effort, and (3) the psychological rehabilitation effort.

Therapy for Persons with Impaired Hearing

Therapy for persons with impaired hearing is generally speech-oriented because of the close relationship that exists between speech and hearing. In a suggested plan of instruction for hard-of-hearing children, Irwin (1953) stresses three phases of hearing therapy: (1) speech correction and conservation, (2) auditory training, and (3) speechreading.

In *speech correction and conservation,* therapy is to be directed toward the improvement of articulation; voice quality; phrasing and timing of thought units; and variations in pitch, rate, volume, and intensity level as required by the particular situation. *Auditory training* is to be concerned with the development of three types of auditory discriminations: (1) gross discriminations, as with highly different sounds such as drums, horns, and bells (note the exclusive use of musical sounds); (2) simple speech discriminations, as with vowel sounds; and (3) difficult speech discriminations, as with consonants and vowels in syllables.

Speechreading is another, and perhaps more correct, term for lip reading. In explaining this phase of hearing therapy, Irwin refers to various methods of speechreading as developed by Bruhn, Nitchie, Kinzie, Jena, Mason, and Markovin. In brief, these might be said to range from the use of syllable drills to dramatized life situations. One method advocates the use of key words, phrases, sentences, and stories related to particular movements. Another calls attention to the "feel" of the movement of the sound. Still another admits a combination of all the other individual methods.

These same aspects of hearing therapy were brought out in a seminar, Speech Problems Due to Hearing Loss, conducted by Norton (1959) at a workshop on speech therapy. Here, auditory training was interpreted to include training in the use of hearing aids as well as the development of sound discrimination. In addition, the members of the seminar strongly advocated that the child with impaired hearing be given ample opportunity to develop his residual hearing. This latter recommendation was based on the belief that every bit of residual hearing present, regardless of how small the amount, can be used profitably.

Therapy for Persons with Impaired Speech

When classified according to the behavior itself, speech disorders seem to fall into four categories—articulation, time, voice, and symbolization. Disorders of articulation include substitutions, omissions, additions, and distortions of speech sounds. Disorder of time or rhythm occurs in speech that is defective in the timing of its utterances. A voice disorder may be characterized by an abnormality in any one or more of the three subdimensions of the tones of speech—loudness, pitch, and quality. Disorders of symbolization refer to difficulties of formulation, comprehension, and expression of meanings (Van Riper, 1963, pp. 18–32).

Although these four major types of speech disorders can be distinctive entities, the same person may have deficiencies in more than one of these dimensions. Certain disorders almost always have multiple features of abnormality. These include cleft-palate speech, deaf and hard-of-hearing speech, cerebral palsy, and aphasia (Van Riper, 1963, p. 33).

Cleft-Palate Speech

Cleft-palate speech, as described by Van Riper (1963, p. 33), is characterized by articulation errors, hypernasality, and a faltering and labored rhythm caused by poor breath control due to nasal leakage of air. Therapy for persons with cleft-palate speech, therefore, cannot be limited to a single approach. This idea also is advanced by Fletcher (1966) in an article emphasizing the regional distribution of developmental disturbances affecting the speech production of cleft-palate children. Because he believes that various disabilities have interacting effects on the speech of the cleft of palate, Fletcher contends that a single therapeutic approach to the problems of cleft-palate speech cannot be expected to produce the best results.

Deaf and Hard-of-Hearing Speech

Deaf and hard-of-hearing speech is characterized by abnormal pitch, intensity, and quality; by unusual rhythms; and by many articulation errors (Van Riper, 1963, p. 34). Therapy for persons with deaf and hard-of-hearing speech is to be directed toward the improvement of articulation, voice quality, phrasing and timing of thought units, and the development of control in pitch, rate, and volume.

Cerebral Palsy

Speech disorders occur in over 70 percent of all cases of cerebral palsy. Many of these disorders are caused by lack of control in using the tongue and lips and in breathing; some are secondary to loss of hearing, which is a frequent concomitant of cerebral palsy. Although speech therapy for the cerebral palsied is directed mainly toward improvement of the ability to communicate, whether it be by speech or other methods, it can exert a positive influence on the development of proper habits of breathing, chewing, and swallowing. Indirectly, it contributes to the improvement of social graces by eliminating drooling and grimacing (Perlstein, 1960).

Aphasia

The young aphasic child who has not learned to speak and to use language symbols in general has not developed behaviors related to symbol usage. The problem in dealing with him is one of special training to compensate for his atypical development. The normal adult, however, usually has learned to speak, read, write, and otherwise use language symbols. In contrast to the atypical development of the child, the adult aphasic is characterized by modifications of behavior. The problem in dealing with him is mainly one of rehabilitation (Berry and Eisenson, 1956, p. 387).

Therapy for aphasic persons is concerned primarily with the development or recovery of language ability through improvement in formulating, comprehending, and expressing meanings. Attention also is given to the associated problems of articulation, phonation, and fluency. The varying patterns of disability in this area necessitate individual treatment of each case (Van Riper, 1963, pp. 445–448).

Therapy for Persons with Crippling Conditions

Crippling conditions, whether they are congenital in origin, developmental, or acquired, are characterized by motor dysfunction of some sort or another. The specific problem may relate to a condition such as muscular weakness, paralysis, lack of balance, lack of coordination, restricted joint motion, or amputation. Although certain general principles of muscle strengthening and/or muscle reeducation will apply to most crippling conditions, the psychological approach to persons having congenital handicaps will very likely differ from that used in case of progressive disease or temporary traumatic conditions. Therefore, brief consideration is given here to crippling conditions in the light of their causes.

Congenital Abnormalities

Of primary concern in therapy for the person with a congenital defect is the kind of body image he is forming, or has already formed, in response to the attitudes of others toward him. Care must be taken to prevent the congenitally deformed person's sense of difference from degenerating into a sense of inferiority and even shame. In addition, he must be helped to attain the greatest degree of independence that his condition will allow in order to ensure his proper emotional and social growth (Work, 1959).

As a crippling condition, cerebral palsy is characterized by any one or more of many abnormal motor functions. Specific therapy for the cerebral palsied consists of improvement in locomotion, stretching of contractures, muscle reeducation and strengthening, and improvement in balance. Psychological preparation should always precede the special techniques used in motor reeducation (Perlstein, 1960, p. 153).

Erb's palsy is a condition resulting in paralysis of the muscles of the shoulder, arm, and hand. Because disuse of these defective body parts can reduce their functional potential, therapy should take the form of a work incentive (Connor, 1958, p. 431).

Spina bifida is a congenital gap in the posterior vertebral column that causes partial or complete flaccid paralysis of the lower extremities (Gartland, 1965, p. 115). In some conditions of spina bifida, bracing is used to promote body locomotion. The person with spina bifida is also in great need of psychological support and stimulus to action within his capacity.

Congenital orthopedic deformities derive from congenital malformations of any part of the musculoskeletal system. The most common of these deformities are clubfoot and congenital dislocation of the hip. Therapy for these two conditions is directed primarily toward correction of the malformations through any one or more of the following approaches: use of plaster casts, plates, or bars; surgery; and exercise (Gartland, 1965, pp. 38, 40, 46).

The congenital amputee is that person who has been born with a complete or partial loss of an extremity. The fundamental goal of therapy for the congenital amputee is the attainment of an acceptable degree of function in grasping and walking. This is accomplished by fitting the amputee with a standard prosthesis and by motivating him to use it (Frantz, 1959, p. 105).

Infection

Anterior poliomyelitis is an acute infectious disease caused by a filterable virus. The most common type of poliomyelitis, the spinal form, can leave the patient with flaccid paralysis of the muscles of his trunk and extremities. During the acute stage of muscle spasm, treatment should entail mainly rest and quiet. After the period of painful muscle spasm is over, therapy includes passive exercise to preserve joint motion and prevent contractures and active exercise to develop muscle strength and function. In some instances, this period of maximum recovery extends for as long as two years following the onset of the disease. The paralysis that still remains after this period is permanent. Some of its crippling effects, however, can be lessened through the use of orthopedic surgical procedures (Gartland, 1965, pp. 111–113).

Skeletal tuberculosis can develop in a person who has or has had a primary tuberculosis focus elsewhere in the body. In about 90 percent of patients, the spine, hip joints, or knee joints are affected. The joints of the upper extremities are affected more frequently in adults than in children. Treatment for tuberculosis infection of bones and joints consists of immobilization and chemotherapy (Gartland, 1965, pp. 100, 104). The therapeutic approach to this type of patient is essentially supportive.

Infectious arthritis is a condition of joint infection. Direct therapy involves surgical procedures followed by joint immobilization and support in traction or a plaster splint. Here, again, psychological support is also important (Gartland, 1965, pp. 91–93). Chronic arthritis refers to a condition of joint inflammation that persists over a long period of time. The two most common types of this disease are rheumatoid arthritis and osteoarthritis. "The goals of rehabilitation for patients with chronic arthritis are: (1) relief of pain, (2) achievement of locomotion and self-care, and (3) psychosocial adjustment" (Hirschberg, Lewis, and Thomas, 1964, p. 315). Myositis, inflammation of the muscle, is similar in effect to arthritis and, therefore, requires a similar therapeutic approach (Connor, 1958, p. 434).

Epiphysitis is a crippling condition frequently caused by an involvement at the head of the femur or at the tibia. Treatment for epiphysitis usually involves immobilization of the affected limb (Connor, 1958, p. 434). The total healing process, beginning with complete and absolute recumbency and continuing with limited ambulation that is aided by protection from weight bearing, may take from twelve to thirty-six months (Gartland, 1965, p. 66). The duration of the healing process implies the need for continued psychological support and encouragement.

Metabolic Disturbances

Progressive muscular dystrophy is a degenerative disease of muscle tissue. Although this disease is continuously progressive, the rate of para- lytic involvement is not constant. In rehabilitating the person with muscular dystrophy, as with all cases of progressive diseases, efforts should be directed toward performance on a level of function that can be main- tained for a given period of time. This level might well be submaximal so that added neurologic deterioration need not immediately change the status and organization of the patient's setup (Hirschberg, Lewis, and Thomas, 1964, pp. 170–172).

The person with myasthenia gravis suffers periods of excessive muscle fatigue, alternating sometimes with long periods of remission or tem- porary improvement. Treatment for this disease consists mainly in the administration of a parasympathetic stimulant at the time of muscle fatigue. A degree of muscle strength can also be restored by rest (Gart- land, 1965, pp. 119–120). The therapeutic approach in general should be psychologically supportive.

Traumatic Conditions

Trauma can cause a variety of crippling conditions, the most common of which is probably the fracture. Treatment for a fracture consists of immobilizing the involved part through use of a plaster cast (Connor, 1958, p. 435). This is not incompatible with a degree of normal daily activity. The therapeutic approach will fit the needs of the particular person in the attending circumstances.

Severe burns often cause physiological damage that can be repaired only by means of plastic surgery. During the initial stage of the healing process following surgery, the goal of therapy for the person with burns is to stimulate circulation and to maintain muscle tone and joint motion through activity of the uninjured parts. When kinetic therapy for the injured part is indicated, care must be taken to select an activity that will prevent contractures but will not place undue strain on the new tissue. This activity should also initiate correct use of the muscle of the injured area (Gleave, 1947, pp. 154–156).

Miscellaneous Crippling Conditions

Tumors and multiple sclerosis are considered crippling conditions when they cause motor dysfunction. This occurs when the tumor, or enlargement, interferes with normal body motion and when the neural involvement of multiple sclerosis causes difficulties in muscular coordination (Connor, 1958, p. 436). Therapy for these two conditions is both medical and psychologically supportive.

References

AINSWORTH, S. H. The education of children with speech handicaps. In W. M. Cruickshank and G. O. Johnson (Eds.), *Education of exceptional children and youth*. Englewood Cliffs, N.J.: Prentice-Hall, 1958. Pp. 386–428.

BERRY, MILDRED F., and EISENSON, J. *Speech disorders: principles and practices of therapy*. New York: Appleton-Century-Crofts, 1956.

CARROLL, T. J. *Blindness: what it is, what it does, and how to live with it*. Boston: Little, Brown, 1961.

CONNOR, FRANCES. The education of crippled children. In W. M. Cruickshank and G. O. Johnson (Eds.), *Education of exceptional children and youth*. Englewood Cliffs, N.J.: Prentice-Hall, 1958. Pp. 429–497.

CRUICKSHANK, W. M. Development of education for exceptional children. In W. M. Cruickshank and G. O. Johnson (Eds.), *Education of exceptional children and youth*. Englewood Cliffs, N.J.: Prentice-Hall, 1958, Pp. 3–42.

DAUTERMAN, W. L. New concepts in rehabilitation of the adult blind. In E. T. Gaston (Ed.), *Music therapy 1956*. Lawrence, Kan.: Allen Press, 1957. Pp. 183–184.

FLETCHER, S. G. Cleft palate: a broader view. *J. Sp. Hear. Dis.*, 1966, 31, 3–12.

FRANTZ, C. H. The child with an amputation. In E. E. Martmer (Ed.), *The child with a handicap*. Springfield, Ill.: Charles C Thomas, 1959. Pp. 90–127.

GARTLAND, J. J. *Fundamentals of orthopedics*. Philadelphia: Saunders, 1965.

GLEAVE, G. MARGARET. Occupational therapy in children's hospitals and pediatric services. In Helen S. Willard and Clare S. Spackman (Eds.), *Principles of occupational therapy*. Philadelphia: Lippincott, 1947. Pp. 141–174.

HIRSCHBERG, G. G., LEWIS, L., and THOMAS, DOROTHY. *Rehabilitation*. Philadelphia: Lippincott, 1964.

HURLIN, R. G. Estimated prevalence of blindness in the United States, 1960. *Sight Saving Rev.*, 1962, 32, 162–165.

IRWIN, RUTH BECKEY. *Speech and hearing therapy*. Englewood Cliffs, N.J.: Prentice-Hall, 1953.

KLEFFNER, F. R. Teaching aphasic children. In J. F. Magary and J. R. Eichorn (Eds.), *The exceptional child*. New York: Holt, 1960. Pp. 330–337.

LONGERICH, MARY COATES, and BORDEAUX, JEAN. *Aphasia therapeutics*. New York: Macmillan, 1954.

NORTON, HELEN. On speech problems due to hearing loss. In W. T. Daley and E. M. Pritchett (Eds.), *Speech therapy*. Washington, D.C.: Catholic, 1959. Pp. 138–147.

PERLSTEIN, M. A. The child with cerebral palsy. In J. F. Magary and J. R. Eichorn (Eds.), *The exceptional child*. New York: Holt, 1960. Pp. 151–155.

POMEROY, JANET. *Recreation for the physically handicapped*. New York: Macmillan, 1964.

UNKEFER, R. F. Music therapy for blind clients. In E. T. Gaston (Ed.), *Music therapy 1955*. Lawrence, Kan.: Allen Press, 1956. Pp. 193–196.

VAN RIPER, C. *Speech correction, principles and methods*. (4th ed.) Englewood Cliffs, N.J.: Prentice-Hall, 1963.

WEPMAN, J. M. *Recovery from aphasia*. New York: Ronald, 1951.

WORK, H. H. The role of the psychiatrist. In E. E. Martmer (Ed.), *The child with a handicap*. Springfield, Ill.: Charles C Thomas, 1959. Pp. 30–43.

9

MUSIC THERAPY FOR THE
PHYSICALLY DISABLED

SISTER M. JOSEPHA, O.S.F.

In the preceding chapter the nature of those physical disabilities in which music therapy could be used as a part of the treatment was described briefly and generally. Treatment aims were set down. Specific literature on the use of music therapy for treating the physically disabled will be considered in this chapter, and the same classification of physical disabilities and order of presentation will be followed as in Chapter 8. The literature varies from opinions through descriptive studies to scientifically oriented investigations.

Music Therapy for Persons with Impaired Vision

Literature concerning the use of music with the blind consists of articles describing music practices and master's theses and doctoral dissertations discusssing specific studies and investigations. Although some works relate to a functional use of music in the rehabilitation of the blind, a greater part of the literature reviews the subject from the standpoint of music education. In a later chapter on music therapy and music education, it will be seen that each overlaps the other from time to time, and on occasion one cannot be well distinguished from the other. Even in these works, occasional references are made to particular therapeutic values that music appears to have had for the blind.

The music practices described in articles seem to parallel those followed in the music curricula of most elementary and secondary schools. Gilliland (1955) summarizes the activities by classifying them into four categories—singing, listening, playing, and dancing. Beetz (1955) tells of a program that includes courses in music theory and class and private instruction on musical instruments. Grupp (1964) notes that some present-day school bands are made up of both blind and sighted students because there is an increasing number of blind students attending public schools. He shows how this program can be handled successfully—even including a marching band. Crocker (1957) describes a creative, therapeutic approach in the teaching of piano to the blind child of preschool age. She claims that piano is not widely used in training programs for the very young child, although piano instruction is generally offered to students in schools for the blind. Baldwin (1955) reports her observations of blind students participating in such music activities as rhythm band, pantomime, eurhythmics, playing piano and flutophone, and listening to talking books (phonograph records) for the purpose of music appreciation.

These same educators and music therapists believe the blind can derive positive benefits, over and above those they derive in common with the sighted, from participation in music. Crocker (1957) stresses the importance of using music with the blind as a means of emotional expression that is socially acceptable and inwardly gratifying. Although this particular value of music also is available to the sighted, it takes on a therapeutic significance for the blind because they are exposed constantly to frustrations that demand emotional release. Crocker also maintains that piano playing can have specific values for blind children as a means of integrating the aural, kinesthetic, and tactile modalities of learning.

Both Gilliland (1955, p. 587) and Baldwin (1955, p. 599) have described the values that eurhythmics, or movement to rhythm, can have for blind children. Gilliland believed this activity gives them physical security and helps them develop grace of carriage and feelings of independence. Sighted children can derive similar values from participation in eurhythmics, but they can also attain them through the use of vision. According to Baldwin, free eurhythmics affords the blind a satisfying release that enables them to move about with the bodily freedom of sighted children.

Arje and Berryman (1966) report that *educational rhythmics*—a technique involving coordination of movement, music, and words—has definite therapeutic values for the blind child. While witnessing a demonstration of this approach, Arje and Berryman observed that blind children who were being exposed to this therapy tended to react with increased freedom and poise and with a more pronounced sense of direction. Educational rhythmics, as a method of practical application of coordinated movement in conjunction with music, was organized by Robins and Robins (1965) primarily for use with mentally handicapped children.

Beetz (1955) claims that not only blind people but also many sighted people feel their life and education would be incomplete without music. Because music has many recreational aspects and because many recreational activities are not available to the blind, he concludes that blind people are often attracted to the study of music.

Alvin (1965, pp. 125–130) believes that the blind person is "forced" by his blindness to develop keen aural and tactile sensibilities. This can be said to guarantee him a degree of success in musical achievement that, in turn, helps to satisfy his peculiar need for security and communication. Concerning communication, Alvin holds that the very expressiveness of music in color and dynamics makes it an effective substitute for the form of communication missed by the blind child—that conveyed through gestures and facial expression. She also contends that musical activities can divert the blind child from egocentricity by helping him become a part of the environment he cannot see.

Research literature concerning the use of music with the blind includes investigations of the status of current practices, the development of adequate teaching procedures, the effectiveness of music in rehabilitation programs, and the comparison of the sighted and the blind in certain areas of musical performance. Four studies describe current practices in music programs for the blind. Two investigate practices in the general music education curriculum and two investigate practices in the instrumental program. All four studies survey objectives, practices, methods, and procedures, both for purposes of evaluation and to obtain information that might contribute to the further progress of those handicapped through loss of sight.

Haldiman (1953) studied music programs in residential schools for the blind. She obtained her information primarily through a questionnaire sent to seventy-five schools in mainland United States, Canada, Hawaii, and Puerto Rico. Her other sources of information were reading, personal observation, research at two schools, personal interviews, and materials for the blind. Her summary of the music curricula shows them to be similar to regular music education programs, but with three added points of emphasis: (1) the use of vocal music to relax muscles of the throat, chest, and diaphragm (this is considered significant because the blind are inclined to be tense and find physical repose and relaxation difficult to attain); (2) the learning of music history and appreciation as a substitute for attendance at concerts and operas; and (3) the study of harmony for an adequate understanding of braille music. Although piano tuning seems to head the list in vocational training, the lack of available music literature in braille and the blind person's inability to sight-read are considered handicaps to his pursuit of professional music. Haldiman concludes that music is given special emphasis in schools for the blind because of the intrinsic values it seems to have for those areas that are of principal interest in the education of the blind—personal and social adjustment, psychological development, and economic independence.

The study by Elam (1958) consists of an investigation of the methods and procedures employed in teaching music to the blind at a particular state school. Elam developed her study through a review of pertinent literature, observations, tape recordings, and an analysis and appraisal of the data. The music activities observed in this study were classified according to the three levels of primary, intermediate, and advanced music. The primary music program (grade 1) included singing, rhythm, listening, instrumental, and creative activities. Part-singing and eurhythmics were added at the intermediate level (grades 2 to 4). Braille music and music appreciation were stressed in the advanced program (grades 5 to 7). The methods and procedures followed were based mostly on five general principles for education of the blind—individualization, concreteness, unified instruction, added stimulation, and self-actualization. At the conclusion of her study, Elam confirms these three facts: (1) Educational processes for the blind must be tangible and concrete, (2) creativity is necessary for easing rigidity as well as for developing spontaneity of thought and action, and (3) activities on lower grade levels should involve the whole child.

The first of the two studies concerned with instrumental music programs for the blind centers exclusively on use of the piano. McCuskey (1944) surveyed seven schools having instrumental instruction for the blind. She investigated several aspects of piano instruction including prepiano experiences with music, planning the lesson, introducing notation, ear training, and materials for beginning piano. The results of the survey showed that five out of the seven schools stressed private piano instruction. There was also evidence that performing popular music was the most common way for the blind to secure an income through music. Because such music lends itself to an individualized approach, it is less rigid in its demands and more adaptable to the handicap of blindness. McCuskey recommended that the class-piano approach be used more frequently in teaching the visually handicapped child, because the class approach can foster socialization and cooperative responsibility, consequently dissipating the aloneness of the child.

Cascio (1954) investigated the status of general instrumental programs for the blind. The particular purpose of his study was to ascertain the status of the teaching personnel, the methods of teaching, and the importance of instrumental performance for the visually handicapped. Following the normative survey method, he sent a checklist to all state superintendents of schools in the United States and a questionnaire to all the schools he knew of in which the visually handicapped were taught. He discussed the curricula and techniques revealed in this study from a purely educational viewpoint. The values he attributed to music were mainly those that the blind person experiences in common with the sighted. However, one outcome of his study is particularly significant: There was an indication that considerably more emphasis is being placed on music in schools for the blind than in other schools.

Three studies are related to the development of adequate teaching procedures in music programs for the blind. The first is a study by Stoltz (1939) of the reactions of elementary children to a modern music education program in a residential school for the blind and was an attempt to discover the materials and procedures that had proved practicable in teaching music to the visually handicapped. The curriculum that was compiled as a result of this study seems to parallel regular music education curricula in both content and procedure. One exception was made for the blind: Models were used as an aid in forming concepts of certain material objects. The study focuses on the need for considering two objectives when teaching the blind child: (1) to enable him to take an independent place in the world of the sighted through developing his initiative, self-confidence, and cooperation; and (2) to lead him to realize he has many abilities and capacities that place him on an equal footing with the sighted.

The work of Hoy (1954) is based on a questionnaire sent to piano teachers in schools for the blind in the United States and Canada. The work is of educational significance for the music therapist. In it, Hoy gives a clear explanation of the relation of braille music to the braille alphabet, and indicates the exact point in the learning of braille at which the child should be ready to begin his first piano book. He also explains the two general methods—*reading and playing* and *memorizing and playing*—that are employed by the visually handicapped in learning to play particular selections on the piano. This knowledge, plus a list of method books and suggested procedures, might prove a valuable aid to the therapist who needs guidance in the teaching aspects of this activity.

DiPasquale's (1956) thesis was intended as a beginning instrumental program for use in institutions for blind children. It includes a long list of substitute devices to be used in explaining problems to the students. These problems relate mainly to descriptions of instruments, manners of holding them, and required embouchures. DiPasquale also suggests a modified technique for conducting an instrumental ensemble of blind performers. His work is of value as a system of adaptive techniques for the presentation of ideas that normally depend on sight for their proper understanding.

Research literature relating to the effectiveness of music in the rehabilitation of the blind consists of three studies. The bases of the findings are experimental, experiential, and exploratory. The experimental study of Hartley (1954) deals with the effectiveness of music activities in aiding the blind child's individual growth and adjustment to his physical limitation. In this work, Hartley presents several considerations of childhood blindness and their indications for musical experiences that he derived from clinical experimentation. Because of the absence of visual stimuli, the blind child is characterized by bodily inaction and a retarded organization of physical faculties. Perception of auditory and tactual stimuli is basic to his independent movement. Music has several important applications: It can be used to provide the necessary stimulus for movement; it can facilitate action without emphasizing an isolated physical act; and its demand for various levels of physical skill and bodily coordination leads to expansion of the blind child's physical capability. Music can help to develop social awareness because it is social by nature and demands a great deal of group participation. At the end of his study, Hartley cites several areas of improvement that he observed to be the result of the musical activities. He claims they prove that functional music can have many beneficial effects on the life of a blind child when it is applied scientifically.

Schapiro's (1955) work utilizes piano experiences in the rehabilitation of the blind adult. Her findings and recommendations are based mainly on her direct experiences in this area. She has organized them according to problems, basic aims, and precautions, and follows this with a detailed description of the first ten lessons to be given at the piano. Schapiro believes that the therapeutic possibilities of piano playing lie in two main areas: the constructive interaction resulting from the therapist-client relationship, and the cycle of personal gratification → sense of accomplishment → self-confidence → motivation → real learning. She also believes that the development of a musical skill gives the blind person the power to reproduce music and experience it at will—a power not possible in many other skill areas. She lists the values she observed music to have for the blind person as a positive influence on his accepting his physical condition, as a means of helping him to construct or reconstruct his self-confidence, and as a means of stimulating his interests.

Unkefer (1958) reports a research project in which a tentative two-year music therapy program was developed for use in a rehabilitation program for the adult blind. The first part of the project was necessarily exploratory. In the ensuing study, uses of music that tended toward goals of hobby formation or the development of leisure-time activities were recognized as being valuable but were excluded from the discussion. Unkefer classified the music activities in the project as creative, educational, recreational, and capable of promoting the development of manual skill. He called attention to those music activities that appeared to have significance in the adjustment phase of the rehabilitation process and to those that yielded early and important diagnostic materials. He also indicated the therapeutic value of relationships achieved by the guidance of the music therapist. These several considerations formed the basis of his selection and use of six case studies for descriptive purposes. In cases 1 and 2, successful music experience was substituted for earlier unsuccessful experience. Cases 3 and 4 illustrated the use of music as an aid to diagnostic appraisal. Cases 5 and 6 gave examples of supportive relationships that can be attained through musical experiences. In his conclusions, Unkefer stated that beside serving as a means of identifying particular values of music in the rehabilitation of the blind, the project suggested continued effort in the use of music for travel-training and the use of rhythmic music to facilitate smooth walking movements in the congenitally blind.

Research literature on the use of music with the blind also includes three comparative studies of the blind and the sighted. In the first of these studies, Grissom (1957) compared problems of teaching voice to sighted and sightless students in order to determine whether the teaching requirements for each group were different. Although her findings revealed that frequent special attention had to be given to the blind student's problems of breathing and muscular tension, she concluded that the teaching approach for both groups of students was essentially the same.

The second comparative study is not concerned specifically with music, but its results may have implications for the use of music with the blind. In this study, Schwartz and Steer (1962) compared the reactions of congenitally blind and sighted subjects to delayed auditory feedback. The subjects of this study were seventeen young adult males. Seven of them were congenitally blind, ten had normal vision, and all had normal speech and hearing. They were presented with two stories, one through listening and one through silent reading. Recordings were made of their impromptu retellings of the stories under synchronous feedback and under three different conditions of delay. The amplification levels for these feedback conditions were based on each subject's determination of his own tolerable loudness level. The blind subjects showed a reduced phonation/time ratio under all conditions of feedback. They also tended to have lower indices of major sound-pressure level than the sighted for synchronous feedback. Both groups showed a reduction in the index of sound-pressure level under conditions of delay. Schwartz and Steer concluded that the gross difference between the phonation/time ratios of the blind and the sighted seemed to confirm the supposition that blind persons are more susceptible to sidetone alterations than the sighted because they depend to a greater degree on auditory cues in the environment.

The third comparative study is by Heim (1963), who compared the scores made by students on the secondary level in residential schools for the blind with norms established for sighted students on the Wing Standardised Tests of Musical Intelligence. One hundred and twenty-five students from seven schools were selected as subjects for the test. The series of seven tests covered various areas of music ability and appreciation. None of the tests required the students to read a musical score. Although the results of the tests showed fewer scores in the middle range of ability than would have been expected, the median scores for both boys and girls were in keeping with the expectancies for sighted subjects of the same age. The standard deviation indicated no great difference in the distribution of scores between the sexes. On the basis of the data gathered in this study, the blind are not superior to the sighted in music ability.

In conclusion, articles and clinical reports about the use of music with the blind were observed to be mainly descriptions of music practices and techniques in this area. The reports were generally of educational significance, although they had occasional references to particular therapeutic values that music appears to have for the blind. Few works directly concerned the functional use of music with the blind.

In an earlier discussion of rehabilitation of the blinded person, reference was made to four main phases of rehabilitation: (1) training the other senses to take over the role of sight, (2) training in skills and the use of devices, (3) restoring psychological security, and (4) educating society toward him and assisting him to meet the prevailing attitude. Examination of the various approaches presented in the research literature shows that, to some extent at least, the first three phases are being accomplished. There seem to be no music activities directed specifically to the realization of the fourth phase, unless it could be inferred that the attitude of society toward the blind is influenced indirectly by the promotion and accomplishment of the first three phases. This is brought out in a case study presented in the latter part of this chapter.

Music Therapy for Persons with Impaired Hearing

Literature concerning music therapy for the deaf and the hard-of-hearing consists mainly of articles and clinical reports on the use of music at institutions for the deaf. These accounts indicate that some therapists and teachers have found music to be of value for the auditorially disabled, primarily as a positive influence on their development of a rhythmic sense. The few correlation studies and experiments that have been done also are concerned with rhythm, although the amount of published research in this area is minimal. Certainly the use of rhythm offers the greatest benefit to the deaf and hard-of-hearing. It should be remembered that these handicapped people do not hear music as the normal person does.

There seems to be general agreement among therapists and teachers about the particular values that rhythm has for the auditorially disabled, but the reports vary slightly with respect to approach and emphasis. Lane (1953) cites the use of rhythm as an underlying factor in attaining the following objectives for the deaf child: (1) improved bodily coordination, (2) improved speech through better speech rhythms and correct accent, and (3) social habilitation through the acquisition of skill and grace in social dancing. Dattilo (1953) stresses the use of music for the development of rhythmic sense, both as a preliminary step toward the development of poise, grace, and balance, and as a foundation for speech through accent and phrasing. Harbert (1953) presents a case study of a deaf child whose enjoyment of rhythmic response led to a more positive attitude toward treatment.

The deaf child's perception of music is based almost exclusively on his tactile sense. Given sufficient opportunity and guidance in this respect, he can learn to distinguish musical vibrations in terms of rhythm and accent, but only gross pitch difference. Lane (1953) describes a program in which deaf children learned to discriminate gross pitch differences through the sense of touch. With fingertips on the sounding board of the piano and eyes closed, these children replied "high" or "low" as the teacher played chords in extreme registers on the piano. This approach is mentioned by Gilliland (1955) as being in common use. Sister Giovanni (1960) believes that a deaf child can become acquainted with the concepts of high and low sounds more effectively by playing the piano himself. She holds that the vibrations he produces on the piano can help him gain a better concept of high and low as they are related to his own voice production.

Alvin (1965, pp. 130–136) discusses the problem of deafness with regard to the limitations it can place on the learning process and to the drastic way it can alter personality. Because deafness impairs or prevents the acquisition of language, it is frequently a barrier to social contacts. Consequently, the deaf person tends toward withdrawal, depression, and neuroticism. Alvin believes that the deaf person's experience of musical vibration through his tactile sense is for him an important means of contact with the world of sound.

Wecker (1939) reports an experiment conducted in public schools to "determine whether the completely deaf child could be brought to an appreciation of music, and through appreciation, to a self-expression in music somewhat approximating that of the normal child" (p. 47). Twelve children, classified as profoundly deaf, were given music through headphones with individual volume controls. After a period of exposure, they were asked to beat responses to the vibratory stimuli. They were able to respond, progressing from simple to double and triple rhythm. Finally, a selected group of four children beat a correct rhythmic pattern with a drum and tympani sticks to the music of an orchestra, giving evidence of individual response and expression to rhythmic stimuli. It should not be forgotten, however, that deaf children do not "hear" music.

Because the only pitch experience of the deaf child is on his own monotone level (usually middle C), the experiment included attempts to teach the children pitch discrimination with middle C as the starting point. The oboe was selected for this study because of its intensity. Wecker (1939) concluded that "If a deaf child can but react to a very narrow range of pitch differences, he can be taught to speak with the same natural voice inflections used by a person with normal hearing" (p. 48). The strength of this conclusion does not seem warranted.

Madsen and Mears (1965) report an experiment conducted in a psychology of music class to determine whether tactile thresholds have specific relationships to intensity and frequency levels of sound stimuli. In this experiment, an elaborate specially designed mechanism was used to measure tactile threshold with and without sound stimuli and with the sound stimulus varying in both frequency and intensity. Care was taken to determine skin response alone. The possibility of bone conduction and excitation of hair follicles was eliminated by using the arch of the foot as the excitation area. Two pure tones, one of 50 cycles per second (cps) and the other of 5,000 cps, were presented at sound pressure levels of 60 and 100 decibles. Deaf subjects were used for the experiment so that the possible tactile effects of sound could be isolated. The results of this study indicated the following: "(1) Sound vibration does have a significant effect upon the threshold of the tactile sense; (2) A 50-cps tone at both high and low pressure levels *desensitizes* the skin and raises the tactile threshold; and (3) A 5,000-cps tone at both high and low pressure levels seemed to *sensitize* the skin (although this was not statistically significant)" (p. 67).

Traughber (1959) tested the ability of deaf children to discriminate musical stimuli such as music and noise, different rhythms, high and low tones, qualities of chords, intervals, musical instruments, and degrees of intensity. The thirty-seven subjects, congenitally deaf adolescents institutionalized at a school for the deaf, were classified as aphasic, nonaphasic, with recruitment, without recruitment, and aphasic with recruitment. The tests consisted of randomized paired items played from a tape, both in a free field and through earphones.

Some subjects were able to discriminate between noise and music, but only one subject could discriminate significantly between high and low tones. The group as a whole responded significantly to the discrimination tests of rhythm and to both chordal and intervallic qualities. The group did not respond significantly to different levels of intensity. Discriminations in general seemed to be better when the sounds were played in a free field. The subject's ability to discriminate appeared to have no relationship to either the phenomenon of recruitment or the degree of hearing loss.

Traughber concluded that most so-called deaf children can perceive some of the various components of music and, consequently, that music should be used to help him form rudimentary concepts of sound and to provide an environment that he can experience in common with the normal child. He also recommended that music for the deaf child be played in a free field because this seemed to afford greater opportunity for tactual discriminations than did the use of earphones.

In conclusion, it has been observed that articles and reports on the use of music with the auditorially disabled emphasize the value of music as a positive influence, particularly in the development of rhythmic sense. Although the accounts seem to relate the development of rhythmic sense primarily to the development of speech, some reference is made to the value rhythm has for the development of grace, poise, and body coordination. In one instance, rhythm was considered a dominant factor in communication and self-expression.

These various uses of music with the auditorially disabled are exemplified in the clinical reports that are presented in Chapter 11. The report of Crigler and Snively also brings to light an approach that is seldom mentioned in the literature—the use of music as a diagnostic tool. The purpose of this approach is to supplement the knowledge obtained from the audiogram. This method has particular significance for work with deaf children too young to respond to ordinary testing procedures.

The amount of research literature concerning the use of music with the auditorially disabled is meager, but Ewing's (1958) book may be particularly useful to the music therapist. The few studies that have been done lend support to most of the clinical practices described. Their findings may be summarized as follows:

1. There is a positive relationship between motor organization and the ability to read lips.
2. There is little correlation between the ability to discriminate pure-tone frequency and the ability to discriminate speech.
3. Deaf children are able to respond to rhythm.
4. Deaf children are able to discriminate and match pitch.
5. Exposure to amplified sound appears to influence the development of normal responsiveness to sound in infants originally diagnosed as deaf.
6. Deaf children can be brought to some appreciation of music and,

through this appreciation, to a self-expression somewhat approximating that of normal children.

7. Participation in music therapy can help deaf children develop increased self-esteem, better interpersonal relationships, and a more profound awareness of the world around them.

Perhaps the implications of these findings are that therapists should give attention to the psychological benefits deaf children can derive from musical experience as well as to benefits related to the development of spoken language. Whatever expands the sensory world of the impaired has far greater importance than would the same sensory expansion for the unimpaired.

Music Therapy for Persons with Impaired Speech

Speech defects frequently are divided into the four categories of articulation, phonation, rhythm, and language dysfunction. A single speech-defective person may exhibit deficiencies in two or more of these categories at the same time. For example, brain-damaged adults often manifest impairment of language function as well as of articulation, and most cleft-palate children have defects of both articulation and voice (Berry and Eisenson, 1956, pp. 316, 323–325). Sometimes the overlapping of the same basic speech defects in categories of speech-defective individuals emphasizes the need to plan music therapy techniques in light of the speech defect itself. The manner in which this can be done is outlined and defined clearly in the report of Wells and Helmus reviewed in Chapter 11.

The two case studies appended to the report of Wells and Helmus describe how treatment was directed simultaneously toward correction of the speech disorder and resolution of the accompanying emotional problem. Initial attention was given to lip and tongue exercises that were motivated through song and supplemented by other musical and rhythmic activities. Although the basic techniques were the same, they were easily adapted to the different age levels through the appropriate selection of materials. In both cases, the resolution of emotional conflict was promoted through guided, successful accomplishment in supplementary music activities as well as in speech performance.

At other times, the presence of several speech impairments in the same person points up the need to plan music therapy techniques in light of the total disability. This is especially true with regard to persons with cleft-palate speech, deaf and hard-of-hearing speech, cerebral palsy, and aphasia.

Cleft-Palate Speech

It is in the area of speech habilitation that music has been used with cleft-palate children. Although recent years have witnessed progress in speech habilitation programs for these children, published articles and research describing the use of music are practically nonexistent. Therefore, music therapy for cleft-palate children is based predominantly on current practices in music therapy and their relationship both to already established principles in the field of speech therapy and to continuing research developments.

In a review of the literature in the field of speech therapy, McDonald and Baker (1951) point out that speech correctionists generally have recognized three major speech-production problems in the cleft-palate patient—hypernasality, nasal emission, and misarticulation. They proceed to clarify these problems by presenting a summary of the various theories about the nature of cleft-palate speech that have been developed through research, observation, and clinical experience.

Hypernasality, according to many writers, is the result of failure to effect a velopharyngeal closure. McDonald and Baker list various interpretations of this theory according to such authorities as West, Kennedy, and Carr; Nusbaum, Foley, and Wells; Kanter, Harrington, and others. This is followed by a brief summary of the findings of Russell, Williamson, Hixon, and Kelly, wherein nasality seems to be associated with conditions other than the velopharyngeal closure, such as throat and mouth tension, small mouth openings, and cavity relationships. McDonald and Baker (1951) conclude with their own hypothesis concerning hypernasality:

> There is a critical point in the degree of closure of the nasopharynx. It is at this critical point that a characteristic balance or ratio is established between oral and nasal resonance. If this critical point is not reached, "nasality" will occur. . . . We further hypothesize that at least some of the cleft palate patient's "nasality" results from his persistent habit of elevating the mandible and the dorsum of the tongue during speech (p. 11).

Nasal emission, in the opinion of McDonald and Baker, has not always been clearly distinguished from nasality. Findings of the only available research—that of Nusbaum, Foley, and Wells—indicate that vowel sounds free from nasality may be made even when air is escaping through the nose. The concluding hypothesis associates nasal emission principally with mandibular and lingual position and movement and only secondarily to "(1) the degree of patency of the nasopharyngeal port; (2) the degree of constriction of the pharynx; and (3) the habitual use of excessive air pressure which the cleft palate patient appears to develop to compensate for his 'leak' " (McDonald and Baker, 1951, p. 12).

The problem of misarticulation has been attributed to various conditions such as improper articulatory adjustments of the tongue caused by anomaly in structure or developmental function; general speech retardation; or hearing loss. McDonald and Baker (1951, p. 13) conclude with their own hypothesis that the articulatory mutilations of the cleft-palate patient are the result of his habit of talking with the jaw elevated and the dorsum of the tongue held high in the back of the mouth. This, in turn, makes it impossible for the speaker to make free use of the tip of the tongue, which is necessary for the accurate production of many speech sounds.

Michel has submitted a report, presented in Chapter 11, of current clinical practices in the use of music with the cleft of palate. The music therapy techniques described by him were directed toward the solution of the three problems we have been discussing. Attempts were made to correct hypernasality through singing, playing the flutophone and kazoo, and using open-throat exercises with free tones. Treatment was directed toward the reduction of nasal emission through playing the instruments, which served both to facilitate and motivate correct breath-stream direction. Correction of misarticulation was approached through the use of selected articulation exercises in song.

Playing simple wind instruments comes under the category of "blowing" in speech therapy techniques for cleft-palate conditions. Speech correctionists formerly placed great reliance on blowing exercises that consisted of blowing up balloons and puffing at bits of paper and cotton as well as tooting on whistles and playing harmonicas. Although these techniques are still in use, they are no longer treated with the same emphasis (Johnson, Brown, Curtis, Edney, and Keaster, 1956, p. 342).

McDonald and Baker (1951) point out several commonly held objections to the use of blowing, especially as a routine exercise. These are (1) exclusive concentration on velopharyngeal closure; (2) difference in types of movement used in blowing and in speaking; (3) possible development of undesirable accessory movements; (4) use of too much air pressure; (5) psychological problems created by failure and frustration in initial blowing exercises; and (6) observed development of nearly normal speech, in some cleft-palate patients, without the use of blowing exercises.

The music therapy techniques described by Michel in Chapter 11 seem to have avoided some of these objections. Exclusive concentration on velopharyngeal closure seems to have been unlikely, inasmuch as the activities included group singing as well as playing pre-band instruments. The patient's monitoring of his own speech for correct sound discrimination was encouraged through ear training. This is in accord with recent evidence that nasal emission of air during speech can be reduced effectively by concentrating clinical attention "on what is heard rather than on the portal of emission" (Johnson et al., 1956, p. 342). Because a person does not speak as he blows, more acceptable therapy is concerned with directing the flow of air through the mouth and throat as resonators (Cypreansen, Wiley, and Laase, 1959, p. 133). This approach was effected by playing the kazoo, an instrument through which one hums. Use of too much air pressure was avoided by utilizing actual instruments instead of simple blowing. Overblowing on instruments causes poor tone quality. Therefore, playing these instruments can facilitate control of air pressure by directing attention to the sound being produced rather than to the blowing process itself.

The present-day attitude toward the use of blowing exercises with the cleft-palate patient is not as negative as it might at first seem. McDonald and Baker (1951) suggest that blowing exercises can and should be used under the following conditions: (1) presence of little or no perceptible movement in the velum or the pharyngeal walls—blowing exercises might initiate such movement; (2) the need for modification of mandibular and lingual habits—blowing exercises can increase mobility of the velopharyngeal structures; and (3) emotional resistance to speech therapy—blowing exercises, as a nonspeech activity, may serve as motivation. Although the report on the music therapy techniques used by Michel does not point to any specific relation of the activities to these three conditions, the relationship is obvious, especially to conditions 1 and 3. The use of open-throat exercises and the playing of simple wind instruments coincides with condition 2. In all, there seems to be a definite correlation of current music therapy techniques for conditions of cleft palate, as described by Michel, with the principles of speech therapy in this same area.

Deaf and Hard-of-Hearing Speech

In Chapter 8, it was noted that therapy for persons with impaired hearing tended to be speech-oriented. Although articles and clinical reports cited earlier in this chapter show that music has positive values for the development of speech in the auditorially disabled, they also refer to the values music has for the development of poise, balance, communication, and self-expression. Because these various developments are closely related, speech problems have been discussed in the general section dealing with music therapy for persons with impaired hearing (p. 117).

Cerebral Palsy

Speech disorders of the person with cerebral palsy are caused mainly by his inability to control the use of his tongue, lips, and breathing. Such inabilities result from motor dysfunction. This is usually only one aspect of a general neurological condition. Therefore, speech rehabilitation of the cerebral palsied will be included in the following chapter, where cerebral palsy is treated in its totality.

Aphasia

Although literature concerning the use of music with aphasia is sparse, the few articles and clinical reports on the subject do credit music with having therapeutic value for aphasic persons in several ways: (1) as an intervening wedge in communication, (2) as a means of increasing propositional speech, (3) as an indirect influence on speech improvement, and (4) as an emotional outlet and a means of experiencing feelingful relationships with others.

Palmer refers to the use of music as an intervening wedge in the so-called congenital or developmental aphasias. He cites cases handled through an extensive home program in which the parents are advised to expose their child to music constantly along with other items in the treatment program. After three months of this routine, the child is re-examined; it is not uncommon for him to begin to talk toward the latter part of the three-month period, even though he may have shown little or no linguistic comprehension and had uttered no meaningful word prior to treatment. Palmer (1953) gives another example, that of a precociously developed child of eighteen months who had suffered severe encephalitis and was left without comprehension or speech. When either of the parents would sing a song the child had learned before illness, "he would immediately start to sing it, quietly, with good diction, and with every indication of understanding" (p. 164). Some language ability was developed in this child, apparently through the influence of his musical participation.

In some cases of adult aphasia, melodic patterns have been used to bring about an increase in elemental units of propositional speech. According to Palmer (1953, p. 165), this approach is used best with the aphasic who does not have an actual language loss, but whose speech shows considerable limitation in those elements subserving general meaning—the reflex melodic, rhythmic, and accentual functions of language.

When this approach is used with children having severe conditions, attention is given to meaningful intonations rather than words.

It is difficult to determine the degree of contribution by music therapy to the improvement of speech. Goodglass (1963) recognizes music as having an indirect influence on speech in ordinary conversation because it provides a basis for relationship with other patients. Klingler and Peter (1963) also consider its influence to be indirect, a source of motivation for speech through successful accomplishment. They noticed that several persons with little or no speech appeared to lack motivation because of past failures in speech attempts. These patients frequently produced their first words while trying to sing with other patients. This success seemed to contribute toward a more positive outlook and better motivation in other therapies.

The use of music as an emotional outlet is not new. The ability to gain emotional gratification from musical experiences, and particularly from repeating familiar musical experiences, is a type of music appreciation available even to the aphasic. Goodglass (1963) claims that in cases of aphasia where a part of the brain that is essential for speech has been injured, it is very common to find some preservation of the ability to appreciate music and, in some degree, to sing. He maintains that there are many patients who have completely lost the power to speak effectively and yet have retained an ability to sing. The patient who has a well-preserved ability to sing usually finds enormous satisfaction in singing. In addition, the relationship he gets by joining musically with other people "is a much more immediately emotionally involving one than one that has to be filtered through speech and the conventions of polite social conversation" (p. 107). Here, music can be said to act as an effective shortcut to the feelings of the patient.

No experimental research studies were found that related specifically to the use of music for aphasia. The articles of Palmer, Goodglass, and Klingler and Peter describe the effects music seems to have had on congenital and adult aphasia, but their reports are observational.

Goodglass (1963) presents rather clear evidence of a physiological condition underlying the dissociation of musical performance from language. His findings describe postmortem conditions of the brain of a patient who had manifested this phenomenon of dissociation and who had died while at the hospital. They are significant in that they show preservation of the structure known as Broca's area and preservation of a small island of tissue near the front tip of the temporal lobe. According to Goodglass (1963), this preservation of the anterior portion of the temporal lobe nearly coincides with that found in earlier cases in which musical abilities have been isolated by brain injury.

Klingler and Peter (1963) describe a program in which singing was used as a therapeutic adjunct in the treatment of the aphasic. They report techniques that not only had proved effective in the past, but also held true in their own experience. These techniques can be summarized as follows: (1) use of a tempo that is slower than normal, but fast enough to afford some challenge; (2) presentation of good sound patterns by means of the therapist's own clear enunciation of words; (3) use of songs with few words at a fairly regular rhythm; and (4) some reminder of the words in the form of visual reinforcement.

In conclusion, it can be said that the general objectives of music therapy for aphasia need not differ from those of other therapies. Music can be used as a positive influence in the special training of the aphasic child and as a means of rehabilitation for the aphasic adult. Music has values for both types of patients in the improvement of communication speech. Music can be, for the child, meaningful intonation that contributes to the development of fundamental speech communication rather than an isolated verbalization of vowels and consonants. The dynamics of melodic patterns, in turn, can influence the development of propositional speech in the adult. Finally, a rich musical background for the child can facilitate the special training that is necessary to compensate for his atypical development, whereas active participation on the part of the aphasic adult can lead to his own rehabilitation.

One of the most important aspects of adult rehabilitation is social. Many aphasic patients are essentially cut off from useful communication with other people and, therefore, have much need for emotional outlets and positive relationships with others.

Singing is the predominant music activity used with aphasics, although a complete musical approach might also include such activities as whistling; exercises in tone matching, inflection, and volume control; and lip and tongue exercises. Music therapy can be used to help the aphasic person achieve an optimal role within the limits of his physical and intellectual capacity. With the medium of music, the therapist can bring about an increase in morale and provide new interests for the patient. The music therapist, in the words of Goodglass, (1963) "can make, essentially, the difference between a patient who cannot be reached, is not interested in staying in the treatment situation and goes home, or goes to a nursing home to vegetate, and one who is an interesting and happy addition to the hospital or to his home" (p. 107).

Music Therapy for Persons with Crippling Conditions

Cerebral palsy purposely is being omitted from this section dealing with the therapeutic values of music for persons with crippling conditions.

Both the vastness of the disability area of cerebral palsy and the amount of related literature warrant its separate consideration. In the succeeding discussion on therapeutic application, however, reference will be made to the cerebral palsied as appropriate subjects for a unique therapeutic approach based on musical improvisation.

Values of Music

Several articles in the literature concerning the use of music with the physically disabled are concerned with the following crippling conditions: tuberculosis of the hip and spine, hemiplegia, Perthes' disease, postpolio conditions, congenital amputation, fracture, Erb-Duchenne paralysis, and muscular dystrophy. These reports indicate that some teachers and therapists have observed that music has definite values for the physical, social, and psychological development and/or adjustment of persons with crippling conditions.

McAlister (1937), Roan (1952), Gilliland (1951), and Sister Josepha (1964) have found that the playing of musical instruments is an effective means for increasing muscular strength and joint motion and for developing coordination. Although the use of music from this physical-functional standpoint is less well known than its use in psychiatric rehabilitation, medical prescription for increased mobility or endurance at a particular point of the body or increased coordination of parts of the body can be achieved through the playing of specific musical instruments. Denenholz (1959) has said that with proper systematizing of the movements and motions involved in instrumental techniques, musical performance becomes a "tool of functional therapy" (p. 67).

In another article, Gilliland (1955) called attention to the beneficial effects that the playing of wind instruments can have on the development of breath control. According to Brim (1951), similar values can be derived from singing. She stated that singing can be used to increase vital capacity because its sustained nature demands much greater inhalation of breath than is necessary either for speaking or for the maintenance of life.

The social benefits afforded by music to the handicapped and the non-handicapped might be said to differ in degree rather than kind. Allen (1955) stressed the use of group music activities to promote interpersonal relationships among handicapped children because these children ordinarily have little or no opportunity to relate to each other as part of a group. Clingman and Belstrom (1939–1940) and Sister Josepha (1964) also have indicated the social value of music as a thing to be shared and as a form of communication.

Normal children have various ways of giving release to their emotions. The handicapped child frequently lacks ordinary means of emotional release. Bruner (1952) believes that music can fulfill a definite need for this child as an avenue of emotional expression. According to the opinions of Crane (1955) and Gilliland (1951), this musical experience can be emotionally stabilizing.

Certain psychological values of music have special significance when applied to the orthopedically handicapped. In its creative aspect, music allows for such individuality in performance that even the physically handicapped child can participate with some degree of success. This, in turn, serves to compensate for his other deficiencies, thus promoting in him feelings of self-confidence and responsibility. Sister Josepha (1950) has related this particular value of musical performance to several types of physically handicapped children. Clingman and Belstrom (1939–1940) also pointed to the value of musical performance in the area of compensation. In addition, they held that it is a boost to the morale of the handicapped child to perform in a group music situation and to know that he is wanted in the group because he, like others, has his contribution to make.

Similar to this last-mentioned value of music is that stressed by Korson (1958), who considers participation in music activities an effective means of giving a sense of accomplishment to the child handicapped almost to the point of helplessness. Music participation, in this instance, can serve to offset the sense of isolation engendered by the child's feelings of uselessness and incompetence.

Therapeutic Applications

Application of music so that it has therapeutic value to persons with crippling conditions requires a variation of emphasis according to the particular disability being treated. This is evident in the following examples of therapeutically directed music activities for specific disabilities.

Clingman and Belstrom (1939–1940) reported the use of selected musical instruments for exercising certain parts of the body. A young girl was taught to play the baritone horn as a means of strengthening her abdominal muscles, which had been in a weak condition for years. Playing the cello was used to overcome residual stiffness of the right arm and wrist of a child who had been afflicted with infantile paralysis. Although physical restoration was the most apparent therapeutic effect in both instances, the musical activity also led to the establishment of feelings of self-confidence and self-worth.

Clingman and Belstrom also cited an instance in which playing a musical instrument was directed toward a psychological goal. A girl, whose right arm ended at the wrist and whose left arm ended at the elbow, was taught to play a trombone that the manufacturer had adapted to her handicap by means of a device permitting the slide to be controlled by foot rather than by hand. The satisfaction and self-confidence that the girl derived from this accomplishment prompted her to attempt to play the piano, even without the use of prosthetic attachments. She was able to play simple soprano and alto parts in this manner.

Brim (1951) described a music program that was planned for post-respirator patients in which singing was used as a means of increasing their vital capacity. Singing classes were conducted for forty-four patients (varying from seventeen to twenty-nine patients per session) over a period of ten months. The group met for thirty minutes each day, five days a week. The primary aim of the program was to stimulate and motivate the desire for better functional achievement. Therapeutic results were both physical and psychological—physical in the development of vital capacity; psychological in the ensuing feelings of self-confidence.

Sister Josepha (1964) has given examples of instrumental performance used as a therapeutic medium for various orthopedic handicaps. In one example, piano performance was used successfully to develop muscle strength and joint motion in the left shoulder, arm, and hand of a young girl who was afflicted with congenital Erb-Duchenne paralysis. Joint motion and muscular strength were developed gradually through the use of music requiring the arm, wrist, and finger motions that are essential to normal function and by approaching those motions in progressive order.

Different musical techniques were used to attain particular therapeutic objectives: Through correct right-hand function, a legato concept was established and used to stimulate individual finger action in the left hand; double-note playing at intervals of fourths and fifths was used to develop an arch in the left hand; melodic progressions were changed over a period of time from scale steps to chord skips for increased finger abduction; musical compositions requiring crossing of hands on the keyboard were selected for the development of horizontal adduction in the shoulder; and gradual increase of note span on the keyboard was used to develop horizontal abduction of the shoulder. To avoid overcompensation in the handicapped shoulder, periods of conscious relaxation were interspersed in each lesson.

The second example concerned the use of piano performance to motivate arm and finger function in a girl with a postpolio condition that permitted only slight use of the right arm and wrist and partial use of the right hand. During her course of study over a period of five years, she showed slight but steady progress in right-hand function. Although complete restoration of physical function was not possible because of this condition, the functional level that she attained at the piano gave her the courage to attempt the performance of other tasks requiring similar manual dexterity.

The third example illustrates therapeutic effects that piano performance can have on a deformed person. A young girl with congenital loss of the left hand was guided in piano playing from one-note arm-playing through advancing degrees of multiple-note playing, facilitated by a specially devised prosthesis. Sister Josepha related the music activity to specific therapeutic results as follows: The demands made on the arm and shoulder helped to strengthen the muscles of the arm and to stimulate normal growth in the arm; facility in the use of the piano prosthesis led to a greater dexterity in the use of the practical prosthesis, especially where the motions of pronation and supination were concerned; the ability to play the piano proved to be an important means of compensation as both a direct attempt to overcome the handicapping condition itself and a substitute for other skills that would never be attainable with this condition; and finally, the need of sharing music promoted the development of social relationships. Four years after this girl began the study of piano, she was introduced to studying the violin. She had to approach the violin in a left-handed fashion, with a prosthesis, using the right hand for fingering and the left arm to draw the bow across the strings. Violin playing afforded this young girl even greater opportunity for social development through the interaction that is demanded by ensemble playing.

In an extensive report of their investigations and experiences in using music therapy with handicapped children, Nordoff and Robbins (1965) cite an instance of a spastic boy's response to a unique therapeutic technique involving drum beating. In beating the drum, this "spastic boy showed his acuity in his perception of rhythmic patterns and his determination to express this in his struggle to master impaired muscular coordination" (p. 35). In this drum-beating approach, the child is asked to stand by a drum, is given sticks, and then is asked to beat along with piano improvisations. Music is improvised to match his beat. This starts a chain of reactions, for the improvisation modifies his reaction and his reaction, in turn, influences a change in improvisation. There seems to be diagnostic value in this activity as a means of stimulating a child to present a "musical-rhythmic picture of himself" (p. 43). Nordoff and Robbins (1965, pp. 52–60) delineate thirteen categories of response to improvised piano music. Three of these relate directly to musical participation through playing and singing, and two relate to the effects of musical idioms and moods.

Research Literature

There is an extreme sparsity of available research literature relating specifically to the therapeutic use of music with the orthopedically disabled. This is a serious lack in the field of music therapy. In "The Interdisciplinary Approach: Music and Medicine" (1964), Gates notes that musicians in general have not realized fully the need for research in the physiological applications of their profession. To help remedy this situation with respect to the teaching of wind instruments, he organized a two-day interdisciplinary seminar on the subject. This seminar was attended by physiologists and musicians who hoped to initiate steps toward the development of "a common vocabulary, body of knowledge, and understanding of principles of respiratory physiology as these apply to the playing of wind instruments" (p. 8).

The physiological aspects of instrumental performance are perhaps recognized more commonly in the area of piano playing. Ortmann (1962) attempted to apply the complex problem of physiologic mechanics to piano technique through the following considerations: the physiological organism, the general aspects of physiological movement, and the touch forms of piano technique. Although his work embodies an experimental study of muscular action used in piano playing and its effects on the piano key and piano tone, some of the material contained therein might well be applied to the therapeutic use of piano performance in orthopedics.

Published articles on the use of music with the orthopedically disabled are concerned with the physical, social, emotional, and psychological values of music. The application of these values in the field of music therapy parallels that in education, but with some differences in respect to degree of need, variations in emphasis, and adaptations. Both instrumental and vocal performances have a rehabilitative significance, especially when they promote physical restoration.

No experimental research relating specifically to the therapeutic use of music in orthopedics has been carried out. At least, no written accounts are available. Inasmuch as almost every kind of physiological involvement can be attained through musical performance, this is an area that would benefit greatly from experimental investigation.

Current Approaches

Many of the contemporary music therapy programs for physical disabilities are characterized by the rehabilitative approach. When this approach is used at an orthopedic hospital or center, it often occurs in a setting that is geared entirely to rehabilitative purposes. The reports of both Kozak and Rogers, which are included in Chapter 11, describe the organization and function of the rehabilitative type of therapeutic setting.

Although current practices in music therapy for the orthopedically disabled seem to relate mainly to the physical aspects of rehabilitation, music is used primarily for its psychological values to them. This is typical of music therapy for the child with muscular dystrophy. The dystrophic child needs to be stimulated to function at his full capacity in order to prevent disuse atrophy of his muscles. But even greater than this is his psychological need for accomplishment and for feeling wanted. The report by Herman in Chapter 11 presents some of the implications this disability area has for the music therapist.

The three reports of current clinical practices mentioned here describe some of the possibilities of therapeutic application of music in this disability area. It is intended that each report demonstrate particular aspects of a vast field of endeavor. Lest this simplification of a complex problem result in an overemphasis of either the psychological or the physical approach, it must be remembered that in function the two are very closely interrelated.

References

ALLEN, ELIZABETH P. Let there be music. *Crippled Child*, 1955, 33, 11–15.
ALVIN, JULIETTE. *Music for the handicapped child*. London: Oxford, 1965.
ARJE, FRANCES B., and BERRYMAN, DORIS L. New help for the severely retarded and emotionally disturbed child. *J. Rehabilit.*, 1966, 32, 14–15, 67.
BALDWIN, LILLIAN. Music and the blind child. In P. Dykema and Hannah M. Cundiff (Eds.), *School music handbook*. Boston: C. C. Birchard, 1955. Pp. 598–606.
BEETZ, C. J. The lighthouse music school for the blind. In E. T. Gaston (Ed.), *Music therapy 1954*. Lawrence, Kan.: Allen Press, 1955. Pp. 104–105.
BERRY, MILDRED F., and EISENSON, J. *Speech disorders: principles and practices of therapy*. New York: Appleton-Century-Crofts, 1956.
BRIM, CHARLOTTE L. Music, vital capacity, and post-respirator patients. *Mus. Educ. J.*, 1951, 37, 18–19.
BRUNER, OLIVE P. Music to aid the handicapped child. In Esther G. Gilliland (Ed.), *Music therapy 1951*. Lawrence, Kan.: Allen Press, 1952. Pp. 3–6.
CASCIO, A. M. The status of instrumental-music education for the visually handicapped. Unpublished master's thesis, Univer. of Wyoming, 1954.
CLINGMAN, E. C., and BELSTROM, C. E. Instrumental music in a school for crippled children. *Mus. Educ. Nat. Conf. Yearb.*, 1939–1940, 30, 105–109.
CRANE, LOIS M. The role of music in the interests and activities of 95 former polio patients. Unpublished master's thesis, Univer. of Texas, 1955.

CROCKER, DOROTHY B. Teaching piano to the young blind child. In E. T. Gaston (Ed.), *Music therapy 1956*. Lawrence, Kan.: Allen Press, 1957. Pp. 175–182.

CYPREANSEN, LUCILLE, WILEY, J. H., and LAASE, L. T. *Speech development, improvement, and correction*. New York: Ronald, 1959.

DATTILO, MILDRED. Music for the deaf. *Bull. NAMT*, 1953, 2, 5.

DENENHOLZ, BARBARA. Music as a tool of physical medicine. In E. H. Schneider (Ed.), *Music therapy 1958*. Lawrence, Kan.: Allen Press, 1959. Pp. 67–86.

DiPASQUALE, H. J. Teaching instrumental music to the blind. Unpublished master's thesis, Duquesne Univer., 1956.

ELAM, MERNA D. Methods employed in teaching music to blind children at the Virginia State School, Hampton. Unpublished master's thesis, Virginia State Coll., 1958.

EWING, SIR A. (Ed.) *The modern educational treatment of deafness*. Manchester, England: Manchester Univer. Press, 1958.

GILLILAND, ESTHER G. Prescriptions set to music—musical instruments in orthopedic therapy. *Except. Child.*, 1951, 18, 68–70.

GILLILAND, ESTHER G. Functional music for the exceptional child in the special schools of Chicago. In P. Dykema and Hannah M. Cundiff (Eds.), *School music handbook*. Boston: C. C. Birchard, 1955. Pp. 585–591.

GIOVANNI, SISTER. Music as an aid in teaching the deaf. In E. H. Schneider (Ed.), *Music therapy 1959*. Lawrence, Kan.: Allen Press, 1960. Pp. 88–90.

GOODGLASS, H. Musical capacity after brain injury. In E. H. Schneider (Ed.), *Music therapy 1962*. Lawrence, Kan.: Allen Press, 1963. Pp. 101–107.

GRISSOM, MARGUERITE A. A comparison of voice teaching problems of sighted and sightless students. Unpublished master's thesis, Univer. of Texas, 1957.

GRUPP, J. Music and the blind. *Instrumentalist*, 1964, 18, 50–51.

HALDIMAN, GERALDINE. Music education for the braille student in residential schools. Unpublished master's thesis, Northwestern Univer., 1953.

HARBERT, WILHELMINA K. Some results from specific techniques in the use of music with exceptional children. In Esther G. Gilliland (Ed.), *Music therapy 1952*. Lawrence, Kan.: Allen Press, 1953. Pp. 147–161.

HARTLEY, W. S. An experimental study to determine the effectiveness of functional music with blind children. Unpublished master's thesis, Coll. of the Pacific, 1954.

HEIM, K. E. Musical aptitude of senior high school students in residential schools for the blind as measured by the *Wing Standardised Tests of Musical Intelligence*. Unpublished master's thesis, Univer. of Kansas, 1963.

HOY, S. A. The development of an adequate teaching procedure for the teaching of piano for the visually handicapped. Unpublished master's thesis, Univer. of South Dakota, 1954.

The interdisciplinary approach: music and medicine. *Rochester Rev.*, 1964, 27, 8–9.

JOHNSON, W., BROWN, S. F., CURTIS, J. F., EDNEY, C. E., and KEASTER, J. *Speech handicapped school children*. (Rev. ed.) New York: Harper & Row, 1956.

JOSEPHA, SISTER M., O.S.F. Music therapy for the handicapped child. *Educ.*, 1950, March, 434–439.

JOSEPHA, SISTER M., O.S.F. Therapeutic values of instrumental performance for severely handicapped children. *J. Mus. Ther.*, 1964, 1, 73–79.

KLINGLER, H., and PETER, D. Techniques in group singing for aphasics. In

E. H. Schneider (Ed.), *Music therapy 1962.* Lawrence, Kan.: Allen Press, 1963. Pp. 108–112.

KORSON, FRANCES. Music therapy for children with muscular dystrophy. In E. T. Gaston (Ed.), *Music therapy 1957.* Lawrence, Kan.: Allen Press, 1958. Pp. 192–198.

LANE, HELEN S. Psychological aspects of rehabilitating the deaf through music. In Esther G. Gilliland (Ed.), *Music therapy 1952.* Lawrence, Kan.: Allen Press, 1953. Pp. 169–172.

MADSEN, C. K., and MEARS, W. G. The effect of sound upon the tactile threshold of deaf subjects. *J. Mus. Ther.,* 1965, *2,* 64–68.

McALISTER, GLADYS M. Instrumental music for crippled children. *Mus. Educ. J.,* 1937, *24,* 28–29.

McCUSKEY, ALICE E. Teaching piano to the visually handicapped. Unpublished master's thesis, Ohio State Univer., 1944.

McDONALD, E. T., and BAKER, H. K. Cleft palate speech; an integration of research and clinical observations. *J. Sp. Hear. Dis.,* 1951, *16,* 9–20.

NORDOFF, P., and ROBBINS, C. *Music therapy for handicapped children.* Blauvelt, N.Y.: Rudolf Steiner Publications, 1965.

ORTMANN, O. *The physiological mechanics of piano technique.* New York: Dutton, 1962.

PALMER, M. F. Musical stimuli in cerebral palsy, aphasia and similar conditions. In Esther G. Gilliland (Ed.), *Music therapy 1952.* Lawrence, Kan.: Allen Press, 1953. Pp. 162–168.

ROAN, MARGARET Z. Music to aid the handicapped child. In Esther G. Gilliland (Ed.), *Music therapy 1951.* Lawrence, Kan.: Allen Press, 1952. Pp. 26–33.

ROBINS, FERRIS, and ROBINS, JENNET. *Educational rhythmics for mentally handicapped children.* New York: Horizon Press, 1965.

SCHAPIRO, JANE E. A technique of using piano in the rehabilitation of the blind adult. Unpublished doctoral dissertation, Teachers Coll., Columbia Univer., 1955.

SCHWARTZ, R. J., and STEER, M. D. Vocal responses to delayed auditory feedback in congenitally blind adults. *J. Sp. Hear. Res.,* 1962, *5,* 228–236.

STOLTZ, ELIZABETH L. Reactions of a group of elementary children in a residence school for the blind to a modern music education program. Unpublished master's thesis, Ohio State Univer., 1939.

TRAUGHBER, S. H. Discriminations made on musical stimuli by children institutionalized for deafness. Unpublished master's thesis, Univer. of Kansas, 1959.

UNKEFER, R. F. Music therapy in the rehabilitation of the adult blind (a research report). Topeka, Kan.: Services for the Blind, State Dept. of Social Welfare of Kansas, 1958.

WECKER, K. Music for totally deaf children. *Mus. Educ. J.,* 1939, *25,* 47–48.

10

THE CEREBRAL PALSIED

Music Therapy for the Cerebral Palsied

ERWIN H. SCHNEIDER

The largest single group of physically handicapped children in our society today is that suffering from cerebral palsy. In all probability, slightly more than 50 percent of children in special schools or institutions for the crippled are cerebral palsied. Because of the growing birth rate, the number of cases will increase. Although in some cases there may be preventive measures, there are no known cures for this condition once it has become established.

Cerebral palsied children (also referred to as brain-damaged children, or by differential diagnosis as athetoid, spastic, ataxic) generally have neuromotor impairment and disturbances in psychological function and emotional control. They specifically exhibit poor motor control, general distractibility, hyperactivity, irritability, and disinhibition. The degree of total disability in any one child usually shows great variability from day to day, and is believed to be caused by general hypersensitivity and affective tone at the time.

These children present a challenge to the fields of habilitation therapy and special education. This is true not only because of an increase in the number of such handicapped children, but also because public acceptance and understanding of this condition have been taking place. Clinical and educational opportunities are being demanded for these children because medical, psychiatric, and educational workers have provided information and techniques that have made possible new therapeutic and educational opportunities.

Values of Music and Musical Activities

Articles and clinical reports indicate that music and musical activities have a beneficial influence on the tension level, distractibility, hypersen-

[136]

sitivity, and affective tone of many cerebral palsied children. Bruner (1952), Cass (1951), Frampton and Rowell (1938), Reeves (1952), Rogers and Thomas (1935), and Snow and Fields (1950) indicate that music and musical activities help to effect needed relaxation. Reeves (1952) further indicates that music helps to attract attention and increase the concentration span. Carlson (1938) points out that music can serve as an agent to minimize the effects of undesirable environmental stimuli. Lesak (1952) and Bruner (1952) suggest that music stimulates or motivates activity. Bruner also believes that music provides emotional release for cerebral palsied children. Fraser (1958) and Doll (1961) have written that listening to music with one or more persons gives a feeling of belonging and encourages positive interpersonal relationships.

Music and musical activities also are believed to have beneficial effects on the motor control of cerebral palsied children. Weigl (1955) reports that musical activities have proved effective in promoting the initially necessary relaxation and then in stimulating activity, strengthening muscles, and improving motor coordination. Fraser (1958) mentions that listening to music "encourages body activities without requiring any verbal participation" (p. 109). Doll (1961), in reporting on dance activities for the cerebral palsied, suggests that children of this type "can sometimes unconsciously master patterns of movement which might involve months of self-defeating efforts in physiotherapy" (p. 80). Boyle (1954) reports that control of motion (arms, fingers) can be obtained through rhythmic exercises on the piano.

Singing activities can be of value in speech therapy programs for cerebral palsied children. Doll (1961) calls attention to the fact that "the sounds of speech therapy can be as readily learned, and much more eagerly practiced to tunes . . ." (p. 80). Weigl (1955) indicates that better breath and vocal control, easier phonation, and tone prolongation are possible through singing activities. Westlake (1951) also emphasizes the value of practicing phonation and tone prolongation through the use of jingles and easy songs in speech training with cerebral palsied children.

Some clinicians caution that relaxation is not necessarily achieved by all such children in musical activities. Palmer (1953), after nearly twenty years of using music in therapy and training programs for cerebral palsied children, reported that

(1) . . . all of the children with useful hearing get a great deal of sociopsychological support from these periods, which is extremely useful in helping them build toward a self-supporting, independent existence; (2) . . . while the literature and the usual reports from such musical periods conducted every day in the special educational classrooms state that relaxation is achieved during music appreciation [listening] and participation, not all children with cerebral palsy are so benefited. Some relax not at all, and some are appreciably more

tense or more discoordinated following such periods. The effect is transient and apparently not harmful in any permanent sense, unless the therapist, in believing music is a relaxant, uses this for relaxation in a child who proceeds in the opposite direction. We are of the opinion that this is a matter of the kind of cerebral palsy that a child has . . . (pp. 165–166).

Fraser (1958) stresses that music and musical activities can be selected in terms of the individual child. She states, "Brain-damaged children can be reached thru [sic] music, but specific uses of music must be determined individually for each child" (p. 109). The experimental work of Schneider (1957) and Lathom (1961) demonstrates that differential diagnosis of cerebral palsy may determine the kind of musical experiences for these children. They provide evidence that the music used also seems to be a controlling factor in the value of any musical experience. These studies are reported in detail in the next section of this chapter.

Research Literature

Research studies, particularly experimental ones, related to the use of music with cerebral palsied children are not plentiful. The complexity of the cerebral palsy condition, which makes experimental study difficult, probably accounts in part for the paucity of research reports. Studies that concern the use of music with cerebral palsied children are basically of two types: (1) those oriented toward determining the *effects of music* as a stimulus on the behavior of cerebral palsied individuals, and (2) those oriented toward determining the *values of music and musical activities* in achieving certain treatment or training objectives. The former studies provide the rationale, in many instances, for the specific applications of music in the therapy and/or training programs for cerebral palsied children. The latter studies are concerned primarily with actual therapeutic applications of music and musical activities.

EFFECTS OF MUSIC

The studies of Ditson (1961), Lathom (1961), Palmer and Zerbe (1945), Schneider (1957), and Staub (1956) were concerned with the effects of music on certain behavioral aspects of cerebral palsied individuals. Palmer and Zerbe (1945) studied the effects of musical tones and rhythms, primarily those of the violin, on the tremor of a twenty-one-year-old male showing symptoms of spastic paralysis and tension athetosis. The experimental method consisted of delivering to the subject a series of auditory stimuli that varied in rate and amplitude as the tremor of athetosis varied. It was possible to increase and control the severity, rate, and stability of the tremor by means of sound and visual stimuli. In a later report, Palmer (1953) indicated that it was possible to demonstrate that different music had different effects on the tremor rate. Slow, calm music produced tremors at the lower limits of rate—about sixty-five per minute. Martial, vigorous music produced tremors as high as one hundred per minute.

Schneider (1957) tried to determine whether certain recorded music had any effect on the performance of cerebral palsied children. He observed and evaluated them on the quantity and quality of their productive work and their overt behavioral manifestations while engaged in the performance of tasks that employed a psychomotor component. The subjects were ten cerebral palsied children, representing spastic, athetoid, ataxic, and mixed types, who were patients in a cerebral palsy clinic and members of a special education class. The study was continued for seven months. Musical recordings used were classified as (1) physically sedative and (2) physically stimulative. Physically sedative music was defined as having flowing melodies, smooth rhythms, moderate tempos, smooth modulations, and the predominant use of string and woodwind instruments. Music classified as physically stimulative exhibited marked rhythms, fast tempos, staccato melodies, syncopated musical figures, and the predominant use of brass and percussive instruments. The experimental tasks included a pegboard activity and a coloring activity. The experimental design called for each subject to perform selected tasks under a control condition of no music. The two experimental conditions were (1) sedative music and (2) stimulative music; during the performance of each subject, previously designated aspects of behavior were noted and recorded.

Schneider concluded that (1) recorded music did affect the quantity and quality of performance on the selected tasks for a majority of the subjects; (2) recorded music seemed to have some effect on various psychological processes of the subjects; and (3) the noted effects of music seemed to be dependent on the type of music used, the overall physical and mental condition of the subjects, and the type of cerebral palsy. Specifically, the physically sedative music seemed to effect relaxation in some children diagnosed as athetoids, whereas the physically stimulative music seemed to have similar effects on some children diagnosed as spastics. The responses were believed to be the result primarily of the mood effects of the music. Tempo and rhythm as motivating and regulating forces also were believed to be of importance, particularly in physically stimulative music. The improvement in performance of the subjects may have been caused by increased ability in concentration.

The fact that not all the subjects were affected by the recorded music was considered to be related to their degree of neuromotor and psychological impairment, their ages, and the amount and kind of therapy they received. It also could have been because of lack of sufficient musical experience. These factors thus appeared to be controlling interrelated variables that partially determined the degree to which music would or would not affect the behavior of such children. The findings seem to give support to Palmer's (1953) notion that the effects of music are related to the types of cerebral palsy and to Fraser's (1958) comment that "music must be determined individually for each child . . ." (p. 109). Fields (1954) also emphasized that knowledge of the patient's injury and prognosis, as well as knowledge of the functional potential of music, is important in determining uses of music with cerebral palsied children.

Ditson (1961) used moderate background music during regularly scheduled speech therapy sessions. Moderate background music was defined as music that was not exciting or stimulating. Subjects were twenty-one cerebral palsied children ranging in age from eighteen months to four years. The background music was used in over seventy therapy sessions, and the effects of the music, in terms of participation and behavioral response, were recorded by the music therapist and the speech therapist. For the periods in which music was used, the McNemar test for significance of change revealed (1) a significant increase in the amount of participation in therapy activities and (2) a significant increase in the display of socially acceptable behavior. The marked improvement in the participation and behavioral attainments of the subjects led Ditson to suggest that background music may be useful in creating a positive atmosphere in therapy sessions for cerebral palsied children. She drew five conclusions: (1) The use of background music serves as a stimulus for physical and verbal participation during speech therapy sessions; (2) the use of moderately stimulative and sedative music promotes a change in the behavior of cerebral palsied children; (3) the use of moderate background music promotes a conditioned response in the cerebral palsied child, thereby enabling him to enter the therapy session without fear; (4) the use of music promotes a marked increase in socially acceptable behavior; and (5) the use of background music serves as a therapeutic tool in cerebral palsy treatment programs.

Lathom (1961) investigated the effects of a musical environment on voluntary muscular control. Devices used included a stationary bicycle for determining degree of control in the lower extremities and a wall pulley for determining degree of control in the upper extremities. Ten subjects performed under conditions of no music, sedative music, and stimulative music for the purpose of determining whether there was a change in the amount of control under each condition. There were several conclusions: (1) Not all the subjects were influenced to the same degree or in the same manner by the three experimental conditions; (2) the athetoid children exhibited better control in response to sedative music, and most of the children diagnosed as spastic seemed to benefit from stimulative music; (3) some subjects reacted to the same music in a different manner on different days; and (4) if music is to effect a beneficial response during activities that involve physical control, it would seem necessary to be careful to choose music that is observed to have a desirable effect on the individual.

This study gives additional support to the concept that the effects of music on specific behaviors of cerebral palsied children seem to be related to differential diagnosis and the type of music used, but that not all cerebral palsied children are affected in the same way by music. Other factors, such as the severity of the condition, age, physical condition, and amount and type of therapy, may also be controlling variables. This concept appears to be true particularly when the music used is extremely stimulative or extremely sedative and when relaxation or physical control is the behavior involved.

Staub (1956), in a study using music as a relaxing agent, worked with eight adult cerebral palsied patients ranging in age from sixteen to twenty-six years. She observed the degree of relaxation present during finger-painting activities accompanied by music, during finger-painting activities without music, and during quiet listening to music. She reported that music helped to induce relaxation in the patients during the finger-painting and listening activities. She did not indicate the type of music used in the study. Personal observation and reports of the subjects were utilized to determine the degree of relaxation present.

THERAPEUTIC APPLICATIONS

Fields (1954) reported a three-year study on the use of music and musical activities in treatment that attempted to increase motor coordination in twenty-eight severely disabled, brain-damaged patients. The patients ranged in age from fifteen to fifty-four years and presented neurological symptoms of spasticity; athetosis; ataxia; tremor; and associated speech, auditory, and visual defects. Psychological characteristics included distractibility, dissociation, perseveration, and reverse field tendencies. The treatment employed was patient participation, using simple rhythm instruments and piano-keyboard activities. Measurable improvement was noted in both gross and fine motor coordination in twenty-four of the twenty-eight patients. The improvement in motor coordination carried over into other activities. These findings were considered to be especially significant with seven of the patients, because other therapy with these patients had either been terminated or confined to activities not related to those used in the experimentation. Fields concluded that "improvement in coordination among twenty-four of the twenty-eight patients treated suggests the value of music as an adjunct in the treatment for brain-damaged patients in the area of coordinated motion" (p. 282).

Glover (1955), in a definitive case study of a brain-injured child, was concerned with (1) developing an educational program of music for the subject with emphasis on piano instruction and (2) determining whether the general mood of the subject could be influenced through music listening, rhythmic activities, and creative activities. Glover also sought to determine whether music could serve to help the subject go to sleep, and whether any emotional reflections of the music were present in the subject's creative activities. The subject was a six-year-old male whose normal behavior pattern was one of slight hyperactivity. Glover reported that music seemed to be a potent factor in influencing the subject's mood. This was demonstrated most effectively on the occasions when music was used as an inducement for sleep. The subject also appeared to be quieter and more attentive during his music lessons than at other times. And, as he played the piano, he demonstrated a spontaneous creativity and released many feelings through music. The subject's schoolteacher believed that his musical activities were an important aspect of his social adjustment. Glover's general conclusion from this study was that music seemed to offer, for this child, a means of sublimating tensions.

Summary

The foregoing review of research studies suggests certain implications for the use of music with cerebral palsied children. These implications can be considered *guidelines* only, because the research reported did not investigate an adequate sampling of the cerebral palsy population. However, as guidelines, they provide direction and concepts for therapists and teachers who work with cerebral palsied children.

First, when music is to be used as a background stimulus for purposes of improvement in motor control or for purposes of relaxation, careful consideration should be given to the differential diagnosis of cerebral palsy. Careful observation should follow to determine whether the child is responding toward the therapeutic goal.

Second, the value of music as a background stimulus in group situations, in which various types of cerebral palsied children are found, would seem to be dependent on the degree of disability, the age of the children, and the degree to which the music is stimulating. With some children, and for some activities, moderately sedative to moderately stimulative music might be valuable in establishing an atmosphere conducive to therapy or learning activities. Music used in this way should be presented just above the threshold of hearing in order not to distract or unduly stimulate. It may be impossible to establish a musical environment for any group of cerebral palsied children that will be of benefit to all the children on any given day. Again, observation of the response of a group to the various types of music is necessary before planning widespread use of this medium in a group situation.

These two basic considerations are essential to the successful use of music or musical activities with cerebral palsied children. They indicate that the differential diagnosis of cerebral palsy may give a clue to the reactions of a child to various types of music, but that the possibility always exists that not all children so diagnosed will react in the same way. Such evidence as is available, however, indicates that music therapy is valuable and worthwhile for cerebral palsied children.

Music Therapy Practices for the Child with Cerebral Palsy

JOHN W. BIXLER

The music therapist in a hospital school works in a double role in his efforts to help the child with cerebral palsy. He is both music educator and music therapist. As a music educator, he is filling the role of the public school music teacher and as such is interested in children who may some day be able to go to public schools. These children must be prepared to take part in a regular school music program. As a music educator, he is concerned with the child's creative life at home and as a member of the social community. He may be dealing with many children who will be doing more listening and who will experience less active participation than others at the same age. Thus, he must also do his best to help the child develop broad interests in all phases of music.

One of the particular problems of the child with cerebral palsy is the difficulty of belonging to a group and making a positive contribution to it. As is the case with many physically handicapped children, the cerebral palsied child tends to live much of his life on a one-to-one basis with adults, be they parents, teachers, or therapists. This is necessitated by the nature of his handicap and by the narrow range of function present in any group of physically handicapped children. Larsen's (1954) study of the experiences of physically handicapped children clearly shows differences in socialization between these children and their nonhandicapped peers of similar socioeconomic status. The reasons for these differences are primarily those of mobility and communication, but there are also strong psychological factors, especially during adolescence, that inhibit good group relationships for the physically handicapped. This problem of group relationships presents a challenge to the music therapist, for music is a meaningful activity that can thrive in a group setting. White (1955) points out the importance of group relationships in helping the child to form a clearer and more accurate picture of himself and the goals for his rehabilitation. This is particularly true of youngsters in their early teens, to whom group activities are an especially important part of life.

Case 1. P was a fourteen-year-old girl with a diagnosis of chronic brain syndrome arising from brain trauma suffered in an automobile accident at the age of twelve. She had a mild dysarthria, a slow walking pattern, and a tremor during any hand activity. She was referred to this facility (a hospital school for physically handicapped children) by a children's psychiatric clinic for observation under group conditions. P was unable to function in a public school setting. Her problems were listed as poor memory, resentment at being stared at, and general negativism, accompanied by refusal to accept the idea that she was different from her peer group and in need of special services.

On admission to the hospital school, she was placed with a music class of twelve intermediate-age pupils having a variety of handicapping conditions but normal intelligence. The goal was to use her reported love of music to help her become a member of the group. In this way, it was hoped that her general attitude toward others and toward herself would undergo improvement. P made no attempt to fit into the music group. She refused a songbook and would not take an instrument of any kind. She was extremely negative and refused all requests. She did volunteer the information that she had played a clarinet during her grade school days and would like to play it again. However, her tremor was so great that she could not hold the instrument.

The basic approach was made through instrumental music, which, it was believed, would present the least threat to her security and permit her to release negative feelings against an inanimate object. She was handed rhythm instruments without comment of any kind. At first she tolerated these for only a short time and would not play. Within a week, it was noted that she no longer objected to the instruments and had begun to make a few movements in time to the music. Her objections then took the form of complaints that she was not able to read music as the others around her could. When asked if she would like to learn to read her own part, she said she probably would "sometime." A significant gain was noted in her desire to play the louder, more aggressive instruments, such as the drum, and to take a few individual lessons in rhythm reading. Her lessons were successful, although she had difficulty remembering the time and place for them.

At this time, the other children in the group were rehearsing for an operetta. On the suggestion that she come to rehearsal, she became upset and declared in anger that she wanted nothing to do with any kind of a stage presentation where she would have to go in front of people. It was explained to her that she already knew the chorus numbers because of listening to the group rehearsals. However, her problem seemed to be centered in the fact that she would be identified with a group of handicapped children. The suggestion was given that she could help usher, an activity involving mainly herself. She readily consented to do this and began to attend rehearsals, but confined her activity to sitting in the back row and criticizing the performance of her classmates.

When another girl her age had to drop out of the cast the day before the first performance, P was asked if she would help out on stage. Her role was that of a court maiden, one of five girls her age who had unison lines to speak and several songs to sing. With some hesitation, she consented to "help a little," but only if she also could be an usher before the performance.

During the operetta, she showed some confusion and needed to be helped with stage directions, but otherwise she sang and acted with freedom and imagination. For the first time, she seemed to identify well with the group, as evidenced by a helpful attitude toward others, her use of the word "we" instead of "I," and by bringing her mother to hear "our" performance.

It was the belief of the staff and her parents that her participation in the operetta was a significant point in her increased awareness of her handicapped condition and need for help. P is presently starting her second year in the school and is most cooperative. Her tremor has lessened enough for her to play the Autoharp in the class band.

Many children with cerebral palsy are unable to enjoy significant group relationships because of their inability to hear sound. This inability frequently results in poor speech communication (Stone and Dayton, 1953). Difficulty in hearing is found in varying degrees among children with cerebral palsy. Singing and playing groups are somewhat meaningless, and rhythm problems are difficult to overcome when the hearing loss is profound. Listening to records for music appreciation often proves boring unless the therapist can find means of increasing the child's awareness of the elements of music through nonauditory means. With increased awareness of sound, the child can be taught to recognize the tone of different instruments, to identify songs, and to develop musical skills that will allow him to be a contributing member of a group, psychologically as well as musically. There are mechanical devices that can be used to bring about an awareness of sound and rhythm. Among these are the oscilloscope (to show an image of sound on a picture tube) and the kymograph (to indicate by tracing rhythm and rhythmic response). Another device that has proved successful elicits tactile sensations and is described in the following case history.

Case 2. C, a nine-year-old boy, had athetoid-type cerebral palsy but could ambulate independently. His gait was poor and was accompanied by considerable falling. He had much involuntary movement of the upper limbs and was quite hyperactive. He was moderately retarded in language development and had a severe bilateral hearing loss. His hearing loss was partially overcome by a hearing aid, but he continued to have much distortion of high frequencies. As a consequence of his condition, C tended to withdraw from his classmates and did not mingle readily during playtime. In the classroom, he had a short attention span and did not participate in class discussions. He had to have directions repeated; although he seemed to hear, he did not respond appropriately.

C was referred to the music program as a kindergarten pupil. One of the primary goals was to provide a group activity in which he could learn acceptable group behavior and where he could develop his attention span while gaining a musical skill that would give him group status. It was decided to capitalize on his fondness for exploring and his mechanical interest, which found expression in handling instruments and attempting to take them apart. However, it was discovered that group instrumental music was highly stimulating to him and the total environment of the music area was too distracting. He played very loudly and with completely uncoordinated rhythm to the annoyance of others in the class. He did not participate in class singing and ignored records. He did enjoy watching filmstrips and sound movies.

Because of his behavior problems, it was decided to drop him from group music and place him in a separate class with two other children having similar hearing problems. A special reproduction system for amplifying vibrations was devised. It consisted of a 12-inch loudspeaker set on a low stand over which a bass drum could be placed. The vibrations of the speaker were amplified by the bass drum. The children then placed their fingertips on the drumhead and were able to feel and hear the music. The vibrations were now strong enough to bounce a coin into the air and thus could be seen. Records with a very prominent beat were played; it also was possible to use a microphone hookup to amplify piano or vocal sounds. Emphasis was placed on gaining skill in matching rhythms until C was able to play on selected beats of a measure. Notated rhythms were placed on the board to help establish a visual-motor response. Gradually, he was led from the drum vibrations to feeling the vibrations of the piano, and finally to listening only. Within a year, he had mastered the playing of rhythms from a printed score. He no longer needed to see the source of sound and was able to depend on his hearing alone.

When C was again enrolled in his regular kindergarten group, all reports were of satisfactory adjustment. His cooperation was excellent, and his attention span increased. Musically, he was at or above the level of his classmates and was able to read from his band book. He took a lively interest in the instruments in the room and learned to play the chord organ and Autoharp. The bass drum continued to be his regular instrument. There had been some carry-over into singing, with increased vocalization and better pitch control. He became a member of a bell-ringing group and has taken part in several operettas.

In a setting such as the hospital school, where the child is exposed to many educational and therapeutic programs, it is difficult to pinpoint the exact extent to which the music therapy program helped this boy. It is believed that he reached most of his goals in musical and physical development. Basic to his progress was his realization that he had a hearing handicap, that he could utilize what residual hearing he had to be successful in group instrumental music, and that he was truly a contributing member of a group formed to produce pleasing sounds. He gained enough skill through his awareness of vibration, meter, and dynamics to make good progress in coordination.

Music can be a valuable means of providing acceptable creative outlets for the child with cerebral palsy, even though he may be so handicapped that he is unable to take an active part in music making (Pomeroy, 1964, p. 226). "Creative," used here, does not mean the original creation of new works, but includes the re-creation of existing works through intelligent, applied thought and the development of a deeper understanding of art, music, literature, or other media. Intelligent listening to records can be a creative activity that has important implications for the future of the child in his home. It is important because it can be the means of something more than mere entertainment. It can be the pathway to a broadening of horizons, an interest in history, and an interest in contemporary thought.

It is the severely handicapped child who needs such interests most, for he is often the most highly dependent on others and unwilling to move toward independence. *Such children usually have not discovered that striving and achievement can be followed by admiration and affection; on the contrary, they believe only helplessness generates kindliness* (Lesser, 1952). The following case study concerns a boy with such feelings and the effective way music listening helped his emotional adjustment.

Case 3. D first was seen at the hospital school as an inpatient at six years of age. His condition was diagnosed as cerebral palsy of moderately severe athetoid type. He had average intelligence. He showed much purposeless motion in his arms and needed heavy weights on both arms and legs for stability. Oral communication was poor because of lack of breath control and involvement of the speech musculature.

As a result of his physical involvement, D was highly frustrated in his early music experiences by his inability to participate actively in group music and to re-create music. He seemed to be extremely sensitive to music and to the moods created by it, and to understand many concepts of, and related to, the theory of music. But he remained unable to express himself in the active way he desired. He would push himself out of the circle of players or burst into tears because he was not able to grasp a rhythm instrument. He was very demanding in his relationships with adults.

The approach to the solution of D's difficulties was to concentrate on the area of his highest interest: intelligent listening to good music reinforced by as much active participation as possible. The active participation was through playing the bass drum with a drum pedal. The intelligent listening was through individual work with appropriately rhythmical records, books, filmstrips, movies, and field trips. In addition, an effort was made to give him a speaking part, even if only a line or two, in every school operetta. This was done for speech therapy goals as well as a means of encouraging walking. He had many original ideas in staging, costuming, and in planning scenery and props.

As D continued to develop his new interests, his adjustment to those persons around him improved. He elicited genuine affection from volunteer students and the staff. He gained a love for opera, and through it a desire to read. In following years, he made several attempts to write librettos for operettas. D considered using music as a means of earning a living, either as a music critic or by operating a record shop with his father. There was a lack of realism in the first goal, but the latter, although dependent on the father's role, was a possibility.

Dramatics can be a useful tool in the hands of the music therapist in helping the child with cerebral palsy improve his behavior patterns. By combining dramatics with music in operetta form, the music therapist sometimes can help the child initiate personality changes that can be reinforced by musical successes. Davis (1952) discusses the value of dramatics as an aspect of the play-therapy technique and the wider area of recreational therapy. He points out that such activity may be redirective, pointing the patient's interest toward more social behavior; that it may help the patient to see his attitude toward himself and his environment; and that it may be integrative, enabling the patient to focus his attention and organize his motor and mental fields into a constructive pattern.

Case 4. B was ten years old when first admitted to the hospital school. He was diagnosed as having spastic cerebral palsy with involvement in his lower limbs. When tested, he was found to have bright-to-normal intelligence. His singing voice was clear and accurate, but he refused to sing in group situations. He gave glowing accounts of his instrumental music accomplishments, but could not produce results that confirmed his claims.

Little had been expected of him at home. He came from a fairly well-to-do family where he seemed to be able to do as he pleased. Some descriptions of him were "careless," "lazy," "lethargic," "immature," "needs prodding," "rude," and "lacks incentive." His behavior in the music class and in private instrumental lessons verified most of these descriptions. He loved the status a trombone gave and could manage it quite easily, but he seemed unable to discipline himself into good practice habits.

One goal set up for B was to capitalize on his singing ability to establish immediate success. He was asked to sing a short solo in a Christmas operetta. This opportunity to sing for his parents spurred him to practice and to an excellent performance.

When rehearsals were begun for the operetta, The Sorcerer's Apprentice, B was encouraged to take the title role, that of a very ambitious, outgoing, dynamic boy. It was hoped that in this way he would identify himself with another personality with more desirable characteristics. Even though he had enjoyed the success and acclaim of his previous operetta, B was reluctant to put forth the effort to learn the lines required. His performance at rehearsals was in his typical slow, lackluster way, with no feeling for the part he was to play. Only a few days before the first performance, while he was helping with scenery and costumes, did he suddenly seem to become aware of his role and begin to feel the part. His singing, walking, talking, and gestures became real and believable. As a result, the morale of the entire group improved.

The most important result was the change in B's attitudes and behavior in the weeks following the operetta. He continued to show a high degree of motivation and enthusiasm. Even his attitude toward music and practice was improved.

A basic technique in working with the child who has cerebral palsy is free use of visual cues to establish neuromotor patterns (the instrumental approach through rhythm reading—that is, playing by reading music symbols). Similar success has been achieved in vocal music. The basic technique is ear training through the rote singing of scales and chord patterns, accompanied by the use of sight-singing materials and a cognitive approach through note and harmony study. This is achieved through much repetition and reference to instrumental technique.

This discussion has been concerned with the problems of the child who has cerebral palsy and the ways in which these problems have been solved through participation in directed musical activities. The typical attitude of these children was overdependence. This was changed through participation in creative musical activities that gradually led to the development of courage and initiative. The unsatisfactory behavior patterns, characterized by lack of incentive and personal discipline, were changed to high motivation and enthusiasm through participation in operettas.

References

BOYLE, CONSTANCE M. Dalcroze eurhythmics and the spastic. *Spastics Quart.*, 1954, *1*, 5–8.

BRUNER, OLIVE P. Music to aid the handicapped. In Esther G. Gilliland (Ed.), *Music therapy 1951*. Lawrence, Kan.: Allen Press, 1952. Pp. 3–6.

CARLSON, E. R. Understanding and guiding the spastic. *Amer. J. Nurs.*, 1938, *39*, 357–366.

CASS, MARION T. *Speech habilitation in cerebral palsy*. New York: Columbia, 1951.

DAVIS, J. *Clinical applications of recreational therapy*. Springfield, Ill.: Charles C Thomas, 1952.

DITSON, RAYMA. A study of the effects of moderate background music on the behavior of cerebral palsied children. *Bull. NAMT*, 1961, *10*, 6.

DOLL, E. E. Therapeutic values of the rhythmic arts in the education of cerebral palsied and brain-injured children. In E. H. Schneider (Ed.), *Music therapy 1960*. Lawrence, Kan.: Allen Press, 1961. Pp. 79–85.

FIELDS, BEATRICE. Music as an adjunct in the treatment of brain-damaged patients. *Amer. J. Phys. Med.*, 1954, *33*, 273–283.

FRAMPTON, M. E., and ROWELL, H. G. *Education of the handicapped, II*. New York: Harcourt, Brace, & World, 1938.

FRASER, LOUISE WHITBECK. Reaching the brain damaged child through music. In E. T. Gaston (Ed.), *Music therapy 1957*. Lawrence, Kan.: Allen Press, 1958. Pp. 109–113.

GLOVER, BARBARA E. A case study on the use of music activities for a brain-injured child. Unpublished master's thesis, Univer. of Kansas, 1955.

LARSEN, E. L. Experiences of physically handicapped children, ages three through six. Unpublished doctoral dissertation, State Univer. of Iowa, 1954.

LATHOM, WANDA. The use of music with cerebral palsied children during activities involving physical control. *Bull. NAMT*, 1961, *10*, 10–16.

LESAK, ELEANOR. Rhythm and movement. In Esther G. Gilliland (Ed.), *Music therapy 1951*. Lawrence, Kan.: Allen Press, 1952. Pp. 49–51.

LESSER, A. Emotional problems associated with handicapping conditions in children. Children's Bureau of Publications, 1952, *336*, 8.

PALMER, M. F. Musical stimuli in cerebral palsy, aphasia, and similar conditions. In Esther G. Gilliland (Ed.), *Music therapy 1952*. Lawrence, Kan.: Allen Press, 1953. Pp. 162–168.

PALMER, M. F., and ZERBE, LOUISE E. Control of athetotic tremors by sound stimuli. *J. Sp. Dis.*, 1945, *4*, 303–319.

POMEROY, JANET. *Recreation for the physically handicapped*. New York: Macmillan, 1964.

REEVES, VIRGINIA. Music to aid the handicapped child. In Esther G. Gilliland (Ed.), *Music therapy 1951*. Lawrence, Kan.: Allen Press, 1952. Pp. 10–13.

ROGERS, GLADYS, and THOMAS, LEAH C. *New pathways for children with cerebral palsy*. New York: Macmillan, 1935.

SCHNEIDER, E. H. Relationships between musical experiences and certain aspects of cerebral palsied children's performance on selected tasks. In E. T. Gaston (Ed.), *Music therapy 1956*. Lawrence, Kan.: Allen Press, 1957. Pp. 250–277.

SNOW, W. B., and FIELDS, BEATRICE. Music as an adjunct in the training of children with cerebral palsy. *Occup. Ther. and Rehabilit.*, 1950, *29*, 147–156.

STAUB, SISTER DOLORES M. The therapeutic values of music in relation to the cerebral palsied. Unpublished master's thesis, Univer. of Notre Dame, 1956.

STONE, ELEANOR B., and DAYTON, J. W. *Corrective therapy for the handicapped child*. Englewood Cliffs, N.J.: Prentice-Hall, 1953.

WEIGL, VALLY. Functional music with cerebral palsied children. In E. T. Gaston (Ed.), *Music therapy 1954*. Lawrence, Kan.: Allen Press, 1955. Pp. 135–143.

WESTLAKE, H. A system for developing speech with cerebral palsied children. *Crippled Child.*, 1951, *29*, 9–11, 28–29.

WHITE, GRACE. Social casework in relation to cerebral palsy. In W. M. Cruickshank and G. M. Raus (Eds.), *Cerebral palsy*. Syracuse, N.Y.: Syracuse University Press, 1955. Pp. 462–500.

11

CLINICAL PRACTICES

Music Therapy for Children
Hospitalized with Muscular Dystrophy

FRANCES KORSON HERMAN

Progressive muscular dystrophy designates an extremely crippling disease characterized by slow, progressive degeneration of the voluntary muscles. Although the involuntary muscles generally are not affected, a rare form of the disease does involve muscles of the heart. The degeneration progresses until all the muscles that normally can be controlled are affected. This is manifested clinically by observed weakness and wasting of the muscles and by contracture formation as a result of muscles becoming replaced by fat and fibrous tissue (Murphy, 1959).

There is neither a known cure nor a specific treatment for muscular dystrophy. Treatment in general is directed toward the prevention, correction, and minimization of contractures and toward the maintenance of functional activities. Diet and medication are prescribed for building body resistance and for stimulating the building or repair of tissues. Nursing care is directed primarily toward teaching the patient to live a full, active life within the limits of his muscle strength (Wiebe, 1961).

Over one-half of the victims of this disease are children between the ages of four and fifteen. When working with them, one must be as aware of their physical limitations as of their emotional needs and difficulties. Those in advanced stages of the condition show marked degrees of weakness and fatigability. Their mobility decreases until eventually they lack the strength to propel their wheelchairs. At this point, they meet growing restrictions in activities with their peers and, if left alone, most of them will resort to excessive viewing of television.

Of particular concern is the possibility of the development of disuse atrophy. According to Milhorat (1954), "Many patients, because of overindulgence, do not perform many functions they are still able to perform and, in short, anticipate the disability that the natural course of the disease produces" (p. 21). A dystrophic child who is emotionally immature because of overprotective parents usually lacks independence and confidence and, therefore, tends to become inactive and lose interest in his work and play. Disuse atrophy can be prevented by keeping muscles working to full capacity. This is especially important with regard to the respiratory musculature that is often found to be reduced in function by as much as 50 percent in later stages of the disease (Murphy, 1959).

These considerations influenced the development of a music therapy program in a children's hospital in Canada. The hospital is an inpatient treatment facility with a school, hospital, and home for forty-eight children crippled by the conditions of muscular dystrophy, cerebral palsy, paraplegia, and other less common disorders. This report is concerned mainly with the dystrophic group consisting of nine boys with muscular dystrophy and two girls with conditions similar in effect.

Aims and Objectives

The music therapy program was based on the following aims and objectives: to reduce the child's isolation through group participation or through activities giving at least a sense of group participation; to provide the child with opportunities to ventilate aggressive feelings and impulses; to help the child develop his latent potentialities and broaden his creative experiences; and to promote function wherever possible for the prevention of disuse atrophy.

The program included group musical activities that would help the patients establish more active and positive relationships with peers, family, and friends. Music activities also were planned to help the children gain recognition of their residual strengths, talents, and capacities, and thereby to distract them from preoccupation with their deficiencies. Meaningful activities were used to stimulate broader interests.

Activities and Procedures

The dystrophic children were integrated with other children in all music activities except melodica playing, which was designed specifically for them. They were able to function successfully at their own level of achievement, along with the other children, in activities such as drum playing, operetta performance, and wheelchair dancing. Group integration did not seem to detract from the positive benefits they were expected to derive from the latter three activities.

MELODICA PLAYING

Respiratory difficulties are common, critical, and often fatal to dystrophic children. Blowing exercise frequently is prescribed for them with the hope that it will help them to maintain function of the respiratory muscles. The musical instrument that seems best suited to this purpose is the Hohner soprano melodica. This is a wind instrument having a piano-like keyboard rather than holes, as does the recorder. Dystrophic patients, who would be unable to cover the recorder holes properly because of weak fingers, can manipulate this keyboard easily.

Although a note-reading approach can be used with the melodica, it was not used with the dystrophic children because of their generally low achievement levels. Use of the number system was found to be a satisfactory substitute. In accord with this system, the notes within the octave were identified by numbers ranging from one through seven, accidental marks were placed directly in front of the numbers concerned, and a change of color was used to designate a change of pitch level for the octave itself. The children learned to read their songs notated in this fashion on large cards with oversized symbols for easy viewing.

Special precautions had to be taken with these children because of their low muscular endurance. In order to avoid fatigue from holding the melodica, a pillow was placed on the knee of the child as a prop for the keyboard portion of the instrument. Care also was taken to have alternating periods of blowing and resting at five-minute intervals.

Initially, each child played the melodica as a solo instrument. Later, each was admitted to a melodica band that was held together by means of piano accompaniment. The ensemble setup served to enhance individual accomplishment and afforded the opportunity for group experience in a cooperative endeavor.

DRUM ACTIVITIES

The major emotional problems of dystrophic children are made evident by aggression and hostility. Yet, these children "are denied a large part of the muscular release for these impulses which are available to the non-dystrophic children. . . . Two major ways seem open to them: an increase of expressed verbal hostility or withdrawal from the outside world to fantasy life, increased passivity and dependency with repression of aggression" (Schoelly and Fraser, 1955).

Because these tendencies were evident in some of the children, it seemed necessary to provide them with opportunities to release emotional tension. A rock 'n' roll drum band was formed. Because these children had little use of either their forearms or their hands, drumsticks were given to all, with the exception of one very weak lad who had to play a brush (percussion type) on a small tambourine perched on his knee. Tall barrel drums were propped into positions that made it possible for them to be played. Piano accompaniment was used to keep the group together. At first, the beating of the drums was loud and aggressive. After a few minutes, it became more subdued. Using music that was contemporary for their peer group seemed to erase feelings of isolation from the outside teen-age world.

MUSIC AND DRAMA

The operetta form, which provides music, dance, drama, art, costumes, and make-up, proved to be an admirably suitable vehicle for the expression of creative ideas by the dystrophic children. Roles were adapted and assigned according to individual physical and emotional needs. The projects were designed so that each child, no matter how handicapped, could make some contribution. This particular type of programing was found to be more successful than anything else attempted. The emphasis it placed on vocal inflection and miming seemed to compensate for the lack of mobility.

WHEELCHAIR DANCING

(The types of wheelchair dancing described here are for immobile groups only and do not apply to paraplegics who normally can propel their own wheelchairs.) One form of wheelchair dancing best suited to the more withdrawn children was accomplished with the aid of two volunteers. One volunteer stood in back of the patient and guided the movement of the patient's chair by pushing; the other faced the patient and held his hands. The patient's initial contribution consisted of permitting his hands to be held and focusing his attention on the person in front of him. He then was encouraged to lead movement of their joined hands and to move rhythmically with his body as much as possible. After several repetitions of these sessions, most of the children gained facility in directing where and how they wished to be moved.

Occasionally, the volunteer help was limited to that of one person. This necessitated pulling the patient's chair while facing him. Various dances were accomplished in this manner. The twist was danced by merely pushing the chair from side to side in the rhythm of the music. The apple dance was highly popular. An apple was placed between the foreheads of the patient and the volunteer (leaning toward the patient), and the chair was pushed around the room until the apple fell. This was an excellent dance for promoting patient involvement. Folk dancing also was accomplished with the help of only one volunteer, who was able to stand in back of the chair and push, because the patient was facing other participants in the activity.

The eleven patients included in the activities described ranged in age from eight to fifteen years. All were in wheelchairs and only three had sufficient strength to wheel their own chairs. The program that was developed for these dystrophic children was both creative and recreative. The major activities were infused with musical adventure and appeared to involve successfully the children's interest. The more subtle effects of the program are expressed best in a statement of the hospital superintendent:

> In watching the proceedings of the program through the years, I was struck with the change it wrought in the personalities of our boys and girls. From a state of dull apathy that existed before the inauguration of the program they blossomed into lively rounded-out beings, full of ready interest, initiative, and joy.
> The happiest vehicles of expression were those associated with music. Music seemed to release them emotionally into the freshness of their natural youthhood. It was of interest to note the abandon produced by the exhilaration of the musical experiences, and the markedly beneficial effect on their physical conditions (Jenkins, 1965).

Music Therapy in a State Hospital for Crippled Children

LUCRETIA ROGERS

The music therapist in this hospital for crippled children is a member of a rehabilitation team composed of various medical specialists and therapists. Collaboration is facilitated by having the music therapist take a two-month orientation course in orthopedics under the supervision of the physical therapy supervisor. All music therapy is initiated upon an order from the orthopedist, the neurologist, or the psychiatrist. Progress notes from music therapy are placed on the patient's medical chart. Music therapy is indicated for the following types of patients:

1. A polio patient with muscular weakness, or one who has had surgical corrections with established, graded exercise routine in physical therapy and is ready for muscular strengthening or further help in muscle reeducation.
2. An arthritic patient with rigid joints and subsequent limited range of motion.
3. A patient with circulatory problems, spina bifida, or paraplegia caused by traumatic spinal lesions.
4. A congenitally blind patient with emotional disturbance, distorted balance, and pseudoretardation, as well as visual disability.
5. An orthopedic patient with deafness, provided that he needs speech therapy that can be facilitated by music.

6. A mentally retarded patient with orthopedic and neurologic problems.

The music therapy program includes a wide range of music activities. Because they are orientated primarily toward rehabilitation, they relate mainly to performance. The following music techniques are commonly used:

1. *Piano.* Practice can be structured to provide an exact amount of resistance, range of motion, finger flexion and extension, and foot dorsiflexion. One advantage of this activity is that it is frequently accessible at home for continued treatment following hospital discharge.
2. *Rhythm band instruments.* These provide an increased vocabulary of movement for the cerebral palsied patient and meet the limitations of the orthopedically handicapped.
3. *Exercises with rhythm.* Properly administered and guided, these can facilitate reciprocity of movement in all four extremities.
4. *Harmonica.* This instrument induces hand control (grasp and release), hand-to-mouth action, and breathing and swallowing, as well as increase in vital capacity.
5. *Mat exercises.* Through this means, a patient can move freely for range-of-motion exercises, stimulated by rhythmic musical accompaniment.
6. *Hand dancing.* This brings the satisfaction of rhythmic expression to those who are nonambulatory.
7. *Marching and crutch walking.* Even though a patient is in a wheelchair that is pushed by another, he is stimulated by the rhythm of the music and is motivated by the satisfaction he derives from the activity. When a pattern of crutch walking has been established in physical therapy, it is implanted more thoroughly in the patient's mind if it is associated with a familiar, well-defined rhythm.
8. *Ukulele, guitar, and mandolin.* These may be used for finger and wrist flexion and extension.
9. *Violin, cornet, trombone, recorder, etc.* These promote hand and finger coordination, as well as range of motion.
10. *Autoharp.* This easy-to-play instrument provides an opportunity for finger and wrist extension and flexion, as well as satisfaction in performance (hearing full-chord tones after only a minimum of physical exertion).
11. *Singing—alone or with others.* This provides an opportunity for esthetic satisfaction, increased vital capacity, and better adjustment and acceptance of hospitalization and treatment.
12. *Preparation and presentation of operettas and music programs.* These activities are important, not only for the motivation and satisfaction

provided, but also because of the aid they give to the development of positive attitudes toward disability. Participation in this type of activity in the hospital setting fosters continued normal participation in school, church, and community groups after discharge.

Therapeutic application of music to a particular orthopedic disability requires adequate knowledge and understanding of the patient's handicap as a basis for selection, evaluation, and possible adaptation of a specific music activity. Sometimes, the music activity itself is the primary therapy; sometimes, it has a supportive relationship to other therapies. The following case studies have been selected to illustrate these two possibilities.

Case 1. The patient was a ten-year-old girl with a diagnosis of rheumatoid arthritis, generalized, affecting all joints. Her characteristic deformities were ulnar deviation of the fingers; wrist drop and ulnar deviation; flexion contractures and deformities of elbows, wrists, knees, and ankles; and involvement of proximal interphalangeal joints of fingers producing fusiform swellings.

The patient was evaluated on piano because this instrument would provide just the right amount of resistance and graded range of motion. Her love of music and her desire to be able to play the piano were positive motivating factors in initiating treatment.

It was necessary to position her at the piano very carefully. Her arms were placed in deltoid slings to remove all strain on shoulders and elbows; her feet were positioned with blocks under them to relieve all strain on ankles, knees, and hips. She was barely able to depress the keys during the first treatment session and could reach only a major third in the key of C. A series of simple finger exercises was arranged by the music therapist (right hand—CDE, DEF, and EFG, using fingers 1 2 3, 2 3 4, and 3 4 5; left hand—CDE, DEF, and EFG, using fingers 5 4 3, 4 3 2, 3 2 1). Simple duets were performed by having the patient play designated single notes with designated fingers while the music therapist improvised an accompanying part.

The patient came for a thirty-minute music therapy session each day of a five-day week. She was in treatment for almost six months. At the end of this time, she was able to extend her fingers from C to A in both left and right hands. She could play each finger individually and finally reached recital performance level. When she was discharged, her parents were given written instructions for use in aiding her continued practice at home.

Case 2. Two four-year-old girls with similar diagnoses—congenital amputees above the elbow with congenital anomalies of lower extremities

—were ordered to music therapy for motivation in using new bilateral upper extremity prostheses. Prosthetic fitting and basic gross motions had been completed in physical therapy. Fine motion and activities of daily living (ADL) were practiced in occupational therapy. (The ADL training board is standard equipment for first lessons in manipulative tasks.) The two patients were assigned to have treatment together so that one could challenge the other.

Wrist bells were used in music therapy. These were grasped in the prosthetic hooks, and a rhythmic choreography was worked out wherein all basic motions were utilized. Stress was placed on the importance of smoothness and dexterity. Both patients took pride in performance and seemed to enjoy greatly their music therapy sessions. In this particular case, music acted as a supportive therapy to physical and occupational therapy.

Music Therapy for Severe Speech Disorders

KAY EWER WELLS

NEAL HELMUS

A diagnostic and treatment center for physically handicapped children in the north central United States serves patients whose problems fall into four general categories—congenital defects, delayed development, accidents, and paralyzing illnesses. The emphasis is on rehabilitation. During a period of two years, this hospital developed a program of coordinated music and speech therapy with patients having aphasia, cleft palate, voice problems, delayed speech, cerebral palsy, and articulation disorders. In this coordinated program an attempt was made to develop workable techniques according to these criteria: methods adaptable for use by the speech or music therapist; specialized music therapy techniques to supplement speech therapy; procedures suited to different age levels; and music activities that could adhere to medical orders for muscle reeducation, approximating the goals of physical and occupational therapy. The following list outlines the music therapy techniques that were adapted for the physical conditions specified.

1. Lip dysfunction—conditions of cleft lip, cerebral palsy, and apraxia: involves inadequate range of motion, speed, and strength of muscle movements.
   a. *Harmonica.* Requires minimal motor control of lip muscles; no tongue movement at this stage; range of motion and strength are involved; no speed for playing scales and simple tunes.

    b. Flutophone. Requires considerably more range of motion and strength; used after enough muscle development to play harmonica easily.

    c. Whistling. Requires finest motor control with maximum range of motion and strength.

    d. Singing. Use of songs with words containing letters, *p, b, m,* initially (least difficult), medially (most difficult), and in the final position; speech exercises, *p-p-p-,* set to music (can be finely graded as to speed and strength) primarily for speed development.

2. Tongue—conditions of cerebral palsy, cleft palate, apraxia, delayed speech, and articulation: involves inadequate range of motion, etc.

    a. Singing. Use of songs with words containing sounds, *t, d, l, k, g, r, s,* and *n,* initially, medially, and in final position. These songs were composed to suit particular needs for speed, strength, or range of motion, for example, "Tom Tinker *told Tillie Atkins terrible tales.*"

    b. Harmonica. For the older patient; calls for speed and strength for accurate placement of tongue.

3. Palate—conditions of cleft palate, cerebral palsy, and tonsillectomy: involves inadequate range of motion, etc. The first four of these activities include emphasis on velopharyngeal closure, eliminating nasal emission of air.

    a. Harmonica. Requires palate-pharyngeal closure; range of motion and speed of muscle movements stimulated.

    b. Flutophone. Same as for harmonica but usable for younger child.

    c. Singing. Can be used with a group younger than that with flutophone; insert *p, ch,* and *sh* sounds into words, especially in the initial position.

    d. Trumpet. For the older patient with adequate breath capacity.

    e. Humming. Expressly for developing velopharyngeal closure and reducing nasal emission; effective.

4. Pitch—conditions of aphasia, voice, and cerebral palsy.

    a. Tone matching. For all age groups; demands development of auditory discrimination; therapist matches tone the patient can produce; use of piano for matching; increase range by moving to adjacent tones; immediate transfer to speech by singing-saying greetings using these tones; match sentence inflection to its exaggerated musical counterpart; when three tones are mastered, start singing nursery rhymes ("Hot Cross Buns"); even older patients do this willingly—and with much hilarity.

    Also, high versus low tones—identifying and matching without help from the therapist; emphasis throughout on using the ears and immediate transference to speech; most effective in daily, or twice daily, fifteen-minute sessions.

5. Loudness—conditions of cerebral palsy, cleft palate, voice, apraxia, and emotional disturbance.
    a. *Singing.* Uses all the techniques listed subsequently under breath control; songs with dramatic content are good; with the younger child use songs such as "Pop Goes the Weasel"; place emphasis on accent and rhythm.
    b. *Rhythm instruments.* Use with singing; imitate sounds of instruments; promote a free and spontaneous atmosphere.
    c. *Oscilloscope.* Use for visual observation and to show loudness.
6. Breath control—conditions of cerebral palsy, cleft palate, and apraxia.
    a. *Singing.* Sustaining tones; expanding number of words and phrases sung on one breath; use of speech exercises with labial and tongue sounds set to music for added interest.
    b. *Rhythmic exercises.* Sing exercises on nonsense syllables emphasizing rhythm; use rhythm instruments with them for added appeal.
    c. *Wind instruments.* Same graded procedure as for singing.
7. Loss of speech—condition of aphasia.
    a. *Singing.* Use of childhood songs to aid automatic word recall; gives confidence and proves the patient able to produce speech; use of sol-fa syllables is especially effective.
    b. *Whistling.* As described in number 1, lip dysfunction.
    c. *Pitch techniques.* As described in number 4, pitch.
    d. *Loudness techniques.* As described in number 5, loudness. Both pitch and loudness techniques are recommended if the aphasic patient has lost normal intonation and inflection.
    e. *Lip and tongue exercises.* Necessary if the aphasic patient has apraxia, or loss of oral-facial muscle control.

Most of the speech patients in this hospital had emotional problems arising from, or underlying, their speech problems. The total treatment plan included the consideration of these emotional factors and the application of the techniques outlined here. The following brief case histories illustrate this approach.

Case 1. M was a four-year-old girl whose speech was unintelligible to everyone except her mother. There was no apparent cause for this, and M had developed a fear of speaking in front of anyone—adults in particular. In both speech and music therapy, attention first was focused on the labial sounds, p, b, m; songs were composed for this purpose. Group music also was included, both for socialization and the mutual support of members of the group, all of whom had speech disorders. Therapy proceeded from the use of simple songs using p, b, m, to the inclusion of sounds made by the tongue. Songs and exercises were designed to give added vocal strength. Much dramatization and many rhythmic activities were also used.

M gradually mastered these sounds. Emphasis then was placed on developing a repertoire of nursery rhymes and similar songs. As a culminating activity, a tape recording of her singing and playing of rhythm instruments was sent to her nursery school class. Subsequently, it was presented as a TV show with M as the "star." Therapy was discontinued once she had developed intelligible speech and had managed to overcome most of her fear of speaking.

Case 2. H was fifteen years old. His speech problem consisted of unintelligibility and nasal emission. He had inadequate lip, tongue, and palate control. All this, plus his facial appearance, was complicated by deep-seated feelings of inferiority. Lip exercises and auditory discrimination were the first points of emphasis in his speech and music therapy. Stress was placed on sounds dependent on lip and tongue. The harmonica was introduced to aid in reducing nasal emission and to increase lip strength and tongue control. Singing was also used as a means of lessening nasal emission and developing better breath control. Next, all blowing and lip exercises were intensified to increase the speed and strength of muscle response. At this point, emphasis was shifted again to sounds formed in the back of the mouth. The therapists demonstrated how the back of the tongue should be raised against the palate to reduce the use of glottal stoppage in speech. An increase of muscle strength was obtained through a gradual intensification of the blowing and lip exercises.

H tended to improve in therapy but to revert to old patterns when away from it. Therefore, strong emphasis was placed on the transference of progress made in the therapy sessions to other situations. All the departments he attended were informed of his work in speech and music therapy. This tactic contributed greatly to his progress. As his sound vocabulary increased, so did his self-confidence. It was further enhanced by the praise he received from others for the proficiency he had developed on the harmonica. He was able to gain lip, tongue, and palate control sufficient for adequate speech. At this point, his therapy was discontinued.

Music Therapy in Speech Habilitation of Cleft-Palate Children

DONALD E. MICHEL

In recent years, considerable progress has been made in habilitation techniques for cleft-palate, speech-handicapped children. This report describes music therapy techniques used in four summer speech therapy programs for cleft-palate children.

These residential programs were based on the idea that a concentrated period of work with the whole child would produce lasting improvement in speech. There was much concentrated, individual speech therapy, but there were also activities such as music, art, drama, and recreation. These activities were focused on speech therapy goals for the children.

In preparation for the first summer clinic (1960), a search of the literature was made, but little information was found concerning music therapy applied to this specific disorder. Considerable experience had been reported in the use of music as a tool in speech therapy in general, but not for cleft-palate children. Kaplan (1955) stated four purposes for music with speech therapy: (1) to provide a form of therapy, (2) to provide recreation, (3) to give the child something to take back with him to his home community, and (4) to give the child some skill in a new modality —music—in order to build his self-confidence. Because Kaplan reported success in the use of music toward such goals for speech-handicapped children, some of whom had cleft palates, his goals were adopted for the residential speech therapy program. More specifically, music therapy goals were to provide new listening experiences for the children, to utilize music activities in speech therapy exercises, and to direct the socializing effects of musical group efforts toward the general as well as the specific speech and personality needs of the children (Michel, 1961).

The two basic methods employed during the first summer's clinic were group singing and the learning of pre-band instruments. Pre-band instruments were used to teach the children to expel air through the mouth rather than through the nasal passages, a common problem in cleft-palate speech. The fact is notable that most of the children wanted to purchase the flutophones they had been loaned so they might take them home and play them. The music activity resulted in some group support for individual efforts when individuals or pairs of children performed in front of the group. Positive results of the socializing influence of group singing were obtained. There was evidence of better cooperation, less shyness, and the development of group identification among the children. Carry-over value was observed in the acquisition of some group-singing skill and the learning of typical songs. The group singing also provided a new means for drill on correct speech sounds.

During the second clinic, individual music sessions were organized for the children in addition to group singing. They learned how to blow wind instruments and studied singing individually. Improved materials were used, for example, recordings designed specifically for speech correction (Sisters Mary Arthur and Mary Elaine, 1959). Two therapists, working together with the group, were more effective than one in providing leadership and individual attention. A tape recorder proved useful as a means of stimulating interest, providing on-the-spot appraisal by the children, and evaluating progress. The children quickly learned to accept and use the tape recorder, even for recording individual performances; the individual recordings served as a basis for later criticism of speech patterns. The conclusions, reported previously, follow:

Not only were the children able to reap the benefits of musical participation in terms of expanded perception of sounds in general—pitch, range, vocal quality, etc.—through singing and other forms of music, but also, many of them were enabled to learn concepts of correct speech articulation through . . . music. . . . The learning of improved social skills . . . and the development of increased self-confidence through individual and group musical accomplishments were . . . benefits realized by many children (Michel, 1962, p. 115).

The third clinic achieved further refinements in procedures and evaluation. In addition to regular sessions conducted with the children in a group, programed learning techniques were used in working with individual children on a song designed for improving articulation.

A musicality test, pitch matching, and a general assessment of the musical potential of these children seemed to show that they were considerably below average in musical experiences and aptitude. Considering their disability, it was not surprising that this should be so. Moreover, it was apparent that most of them were from culturally deprived areas, which probably accounted in part for their low music potential.

A particular effort was made to stimulate spontaneous speech. Students from a summer music camp came into the music sessions to demonstrate and talk about their instruments. The cleft-palate children were forced to make themselves clearly understood in asking questions of the campers. An important discovery was made by the cleft-palate children when one of the music campers, who played the trombone, turned out to have a cleft palate himself.

A brief experiment was made in the use of an inexpensive toy musical instrument, the kazoo, which might be highly useful in speech-correction exercises for cleft-palate children.

Not only were the subjects required to minimize nasal escape (in playing the kazoo—an instrument through which one hums or sings), but they were also required to produce the various pitches of several songs without relying on a mechanical aid such as a piano keyboard . . . (Linger, 1962).

Refinements developed in music therapy techniques during the 1963 clinic centered on work with individual children, although the group sessions also continued. A case study demonstrates how individual music therapy can operate.

The patient was a ten-year-old male who spoke with much nasality, rushed his speech, and was difficult to understand. In addition, he displayed overt behavioral problems, including refusal to cooperate, aggressiveness toward other children, distractibility, and a general tendency toward destructiveness. He was frequently uncooperative in speech therapy sessions and often was a distracting influence in any group activity. He seemed to show, as observed by the staff, a severe cultural deprivation and a low-average learning ability.

The treatment aims of music therapy were improvement in articulation and breath-stream problems; increase in attention span; assistance toward more cooperative behavior; learning of skills that might lead to better self-concept and social acceptance by peers; provision of open-throat exercises with free tones to reduce nasality; assistance in improving his sense of timing and rhythm; and ear training for monitoring his own speech and making better quality discriminations of all sounds.

The approach was to take a personal interest in the patient, accepting him as he was, and to try to build a bridge of common experience and feeling through music. Fifteen daily sessions were scheduled over a period of three weeks, and many other sessions were scheduled outside the regular daily activity times. After the first several sessions, the patient's attention span increased as he worked consistently on the flutophone. By the end of the clinic, he had memorized the first verse of "Old Folks at Home" and sang it proudly, distinctly, and in a serious manner. He concentrated daily on sustained breath-stream control with long, steady tones on the flutophone, and by the end of the clinic, he had attained much more control than he had had on the first day. In addition, the patient learned to play a simple tune on the piano and a few chords on the Autoharp, which he could use to accompany the singing of the group; and he explored the accordion and tape recorder.

The patient made good progress toward more cooperative behavior, and his general attitude improved greatly. He became less aggressive and even helped the other children, trying to get them to cooperate in group activities. He gained enough self-confidence to move from refusing to sing at first to being willing to sing a solo at the final program of the clinic (Herlong, 1963).

Results of the utilization of music therapy were observed not only in the enthusiasm of the children for their work in music, but also in some specific speech improvements that could be attributed more directly to music therapy than to any other single activity. Music therapy, therefore, has been found to be specifically beneficial in cleft-palate disorders as a means to help children improve sound-quality discriminations; gain better control of the breath stream; learn and practice specific articulation exercises; and gain a sense of self-confidence through accomplishment. Music also provides an acceptable outlet for feelings of frustration, hostility, and aggression. In view of the apparent success of music therapy procedures as treatment for this type of speech disorder, further research should be done, both in underlying theory and concepts and in applied methodology.

Music Therapy for Orthopedic Patients in a Rehabilitative Setting

YOLANDA A. KOZAK

Music therapy in a rehabilitative setting functions with the nursing service, which is composed of specialized personnel trained to meet the demands of orthopedic, general pediatric, and postsurgical problems. The patients are convalescent poliomyelitics; paraplegics; amputee, burn, plastic surgery, and fracture cases; individuals with difficult metabolic problems; and those who have suffered cerebral vascular accidents. Much therapy is planned with consultant orthopedists during clinics held three times each week. The therapies involved are physical, occupational, speech, and music. Other handicaps, such as mental retardation, emotional disturbance, mental illness, senility, or regression, are often present. Of necessity, all these things are considered when planning treatment for the individual patient.

The musical activities used in this rehabilitation center can be classified as exercise to music, speech activities to music, eurhythmics, functional use of the various keyboard and other musical instruments, and music appreciation. Music activities are used to help lessen physical handicaps, to aid in developmental problems, and for supportive assistance to the patient while he is in the hospital. Besides offering activities that are therapeutic in themselves, music therapy is used in support of activities conducted by the other therapies.

Orders for music therapy are received from medical doctors. In the case of a referral by another member of the staff, permission must be received from the patient's medical director before the patient can become involved in music therapy or any other activity at the hospital. Unless a medical problem exists, there is a blanket prescription to treat all patients coming into the hospital for training purposes. This includes young cerebral palsied children who come for evaluation and training, patients coming for speech work, and patients requiring only fitting and training in the use of prostheses.

There are many kinds of patient disabilities and many possibilities for music therapy with them. However, mention will be made of the background and treatment of only three patients selected for case presentation because of the purely orthopedic character of their handicaps.

Case 1. A ten-year-old boy, born with congenital anomalies of all four extremities, had been a patient intermittently and was readmitted to the hospital for a reevaluation and proper fitting of his crutches and prosthesis. The boy came into the music therapy department at his own request, stating that the music teacher at home had been reluctant to let him attempt playing an instrument because of his disabilities. Notwithstanding the fact that his upper extremities were deformed, he had had no operative procedures on them. The objective of his therapy was psychological and supportive assistance.

Although the boy had use of only three digits of the right hand, he was able to play the organ and became quite adept at sustaining tones by means of finger substitution. Because his range of shoulder motion was good, he could move from one octave of the keyboard to another. Despite the elbow contracture, the range of motion at this joint was satisfactory. Because of joint tightness, he lacked adequate force for depressing keys on the piano. However, he was able to manipulate organ keys well. He was happy with the thought of playing the organ and requested that one of his favorite hymns be written down for him. He learned to play this, along with other pieces, and took it home, confident that he had accomplished something.

Case 2. A girl with phocomelia of the lower extremities (a condition in which the limbs are extremely shortened) had been fitted with prostheses. In physical therapy, she was taught to walk with a swing-to gait. Rhythm was used as an aid in smoothing out the gait pattern that had been established. Occupational therapy was directed toward the development of the upper extremities and training in activities of daily living. Music therapy was directed toward control of the upper extremities with concentration on shoulder activity. Because the elbows had been fused approximately at right angles, the Autoharp seemed the appropriate instrument for this exercise.

Case 3. This patient was a male adult who had suffered an attack of polio. Initially, music therapy for him was of the supportive type. Later, as his condition improved, piano work was begun to benefit his left hand because his involvement was more severe on the left side. He had good finger dexterity of the left hand in playing melodies and chord patterns one note at a time. However, he did not have sufficient strength in his fingers to keep the distal finger joints partially flexed in a normal playing position. Much of the power for moving the fingers to play arpeggio-like patterns came from wrist and arm motions rather than from the individual fingers.

The right hand appeared to function well. The patient became interested in the chord organ, which he learned to play. Eventually, he began to recognize for himself that this type of exercise was beneficial and thereafter was motivated to continue making use of both hands in playing keyboard instruments.

Among the severely handicapped are occasional congenital bilateral upper amputees. A child with such disability is trained to use his feet to meet the needs of daily living. The music therapist may employ various methods to help develop skill in foot control. He can encourage and direct a patient to perform rhythmic activities and actions to songs with his feet, to play rhythm instruments with his feet, and to hold a horn with his feet. If a portable organ is placed on the floor in an appropriate position, the patient can learn to play it with his feet. After upper prostheses are fitted and training begins, the music therapist can use rhythm—alone, with a melody, or in a song—as a stimulus for the development of control of the artificial limbs.

The material in this report, although not comprehensive, indicates the necessary resourcefulness and imagination of the therapist in applying music therapy to the orthopedically disabled.

Case Reports

Music Therapy for Persons with Impaired Vision
—NORMA SHARPE

E was a sixteen-year-old blind patient at a training and residential school for the blind. She was afflicted with blindness at the age of six as a result of tuberculosis, but retained minimal sensitivity to light and shade contrast. Because of her psychotic behavior, she was referred to a nearby psychiatric hospital for treatment.

The ward staff reported E to be generally pleasant, but with unpredictable moods and temper tantrums. Although she had run away once from the school for the blind, E was given privileges from a closed ward within a year of her admission to this hospital.

E was referred to music therapy by the ward staff who had observed that she played the piano. The music therapist, after establishing initial rapport, asked her to play some of her pieces. She chose "Spring Song" and "Trumpet March," which she played with accuracy and in good rhythm. She had been taught by the braille system and eagerly showed the music therapist her braille music book.

E subsequently learned new pieces for the piano, some of which she taught herself, and others that the music therapist taught her by rote. The rote instructions included explanations of enough music theory to facilitate a better understanding of the piece by the patient. E also learned words of songs by rote and sang them to her own accompaniments.

During the summer months, E became interested in learning to play two musical instruments she had heard played by a music therapy student, the Autoharp and the melodica. She learned to play both of these instruments by the kinesthetic method and seemed to enjoy the experience.

E was always courteous and cheerful during music sessions and, at times, showed mischievous humor. She performed in ward programs, in a worker's music club talent show, and in recital. She appeared to be grateful when her psychiatrist came to hear her perform at a concert. She participated in a program for the local branch of the Institute for the Blind, and seemed very pleased to entertain other blind people.

Except for occasional temper outbursts when her requests were not granted immediately, E's behavior became more tractable. She was learning to share staff attention with other patients. Her musical contributions had been a major factor in helping her realize reward based on merit rather than demand and in developing a degree of self-esteem by means of successful adjustment to her visual handicap.

Music Therapy for Persons with Impaired Hearing
—CAROL A. CRIGLER and MICKIE M. SNIVELY

Because a very young child with an unknown degree of hearing loss is unable to follow directions for hearing tests, it is virtually impossible to judge the degree of his deafness. For this reason, two-year-old J was referred to music therapy. The speech therapist hoped that some idea of the degree of J's deafness could be gained by his response to musical instruments and noisemakers. Because a child normally learns to talk between the ages of three and five, it was also desired that he become familiar with the concept of sound and want to communicate with others so a speech therapist later could help him develop spoken language and lip reading.

J's parents thought him deaf since birth. His records showed him to have a bilateral hearing loss, probably of the inner ear, and a history of ear infections since the age of three months. Speech therapists adjudged him to have a severe hearing loss for social purposes. J appeared to be alert, cheerful, and eager to participate in most activities.

Sessions with two music therapists were held twice weekly for half-hour periods. In addition to becoming acquainted with J in initial sessions, the therapists made sounds with the instruments behind J's back. If he turned to see what was there, the instrument was demonstrated, and he and the therapist would play with it. A variety of instruments and noise-makers were used, including piano, clarinet, tambourine, rattles, whistles, drums, cymbals, ratchets, melody bells, and so on. Note was made of those instruments to which J responded. The fact that he turned his head so that his left ear was in better position to identify the sound was of importance.

Many games were played after the several weeks of testing. J enjoyed strumming an Autoharp placed on a wooden floor, especially when his ear was in contact with the instrument. He liked to place his hand on the piano while the therapist pounded chords. He wrapped his legs around a large bongo drum while he pounded it with a drumstick. He reacted with glee to the experience of crashing a pair of cymbals together and then immediately placing one on each ear. It appeared that J was responding with enthusiasm to some aspects of sound. His ability to take directions and ideas from the therapists steadily increased, as did his ability to relay messages of his own.

After four months, J was joined by C, another two-year-old boy, who had been referred by the speech therapy department for similar reasons. C, although curious about his surroundings, cried and ranted when separated from his mother. He was destructive with the instruments and toys presented to him and did not respond to nonverbal directions from the therapists. He reacted to J either in a hostile manner or not at all.

In testing C with instruments and noisemakers, it was immediately apparent that he reacted to many more than had J. However, his attention span was so short and his hostility so apparent that when given an instrument to explore, he would usually toss it across the room.

With constant encouragement, C gradually lessened his destructive behavior and demonstrated an interest in the bongo drums, piano, many rhythm instruments, and even melody bells. Both boys learned to blow toy horns in an effort to develop breath control as a preparation for spoken language. Follow the Leader became a favorite game for learning to follow the person in charge.

Two months later, both boys were fitted with earphones to make use of the residual hearing that their responses to music indicated they had. With a hearing aid fitted to his left ear, J was found to have a pure-tone loss of approximately 100 decibels in the right ear and 80 to 85 decibels in the left ear. It was felt at this time that he was ready for speech training and lip reading. C was fitted with a hearing aid to his right ear and was found to have a pure-tone loss of approximately 85 decibels in the right ear and 90 to 100 decibels in the left.

The response of these two children shows that music therapy has possibilities for helping very young children with severe hearing loss to develop familiarity with sound, and for encouraging a desire to communicate with others.

References

ARTHUR, SISTER MARY, and ELAINE, SISTER MARY. *We speak through music* (music and recordings). Valhalla, N.Y.: Stanbow Productions, 1959.

HERLONG, VIRGINIA P. Music therapy with "R. C."—a cleft palate child. Unpublished manuscript, Florida State Univer., 1963.

JENKINS, MARJORIE. Personal communication, April 1, 1965.

KAPLAN, M. Music therapy in the speech program. *Except. Child.*, 1955, 22, 112–117.

LINGER, B. H. Programmed learning techniques in music therapy for cleft palate children. Unpublished manuscript, Florida State Univer., 1962.

Michel, D. E. Music therapy in cleft palate disorders. In E. H. Schneider (Ed.), *Music therapy 1960.* Lawrence, Kan.: Allen Press, 1961. Pp. 126–131.

MICHEL, D. E. Music therapy in cleft palate disorders. In E. H. Schneider (Ed.), *Music therapy 1961.* Lawrence, Kan.: Allen Press, 1962. Pp. 111–115.

MILHORAT, A. T. Therapy in muscular dystrophy. *Med. Ann. Distr. Colum.*, 1954, 23, 15–22.

MURPHY, E. G. The child with progressive muscular dystrophy. In E. E. Martmer (Ed.), *The child with a handicap.* Springfield, Ill.: Charles C Thomas, 1959. Pp. 221–232.

SCHOELLY, M. L., and FRASER, A. W. Emotional reactions in muscular dystrophy. *Amer. J. Phys. Med.*, 1955, 34, reprint.

WIEBE, ANNE M. *Orthopedics in nursing.* Philadelphia: Saunders, 1961.

Part IV

MUSIC THERAPY
FOR CHILDREN AND ADOLESCENTS
WITH BEHAVIOR DISORDERS

Donald E. Michel

Child psychiatry is a unique discipline because of the distinctive nature of the problems of children with behavior disorders. Therefore, the music therapist must be especially sensitive to the problems of the emotionally disturbed child. One of the major difficulties of such children is their inability to communicate verbally. However, music is remarkably appropriate in many cases because it is nonverbal communication. Music engages the entire human organism in such fashion that it may well be a most effective medium of intercourse between therapist and patient, patient and peers. Much attention is given the autistic child because there are far greater numbers of them than was previously believed. The loss of love that so often characterizes the behaviorally disordered child can be greatly ameliorated by music and a sensitive therapist. Such music therapy is not esoteric—it functions under the same principles and processes used with other types of patients.

12

THE PSYCHIATRIC APPROACH
AND MUSIC THERAPY

DONALD E. MICHEL

Lustman (1966) has discussed several distinctive factors in the psychiatric approach to treating children and adults that are of interest to music therapists. He says that "child psychiatry [in spite of its relationship to general psychiatry] remains a unique discipline with its own distinctive problems, techniques, and training requirements" (p. 677). The importance of developmental concepts and genetic continuity is at once apparent in the study of the child. Fluctuations in the levels of development and organization often are easily observed.

Communication between child and therapist may be strikingly difficult because speech does not serve to ease it. In many cases, contact by the psychiatrist with parents becomes a necessity, although observation of the child at play yields many clues. *It is quite probable that music is much more than an opening wedge of communication.* Although most responses to music do not require verbalization, they do require organization and are therefore indicative behaviors.

Bakwin and Bakwin (1960) consider almost all types of childhood illnesses as "behavior disorders." This concept has merit, because any illness has its behavioral aspects and, ultimately, if not immediately, affects behavior. However, with the exception of brain damage, the behavior disorders of children and adolescents dealt with in this section are those resulting primarily from functional disturbances, without apparent physiological cause.

Adjustments in infancy and early childhood are chiefly influenced by the relationship of the mother and child. Disturbances of behavior at this early age are due to the infant's response to nourishment and comfort dissatisfactions. It is the mother and her psychological state that chiefly determine the affective experience of the child. What has been termed loss of love and deprivation of love objects seems to be characteristic of children who have had inharmonious or affect-impoverished infancy.

[175]

Later in childhood there are the usual tasks to be mastered, such as eating, bladder and bowel control, and other functions. It is generally at this time that separation from the mother is encountered and adjusted to. Enculturation makes its demands, and some price must be paid. As the child grows older, what was a reactive response may develop into a neurosis with phobias, rituals, and similar behavior disorders.

Disturbances of behavior are nearly always the individual's response to unsatisfactory, frustrating solutions to problems that occur as part of growth and development. Abnormal emotional states—anxiety, phobias, obsessions and compulsions, and impulsions; excessive anger, aggression, negativism, shyness, cruelty, and sexual deviations—and emotional deprivation are problems listed as related to emotional development. Difficulties related to habit and training are tics, disturbances of eating, and so forth. Problems discussed as psychosomatic or organic disturbances with a large psychic component are asthma, skin diseases, ulcerative colitis, and duodenal ulcer. Antisocial behavior may include lying, stealing, running away, setting fires, homicide, and suicide (Bakwin and Bakwin, 1960, pp. 381–560).

Obviously, behavior disorders in children and adolescents cover a wide range of syndromes or patterns. There are other categories of disturbances listed by the same authors that may be considered more on the order of symptoms than syndromes. They include disturbances of speech; difficulties in reading, spelling, writing, and arithmetic; enuresis; and motion sickness (Bakwin and Bakwin, 1960, pp. 325–380).

A description of adolescence and the problems related therein is provided by Caplan (1965), when he defines adolescence as "a psychological process occurring simultaneously with puberty and partly in response to puberty" (p. 93). "There is no developmental phase more flamboyantly stressful to both children and parents than adolescence" (Lustman, 1966, p. 693). Problems develop from a "weakening of the ego. The previously successful defenses are no longer able to cope with the bombardment of impulses . . ." (Caplan, 1965, p. 93). Caplan further describes the pathology of disturbed adolescents as activity that is "presented in some as an exaggeration of normal actions. Action, therefore, is what brings the conflicts to our attention" (p. 92). For the purposes of this section and the following articles, then, adolescence is considered a developmental stage separate from, but related to, childhood.

Some types of disorders in children have drawn more attention than others. Early infantile autism is one of these. The recent formation of The National Society for Autistic Children attests to this growing interest. Contrary to some past opinions, there is high incidence of this disorder. It is the first known psychotic state in man (Lustman, 1966, p. 692). Because of the amount of interest in the syndrome and the consistent and frequent references in the literature to the unusual role played by music in many of the cases of children suffering from the disease, an extended review of such literature is presented in the next chapter. The relationship of autism to schizophrenia is not yet agreed on. Much can be learned from a careful study of the autistic child.

Literature

There is not enough research reported concerning music therapy for children and adolescents with behavior disorders. Reports of experimental research are rare. A few articles illustrate objective observation and evaluation of music therapy procedures, but others are pure testimonials.

Wayne (1944) reported results of an eighteen-month period of teaching instruments to thirty-five maladjusted children. He concluded that music could be of value in relieving tension and promoting socialization among such children. Being a music educator, Wayne concentrated entirely on teaching techniques. He did not report the background of the children's special needs nor provide evaluation of actual treatment benefits.

Since 1951, reports concerning music therapy for disturbed children and adolescents have appeared in the publications of the National Association for Music Therapy. Weir (1952) described her work at a private school. Some cases were presented, but she devoted most of her efforts to describing how music therapy *might* help children with behavior disorders.

Dreikurs and Crocker (1956) referred to music as communication on a nonverbal level and described how this characteristic makes it an ideal tool for working with the psychotic child who has disrupted his communication on logical and verbal levels. They hypothesized that music may increase communication with the psychotic child, thus evoking a subtle acceptance of order so essential in therapeutic endeavors.

. Our experience has shown that music may be a profitable and therapeutic means of eliciting more appropriate emotional responses from a child who ordinarily exhibits little or no appropriate emotional response. This is done by matching the prevailing mood as nearly as possible and then gradually altering the mood of the music in the desired direction. For example, the depressed child likes quiet music and responds more easily to it. The therapist, then, beginning at this level, gradually increases the tempo and excitement of the music and by so doing induces a corresponding mood change in the child thus relieving him of his depression (pp. 65–66).

Some behavior disorders in children and adolescents may result in juvenile delinquency. Lindecker (1955) reported her experiences in working with juvenile delinquents, pointing out the values of music therapy for those held in detention.

Because of the very nature of the music used they seem to lose much of their physical and emotional tension and many of their inhibitions. Thus the staff is able to note behavior patterns which might not be manifest during interviews with probation counselors, psychologists, or outside agency case workers. These observations are valuable . . . when reported to the proper court or agency workers, who frequently gain added insight into their particular cases (p. 118).

Music therapy "acts as an acceptable means of diversion, thus easing tensions created by individual difficulties arising prior to and during detention" (p. 123). Besides facilitating better relationships among the children and between them and the staff members, it also may develop musical ability and interest for use when the child returns to society. Music also can be helpful in modifying moods of children, both individually and in groups.

Harbert (1957) reported on her work with emotionally disturbed children in a university clinic, noting that the clinic accepted all types of handicapped children: "It is impossible to label certain children simply blind, deaf, cerebral palsied, etc., without taking into consideration the fact that in all of these children there is a degree of emotional disturbance, otherwise they would not be coming for help" (p. 157). Several cases were recounted in which the following results from music therapy were observed: development of a sense of security and self-confidence, changed attitudes, better motor response, improved speech, and carry-over values of better communication with members of the family away from the clinic. Most of the work described was done in group activities. Harbert listed other results, including "emotional release . . . growing interest in creative self-expression . . . [and] more satisfactory interpersonal relationships" (p. 164).

Music therapy techniques for handicapped children have been used in public school settings. In a study that applied objective methods of control and observation, public school consultants in special education and in elementary music planned "an experiment . . . to study the effects of music on children who were exhibiting socially unacceptable behavior in the classroom. The study utilized the services of persons in the psychological, musical, and educational departments of the public schools" (Alward and Rule, 1960, p. 153). Using a behavior checklist and structured interviews to identify the disturbed children and their problems (as well as their interests), the investigators structured individual musical experiences designed to develop social awareness, provide for emotional release, build feelings of security, increase the span of attention, help the children accept limits, foster better interpersonal relationships, channel latent musical abilities, and bring about creative self-expression through music. Observation of specific classroom behavior patterns, in the form of certain unacceptable acts by individual children, provided the basis for measuring the change during the music therapy program. In all cases, individual children exhibited changed behavior, and the investigators concluded:

1. Children with withdrawing tendencies seemed to become more outgoing both in the musical activity session and in the classroom. Whether this trend would continue, is speculative.
2. There was not much evidence that the overt actions of a child of normal intelligence were quieted by the musical activities, but his aggressive behavior seemed to take a different form.
3. The music had a quieting effect on the acting-out, mentally retarded child.
4. In the child who was not deeply disturbed, but who was under pressure to achieve, the musical activity sessions seemed to afford relaxation and release from some of the pressures.
5. It was difficult to determine whether it was the specific music activity that was beneficial, or whether it was the personal attention the child received (Alward and Rule, 1960, p. 167).

Greven (1958) incorporated music into the well-accepted techniques of play therapy for disturbed children. Joseph and Heimlich (1959) described how music therapy was used with treatment-resistant children after many other therapeutic approaches had been attempted and abandoned. By having independent observers use an objective rating sheet, the investigators obtained data concerning the children's ability to sustain attention, to achieve release from anxiety, to learn, and to relate to adults and/or peers. Spontaneity, self-esteem, and overall progress also were rated. Although no involved statistical tools were employed, the writers reported definite progress in most of the children.

Singer (1962) described music therapy procedures for children and adolescents in a cottage-plan treatment center. She used case summaries to illustrate music as a treatment medium for two disturbed adolescents (twelve-year-old girls). Basic treatment aims were to develop positive transference and to lessen the girls' tendencies to withdraw and isolate themselves from reality. Both group and individual approaches were used. Observed results in both cases showed music therapy to have operated "not as an insight therapy, but as a means of enabling them to once again re-establish human contacts and, in the loss of their isolation, to live in the world of reality" (p. 22). Although no controlled means of observation and evaluation were employed, the active participation of a psychiatrist in this setting—and his concurrence in observed results—lends some authority to the report.

Wilson (1964) reported on the use of music, among other media, in the program of a special school for emotionally disturbed children. Her description of the total program and of the positive function of music in it is perhaps indicative of future developments.

Gewirtz (1964) has discussed music therapy as a form of supportive psychotherapy and its relationship to the treatment of children. He illustrated how music may serve short-term as well as long-range goals in therapy. No objective data are provided, but the observations of clinical practice and the logical grounds relating music therapy to psychotherapeutic principles seem convincing.

References

ALWARD, EILEEN, and RULE, BETTY. An experiment in musical activities with disturbed children. In E. H. Schneider (Ed.), *Music therapy 1959*. Lawrence, Kan.: Allen Press, 1960. Pp. 153–168.

BAKWIN, H., and BAKWIN, RUTH M. *Behavior disorders in children*. Philadelphia: Saunders, 1960.

CAPLAN, L. M. The disturbed adolescent and problems in his treatment. *J. Mus. Ther.*, 1965, 2, 92–95.

DREIKURS, R., and CROCKER, DOROTHY B. Music therapy with psychotic children. In E. T. Gaston (Ed.), *Music therapy 1955*. Lawrence, Kan.: Allen Press, 1956. Pp. 62–73.

GEWIRTZ, H. Music therapy as a form of supportive psychotherapy with children. *J. Mus. Ther.*, 1964, 1, 61–65.

GREVEN, GEORGIA M. Music as a tool in psychotherapy for children. In E. T. Gaston (Ed.), *Music therapy 1957*. Lawrence, Kan.: Allen Press, 1958. Pp. 105–108.

HARBERT, WILHELMINA K. Treatment of emotionally disturbed children in a music therapy clinic. In E. T. Gaston (Ed.), *Music therapy 1956*. Lawrence, Kan.: Allen Press, 1957. Pp. 156–164.

JOSEPH, H., and HEIMLICH, E. P. The therapeutic use of music with "treatment resistant" children. *Amer. J. ment. Defic.*, 1959, 64, 41–49.

LINDECKER, JANET M. Music therapy for juvenile delinquents. In E. T. Gaston (Ed.), *Music therapy 1954*. Lawrence, Kan.: Allen Press, 1955. Pp. 117–123.

LUSTMAN, S. L. Behavior disorders in childhood and adolescence. In F. C. Redlich and D. X. Freedman (Eds.), *The theory and practice of psychiatry*. New York: Basic Books, Inc., Publishers, 1966. Pp. 676–704.

SINGER, SUE. Music therapy: its application to emotionally disturbed children in a cottage-plan treatment center. *Bull. NAMT*, 1962, 11, 19–22.

WAYNE, M. Instrumental music for the maladjusted child. *Mus. Educ. J.*, 1944, 31, 33–36.

WEIR, LOUISE E. Music therapy at Devereux Ranch School. In Esther G. Gilliland (Ed.), *Music therapy 1951*. Lawrence, Kan.: Allen Press, 1952. Pp. 22–25.

WILSON, ANNAMARY. Special education for the emotionally disturbed child. *J. Mus. Ther.*, 1964, 1, 16–18.

13

EARLY INFANTILE AUTISM

JO ANN EUPER

General Characteristics

Early infantile autism is a syndrome of which the symptoms can usually be traced back to the fourth month of life, but that often does not become disturbingly evident until the first or second year (Rimland, 1964, p. 7). Outstanding characteristics of this syndrome include extreme withdrawal from contact with people; an obsessive need for sameness in the environment; skillful manipulation of objects and often an affectionate relationship to them; a physical appearance of intelligence; and speech pathology ranging from bizarre language, a private metaphorical system, and other uncommunicative forms, to complete mutism (Kanner, 1949).

Autistic children appear to be unaware of persons as such; even in early infancy they fail to assume an anticipatory posture when being picked up and do not adjust their bodies to those of persons holding them (Eisenberg and Kanner, 1956). In contrast to their inability to relate to people, autistic children relate well to objects (other than toy animals and dolls, which they seem to avoid as much as they do the living beings) (Benda, 1952, p. 501). Autistic children show a high degree of interest in forms and usually perform well with the Seguin formboard; this is interpreted by some as an indication of the child's preoccupation with distinction of boundaries and self-other realization (Ritvo and Provence, 1953). The frequent occurrence of head banging and similar autoaggressive behavior is similarly understood by some writers to be the child's means of sharpening his awareness of body boundaries and feeling of entity (Mahler, Furer, and Settlage, 1959, p. 826). His striking ability to spin things has been seen as his attempt to maintain or develop spatial relations (Mahler, Ross, and De Fries, 1949); however, the autistic child does not spin himself, as schizophrenic children often do (Rimland, 1964, p. 73). There is usually an early development of agile, well-coordinated motor behavior (Benda, 1952, p. 501).

An outstanding mark of early infantile autism is speech pathology. Although many autistic children say words, phrases, and sentences very early, giving an impression of precocity, about one-half to two-thirds of them abruptly stop talking and become mute. One-third of all autistic children never use speech; the ones who do usually use it uncommunicatively. Pronoun reversal is common until about age six (Kanner, 1948, p. 717f), and "I" and "you" are not used until about the seventh year (Rimland, 1964, p. 73). Autistic children frequently use metaphoric expressions that are meaningful to others only if the origin of the expression is known; the tracing of these metaphors is usually an involved process and seldom is accomplished (Kanner, 1946).

Many authors have commented on the phenomenal memory of autistic children; very young ones have been known to recite a great quantity of poetry, a list of the Presidents of the United States, and other factual material at an age when the information probably could not be meaningful to them (Kanner, 1949). Also indicative of their astute memories is the obsessive need for sameness; minute, ordinarily unnoticeable changes of environmental arrangements or the order of events sometimes precipitate violent temper tantrums, even though the child shows no further interest after the deviation has been corrected. Intricate patterns constructed from over one hundred blocks have been used to test this trait by changing one block at the second viewing. Deviations are noticed immediately, even when the viewings are separated by several days (Kanner, 1951).

At the outset, it is well to differentiate between autistic behavior, which occurs in other mental illnesses and in mental deficiency, and the syndrome of early infantile autism, which is a separate classification (Kanner, 1944). The child with early infantile autism can be distinguished from the mentally deficient child on the basis of his normal motor development and his intelligent and thoughtful facial expression. He has excellent rote memory and memory for tunes, and sometimes he possesses an amazing vocabulary. There are often wide discrepancies between the autistic child's typically low intelligence quotient (which generally is not measurable because of his lack of cooperation in the testing situation) and his performance in natural situations and on the Seguin formboard. Although autistic children usually function as mental defectives, a distinction is recommended because some have been known to brighten up and perform adequately (Bakwin and Bakwin, 1960, p. 548). Infantile autism is distinguishable from the chronic brain syndrome because of its lack of the incessant pressure of impulsive hyperactivity that is so typical of brain damage (Robinson, 1961), as well as its lack of history of cerebral or neurologic injury or illness. Furthermore, in the chronic brain syndrome, it is usually the motor rather than the speech development that is slow. The reverse is usually true with autism (Bakwin and Bakwin, 1960, p. 548f).

Autism and Schizophrenia

Although some writers do not distinguish autism from schizophrenia (Rimland, 1964, p. 67), most of them do advocate such a distinction. Bakwin and Bakwin (1960) state that "infantile autism presents a clinical picture of its own and deserves a separate place because of the early age at which the symptoms appear" (p. 548). Rimland (1964, p. 67ff) points out many features that distinguish the two. By definition, childhood schizophrenia must follow a period of normal development; autism, however, is present from earliest infancy.

Case histories of autistic children almost invariably describe them as having excellent health and being attractive and well built. By contrast, most schizophrenic children are described as having had poor health from birth, with numerous distinctive physical features not found in autistic children. Electroencephalographic studies tend to indicate a preponderance of positive findings in schizophrenic children and negative findings in autistic children. Rimland further points out that the schizophrenic child usually exhibits a clinging behavior, a strong tendency to mold to adults like plastic or dough. The autistic child, in contrast, is typically stiff and unresponsive to others. In infancy and later childhood, he remains aloof, in apparent unawareness of, or indifference to, the presence or absence of others.

The compulsive need for sameness found in autistic children is not common in childhood schizophrenia. Hallucination, common in schizophrenia, is not reported in cases of autism. Motor performance of autistic children is reportedly much better than that of schizophrenics. The bizarre language patterns of autism, with striking uniformity among cases, have not been reported in schizophrenia; nor has the occurrence of unusual feats of memory and mechanical performance, often reminiscent of the *idiot savant*. Studies of several other aspects, such as the incidence of autism and schizophrenia in twins, their parents' personality characteristics, and familial histories of mental disorder, all point toward sharp distinctions between autistic and schizophrenic syndromes. Studies by Schopler (1964) and Singer and Wynne (1963) tend to support these distinguishing features, which were listed also by Rimland. Early infantile autism must be distinguished from schizophrenia if research in these areas is to be meaningful (Rimland, 1964, p. 68).

Treatment

Despite the abundant disagreement with regard to the classification and etiology of early infantile autism, most writers appear to agree that the primary treatment problem is to stimulate the child to interact with the people in his life (Mahler, 1952). Toward this goal, a variety of methods have been tried, again reflecting the theoretical commitments of those involved. Treatments have included residential and outpatient care; standard suppressive psychotherapy (Escalona, 1948); special physiotherapeutic stimulation (Waal, 1959, p. 444); family counseling (Schulman, 1963); a therapeutically oriented day school (Fenichel, Freedman, and Klapper, 1960); a residential school with elaborate personnel arrangements geared to the provision of mother surrogates (May and May, 1959); intrusion and frustration (Weiland and Rudnik, 1961); and residential team treatment directed toward the development of body image and object relations through well-timed frustrations (Kemph, Cain, and Finch, 1963). All these have been strikingly unsuccessful (Rimland, 1964, p. 17).

Recently the use of drugs has given some hope, but there is insufficient evidence at present, and too little time has elapsed to allow a fair evaluation of it (Rimland, 1964, p. 106). The prognosis is bleak, according to Mahler (1952), and most other writers agree. It has been noted that autistic children seem to fare better with an affectionate, minimally stimulating environment than with intensive professional care (Rimland, 1964, p. 17).

The Autistic Child and Music

A common observation throughout the literature is that autistic children show unusual interest, and often talent, in music. Schulman (1963) cites the case of an autistic child who sang operatic arias at the age of eighteen months, although he did not develop speech until nearly three years of age. Ritvo and Provence (1953) report a child who, at about two and one-half years of age, developed a strong interest in phonograph records, which he played continually; however, he would skip over the parts that used the human voice.

One of Kanner's cases, unusual because in adulthood the patient is considered recovered, became a composer (Rimland, 1964, p. 12). A subject in a case reported by Anastasi and Levee (1960) was such a fine pianist that professional musicians would go to his home to perform with him, despite his unreasonable personality. Although this person was described as an adult *idiot savant*, the information reported indicates that he was an autistic child grown to adulthood (Rimland, 1964, p. 12). A study of over thirty autistic children revealed only one who did not show deep interest in music (Bergman and Escalona, 1949). In another study, one of four autistic children displayed interest described as "extraordinary knowledge of recorded music," two were considered in the class of "musical genius," and the fourth had "an extensive repertoire of popular and classical music" (Despert, 1947). Rimland's (1964) study has led him to the conclusion that musical ability and interest are "almost universal in autistic children" (p. 175).

Beyond the superficial remarks that simply note the child's interest in music as an intriguing symptom, little study of the subject has been made. Sherwin (1953) reports his study of the musical responses of three autistic children. Two of them were identical twins seen for treatment at the age of three and one-half years.

Child D, one of the twins, had shown a profound interest in music at one and one-half years of age, correctly singing scales, folk songs, and selections from a symphony. Upon hearing a familiar song, the child would smile. When anxious, he would rock rhythmically while singing rapidly at a high pitch, often endlessly repeating motives or fragments sequentially in rising pitch. (Sherwin notes the regular use of this musical device to express rising tension.) Although D usually sang with exceptional accuracy, anxiety would cause a screaming tone, distortions, and variations such as rhythmic diminution and distorted melodic inversions. The child never used words in his songs. Although the singing of the therapist seemed to soothe this child, his own singing did not seem to modify his emotional state when he was already anxious.

Child B's interest and ability in music were less marked than those of his twin, D; but they were still more marked than is usual in an ordinary child. His singing increased near the end of therapy, but became less accurate. (Sherwin interpreted this as a subjective expression of involved emotions, rather than a desire for communication.) This child's anxiety seemed to be decreased greatly when the therapist played the piano. When B would stand by the door, indicating his desire to leave, piano music would calm him, and he would climb into the therapist's lap. After approximately six sessions, he would indicate his desire for the stopped music to be resumed by pushing the therapist's hands toward the keyboard, or by guiding the therapist to the instrument. In the seventh month, he indicated selectivity for pieces, sometimes based on familiarity, but usually on his preference for a strong rhythm. The meter and register seemed immaterial, except that B rejected the very low register of pitch.

(*Sherwin concluded that the child's responsiveness to the therapist was based on the association of the therapist with the production of music.*)

Child C, seen at the age of four and one-half years, had revealed great interest in music at fourteen months; by eighteen months, he was able to sing songs by Schubert and Brahms, selections from *Carmen*, various well-known songs, and themes of symphonies. He listened to pieces played on the piano by the therapist and was reluctant to stop, placing the therapist's hands back on the keyboard at the end of a piece. This child had an extraordinary memory for all types of music and would spend long periods listening or singing. His singing was always initiated at his own will. To induce him to sing required one to sing something first; then C would invariably repeat what he had heard. If the last note of a song were omitted, C would supply the correct note. As this child's condition improved, his musical interest and ability waned, his accuracy diminished, and he sang less.

Sherwin (1953) reports Despert's three possible explanations for the frequency of unusual responses of autistic children to music:

1. These children appear to have exceptional acuity to sound.
2. This interest may be a secondary factor based upon the autistic child's preference for objects rather than people, who create words; it is "part of the total 'obsessive preoccupations' of these children . . . with sound, light, or various objects, or play."
3. Rather than being the result of a barrier against verbal human communications, music may be a primary factor functioning to prevent the development of such human communication (p. 829).

These explanations strongly reflect Despert's theoretical orientation.

Other explanations have been offered, each of which reflects the theoretical orientation of the explainer. Rimland (1964, pp. 209, 211) suggests a neurological explanation based on numerous studies of sensory deprivation, neuronal discharge patterning, electrophysiology, and the relationship of heredity to intellect and esthetic values. This author is one of those who favors a theory of physiologic dysfunction as a cause of autism, with a possible genetic element. Sherwin (1953) offers two possibilities:

1. Considering the fact that the overwhelming majority of autistic children are the offspring of very intelligent and sophisticated parents, "music and fine records may play a greater part in the environment of these children than in the average home." [In his three cases, the parents of C were both singers, and the twins' mother sang to them frequently.]
2. Music may appeal to these children because it is inherently less specific than speech (pp. 829–830).

Sherwin believes the autistic child's choice of music as a central preoccupation, or development of musical ability to the exclusion of most other environmental aspects, is significant. He thinks that music may represent a therapeutic approach, at least for the purpose of making contact with these children. He also believes it is possible that music may actually help to improve the autistic condition.

On the other hand, it has been suggested that autism is a fixation at, or a regression to, the primary level of extrauterine life (Mahler, Furer, and Settlage, 1959, p. 827). Writers committed to this theory relate the autistic child's behavioral characteristics to an infantile level of development characteristic of the first four months of life (as interpreted in terms of the psychoanalytic school of thought). Sterba (1946) has attempted to analyze the meaning of music in terms of human psychological processes and concluded that music precipitates a regression to early infantile kinesthetic pleasure as well as the dissolution of ego boundaries. This explanation ascribes to the ordinary enjoyer of music the very same qualities that are attributed to the autistic child by those committed to the psychoanalytic school (Mahler, 1952, p. 297). Thus, the possibility exists that the use of music in the treatment of autistic children may actually impede progress. Mahler, to the contrary, states that "the autistic child is most intolerant of direct human contact. Hence, he must be lured out of his autistic shell with all kinds of devices such as music, rhythmic activities and pleasurable stimulation of his sense organs" (p. 302).

That interest or ability in music is an outstanding characteristic of early infantile autism is reflected in the frequency and way in which it is reported. Such frequent mention of musical preoccupation is not found in the literature concerning other conditions, such as mental deficiency or childhood neurosis, nor in the reported cases of childhood schizophrenia that are clearly not autistic. Although musicality is not universal among autistic children, the writers quoted clearly have been impressed with the presence of musical interest in many children with early infantile autism.

Case Study

A three-month intensive exploratory study of music therapy with an autistic child suggests several treatment considerations.

The subject was a six-year-old boy with a diagnosis of early infantile autism established in two clinics. His symptoms and history conformed well with the clinical picture of autism discussed earlier. Although his mother had stated that he liked music, a thorough exploration of S's abilities indicated that he was not musical himself. Nevertheless, some music activities were probably helpful in improving his relationships with the environment and his peers.

At first S could not imitate the simple activities of another person. He would not observe a demonstration or look at any given object on request. His use of directed observation improved after a few weeks, probably as a result of his increased familiarity with the therapist and the activity period as well as the constant direct efforts to teach him to observe.

Another primary problem for this child was his inability to relate two aspects of his environment. He could march or do other simple exercises rhythmically without music, but the addition of music immediately disorganized him, and he would be unable to continue the exercise. He walked well naturally, but when music was playing he either ignored it, walking rhythmically but not in time to the music, or was completely disorganized by it, developing a very arhythmic gait or stopping altogether. This was seen as a manifestation of S's perceptual and cognitive difficulties: He was unable either to organize parts of the environment into meaningful wholes or to relate himself to his environment purposefully.

Rhythm-band activities were helpful in this area. S was required to play his instrument or clap his hands alternately with another person, without musical accompaniment, thus necessitating that he be attentive to the other person and relate himself deliberately to that person. This was difficult for him, and several weeks of struggling effort passed before he was able to carry this activity beyond a few exchanges. For rhythm-band activity with musical accompaniment, it was first necessary to teach S to continue to play his instrument while the recorded music was playing. This required several weeks. The next step was to teach him to alter the speed of his playing compatibly with tempo changes in the music. Although his playing was seldom rhythmic, he did learn to alter his tempo in the same direction as the alterations in the music. Eventually, his rhythmicity increased also.

Throughout the period of study, S's ability to relate himself to the environment and meet its demands with purposeful responses improved. Although music therapy was only part of S's total treatment program (five half-day special school sessions per week), it was felt to have been of some help in his treatment.

References

ANASTASI, A., and LEVEE, R. F. Intellectual defect and musical talent: a case report. *Amer. J. ment. Defic.*, 1960, 64, 695–703.

BAKWIN, H., and BAKWIN, RUTH M. *Behavior disorders in children*. Philadelphia: Saunders, 1960.

BENDA, C. *Developmental disorders of mentation and cerebral palsies.* New York: Grune & Stratton, 1952.

BERGMAN, P., and ESCALONA, S. Unusual sensitivities in very young children. *Psychoanalytic Study of the Child,* 1949, 3, 4, 333–352.

DESPERT, J. LOUISE. Psychotherapy in child schizophrenia. *Amer. J. Psychiat.,* 1947, *104,* 36–43.

EISENBERG, L., and KANNER, L. Early infantile autism. *Amer. J. Orthopsychiat.,* 1956, *26,* 556–566.

ESCALONA, S. Some considerations regarding psychotherapy with psychotic children. *Bull. Menninger Clin.,* 1948, *12,* 126–134.

FENICHEL, C., FREEDMAN, A., and KLAPPER, Z. A day school for schizophrenic children. *Amer. J. Orthopsychiat.,* 1960, *30,* 130–143.

KANNER, L. Early infantile autism. *J. Pediat.,* 1944, *25,* 211–217.

KANNER, L. Irrelevant and metaphorical language in early infantile autism. *Amer. J. Psychiat.,* 1946, *103,* 242–246.

KANNER, L. *Child psychiatry.* Springfield, Ill.: Charles C Thomas, 1948.

KANNER, L. Problems of nosology and psychodynamics of early infantile autism. *Amer. J. Orthopsychiat.,* 1949, *19,* 416–426.

KANNER, L. The conception of wholes and parts in early infantile autism. *Amer. J. Psychiat.,* 1951, *108,* 23–26.

KEMPH, J., CAIN, A., and FINCH, S. New directions in the inpatient treatment of psychotic children in a training center. *Amer. J. Psychiat.,* 1963, *119,* 934–939.

MAHLER, M. On child psychosis and schizophrenia: autistic and symbiotic infantile psychoses. *Psychoanalytic Study of the Child,* 1952, 7, 286–305.

MAHLER, M., FURER, M., and SETTLAGE, C. F. Severe emotional disturbances in childhood: psychosis. In S. Arieti (Ed.), *American handbook of psychiatry.* New York: Basic Books, Inc., Publishers, 1959. Pp. 816–839.

MAHLER, M., ROSS, J., and DE FRIES, Z. Clinical studies in benign and malignant cases of childhood psychosis (schizophrenic-like). *Amer. J. Orthopsychiat.,* 1949, *19,* 295–305.

MAY, J. M., and MAY, M. A. The treatment and education of the atypical, autistic child in a residential school situation. *Amer. J. ment. Defic.,* 1959, *64,* 435–443.

RIMLAND, B. *Infantile autism.* New York: Appleton-Century-Crofts, 1964.

RITVO, S., and PROVENCE, S. Form perception and imitation in some autistic children: diagnostic findings and their contextual interpretation. *Psychoanalytic Study of the Child,* 1953, 8, 155–161.

ROBINSON, J. F. The psychoses of early childhood. *Amer. J. Orthopsychiat.,* 1961, *31,* 536–550.

SCHOPLER, E. The relationship between early tactile experiences and the treatment of an autistic and a schizophrenic child. *Amer. J. Orthopsychiat.,* 1964, *34,* 339–340.

SCHULMAN, J. L. Management of the child with early infantile autism. *Amer. J. Psychiat.,* 1963, *120,* 250–254.

SHERWIN, A. C. Reactions to music of autistic (schizophrenic) children. *Amer. J. Psychiat.,* 1953, *109,* 823–831.

SINGER, M. T., and WYNNE, L. C. Differentiating characteristics of parents of childhood schizophrenics, childhood neurotics and young adult schizophrenics. *Amer. J. Psychiat.,* 1963, *120,* 234–243.

STERBA, R. Toward the problem of the musical process. *Psychoanalyt. Rev.,* 1946, *33,* 37–42.

WAAL, N. A special technique of psychotherapy with an autistic child. In G. Caplan (Ed.), *Emotional problems of early childhood.* New York: Basic Books, Inc., Publishers, 1959. Pp. 431–449.

WEILAND, I. H., and RUDNIK, R. Considerations of the development and treatment of autistic childhood psychosis. *Psychoanalytic Study of the Child,* 1961, *16,* 549–562.

14

CLINICAL EXPERIENCES
WITH AUTISTIC CHILDREN

Improvised Music as Therapy for Autistic Children

PAUL NORDOFF

CLIVE ROBBINS

Most handicapped children will respond readily to the musical situation in which they find themselves. In addition, they often will disclose particular musical handicaps as expressions of their pathology. This is not true, however, of the autistic child; with him it is not so much a question of discovering his musical handicaps as finding what point of contact he might have with music. This may require many therapy sessions. For the therapist to begin his work, some kind of response from the child is necessary. The child may sing or grunt, or beat the drum briefly in response to music; improvised music can inspire and then accompany various responses having the character of impulses and usually lacking any connection with consciousness. It is then necessary to secure within the child these kinds of responses and to sustain them, allowing him to discover the pleasure and satisfaction of using his body and voice in a shared musical activity. Because each child's response is as individual as he is, the music improvised should be specific for each child. During an active session, the situation usually is changing; the therapist must be ready to lead, to accompany, and to change the music in order to meet existing needs.

The authors have conducted a pilot music therapy project with twenty-six children. At least fifteen of these were extremely autistic; the others were severely ego-disturbed with autistic features. Symbiotic behavior was also much in evidence, and one classically schizophrenic child was included. Some mild to moderate organic involvement was suspected in about seven of the cases and was to some extent verified by long-term differential diagnosis. None of the children treated in this project belonged to the bizarre musical genius class sometimes reported in the literature. It has been suggested that the preoccupation in music shown by autistic children stands out because of the dearth of other interests. Possibly it is an interest in a nonthreatening sphere of experience that avoids direct human contact (recordings and commercials) and frequently serves to reinforce the autistic state. There were a few indications of freak musicality in three children, but these proved to have no significance for treatment. Six children clearly showed musical sensitivity, although this tended to remain limited or stereotyped. Four children possessed a genuine musical intelligence, present in what might be called a normal state of development and function. The fact that two of these freely musically sensitive children began music therapy in the severely autistic condition was of immense importance in the subsequent development of musical rating scales.

The following case description has been chosen to illustrate the use of improvised music in therapy.

When she began therapy, R was a morose six-year-old whose main preoccupation was knotting pieces of string. Her speech was minimal and echolalic, and she did not use personal pronouns. Her behavior was erratic and unpredictable. She had two 10-minute music therapy sessions weekly, in which she beat on a small drum while the therapist accompanied her, trying to engage her interest by varying the rhythm. Although R was not able to follow the therapist's variations for long at the beginning, and would often beat distractedly in her own tempo or sit sucking her thumb, after a month she was able to imitate his rhythmic patterns and accents and follow accelerandi with him. When her song, "R_____ Can Say Hello," was included in the improvisation, she smiled.

Following this period of progress, R's responsiveness ceased; she became negativistic and regressed. For five months she was very evasive and obstreperous and seemed to make no progress in music therapy. Finally she resumed her interest. Through the following month her therapy sessions were extended to twenty minutes each, during which she worked continually at the drum. Music used for this child had much vitality and variety in tempo and dynamics; jazz often was used. When R took initiative in setting a style, the therapist would match it in his improvisations. After another month, during a very energetic session, R began to shout rhythmically with the music, then to sing, "R_____ can beat it, yes she can!" (the words to her jazzy song). Following this breakthrough into song, her drum beating was diminished. It was felt that as drum beating became more expressive of musical-emotional experience, she was propelled into new areas of expressive freedom; unable to resist what was happening to her, she just had to sing.

R became so freely communicative that many songs were developed for her, several on subjects she suggested. Therapy continued in this fashion for another eight months, during which time she began spontaneously to use personal pronouns. Her vocabulary improved consider-ably, and progress in her behavior and responsiveness at home was reported.

Clinical Experiences with Hospitalized Early-Childhood Schizophrenic Children in Music Therapy

BARBARA J. ROMERHAUS

The author worked as a music therapist with a group of young children for a period of two years at a clinical research center. The children, rang-ing in age from two to eight, were diagnosed as having early-childhood schizophrenia, autism, or autism with symbiotic features. The majority of these children were either mute or vocalized for purposes other than communication. Those who did use speech used it in a baffling manner. Naming objects was common, but asking or answering questions was rare. Other speech symptoms were delayed echolalia and pronominal reversal.

The children exhibited extreme withdrawal from interpersonal rela-tionships or fluctuated between withdrawal and excessive clinging to adults. They resisted changes in routine and insisted on preserving same-ness in the environment. Frequently, they engaged in ritualistic behavior centered around the use of their own bodies and/or inanimate objects. Their toy play was inappropriate, often consisting of stereotyped usage of only a part of a toy. Along with this inappropriate use of toys and inanimate objects, the children displayed repetitive and fetish-like pre-occupation with mechanical objects such as light switches and doorknobs. These children either were not toilet trained or displayed inconsistent control. They generally caused feeding problems, having odd habits and preferences.

A five-year-old autistic boy was reported to have some musical ability. He exhibited such autistic features as slight awareness of other people, no communicative speech, and a ritualistic pattern of spinning any toy or object, regardless of its intended use. At the piano, he could play chords in various inversions and scales in octaves. On one occasion, he spontaneously sang a familiar song perfectly in tune, using the appropriate words; then he proceeded to pick out the melody on the piano using one finger. He accomplished this with accuracy.

The responses from this child tend to support Sherwin's (1953) find-ings that there exists in autistic children a preoccupation and unusual absorption in music, a rote memory for melodies, and a preference for singing over speech. This same boy, when listening to any classical music, would gaze at the record player and appear to be in a trance-like state, completely absorbed, for as long as the record played. When the record was changed and fast polkas or pop tunes were played, his attention wandered immediately to other things.

The children had two group music therapy sessions daily. During the first half of each session, they were seated around the piano; during the last half, they participated in a vigorous activity involving more body motility. When the sessions were first initiated, the children resisted staying within the circle around the piano. There was much "escaping" from the circle and loud crying when the "escaped" child was brought back into the group. Gradually, the crying and desire to run from the group decreased, and most of the children came into the circle willingly. Some of them began to participate actively and appropriately. Frequently, children would draw up their own chairs around the piano in preparation for the activity, and two or three would bring chairs for the others.

The activities used during the first half of the session included action songs involving specific body motions such as clapping, stamping, or finger play. Also used were songs referring to different parts of the body and songs intended to help with body identification, or self-image. Rhythm instruments, such as tone blocks, sand blocks, and drums, were introduced. Most of the children learned to play them appropriately for at least short periods of time.

In the more active part of the session, the children were encouraged to use their bodies freely in jumping, running, hopping, and so forth, to appropriate rhythms. Some of them learned to bounce balls and ride bikes to music. Circle games, in which they were required to hold hands with each other and with adults, were encouraged. These games fostered interpersonal interaction. Musical games were successful in evoking appropriate participation from some of the children.

During the course of these music sessions, it was not unusual to see stereotyped movements to music, such as rocking back and forth, shaking the head in rapid motions, and twirling or spinning the body in continuous circles. This behavior seemed to be ritualistic and tended to interfere with more desired responses. Often when the music therapist was on the ward at times other than the scheduled music sessions, a child would lead her to the piano and place her hands on the keys, thus indicating a desire for her to play.

Two years ago, the music therapist began working with S, who was then seven years old. S had begun to use speech at the age of five years. His speech consisted of several appropriate phrases, frequent echolalia, and several rigid speech patterns used for no apparent communicative purpose. Much of his behavior was ritualistic and compulsive, and it was difficult for anyone to break into his familiar patterns and initiate a change in his routine.

S was able to learn songs rapidly and to carry a tune. He enjoyed records and listened attentively, usually sitting still, but sometimes rocking his body in rhythm with the music. About a year ago, he began to show curiosity about the piano, playing a few notes himself, watching and imitating the music therapist's hand positions and movements when she played, and affectionately saying, "This is the piano." He was attentive when the therapist showed him the letter names of the notes and soon learned all of them. His interest remained high as he progressed to the beginner's piano book, and he soon grasped new concepts—for example, the differentiation between right and left hands. He was able to understand the written symbol on the page and transfer it to the actual key on the piano. He also learned how to read and to play with correct fingering. This patient has progressed rapidly in his learning, has maintained consistent interest, and has recently started a second instruction book. He is now living at home and attending a special education first-grade class. He returns to the hospital weekly for his piano lesson.

Music Therapy in a Children's Day-Treatment Center

NATALIE R. WERBNER

Music time at the children's center is primarily a group activity, with an effort made to fill the needs of each child. Music is a voluntary activity, and the children, some of whom are autistic, are free to come and go. The sessions are held in the music room where no toys are in sight; the absence of distracting stimuli, such as exits, stairs, and toys, helps the children focus their attention on the activity and the persons in the room. Active participation of both the regular and volunteer staff has helped the children take part. These adults have served as models for the children, a function that few of their own parents were able to perform in most music activities (Satir, 1965).

One practice has been to use songs of identification. Each person and the appropriate name of his pet became the topic of a song. The therapist printed in capital letters the names of persons and pets, stimulating several children's reading interests. The letters of the names of each child were sung to the tune of "Frère Jacques." Colors have been stressed through songs about various articles of clothing worn by each child, as in "Mary Wore a Red Dress," and by songs spelling out different colors. For the latter songs, the therapist printed the name of each color and enclosed it with a rectangle using appropriately colored ink.

Because the eighteen children enrolled in the center ranged from three and one-half through fifteen years of age, the situation somewhat resembled that of a family group with many interests and needs. The therapist emphasized this variety of needs by pointing out each person's favorite song as it was played and sung, thus strengthening the individual's sense of identity. Not all the children cared for every song, but most children learned to respect the right of the others to have their turns. Evidence that the concept of individual worth had been absorbed by some of the children was provided when one child remarked, "Oh, why don't you play 'Eh Cumpari?' That's Bobby's favorite song."

Two pieces of equipment that have proved useful in therapy for withdrawn children are the accordion and the tape recorder. The accordion allows the therapist to have face-to-face contact with a child and draws the child to it because of its moving parts. At the same time the child is drawn toward the person of the therapist. Thus, the child may proceed from an object relationship to an interpersonal one. The tape recorder has helped give an auditory sense of self to many of the children.

References

SATIR, VIRGINIA. Conjoint family therapy, a guide to theory and technique. Palo Alto, Calif.: Science and Behavior Books, Inc., 1965.

SHERWIN, A. C. Reactions to music of autistic (schizophrenic) children. *Amer. J. Psychiat.*, 1953, *109*, 823–831.

15

OTHER CHILDHOOD DISEASES

J O A N N E U P E R

Behavior Disorders Resulting from Cerebral Damage

"Injury to the brain of so mild a degree as not to give gross changes in motility or in the reflexes may be the basis for a disturbance of behavior. The association of cerebral damage and a behavior disorder is not uncommon" (Bakwin and Bakwin, 1960, p. 517). Although there are many others, the most common causes of organically based behavior disorders are cerebral damage associated with the birth process, encephalitis, and head injuries. According to Bakwin and Bakwin (1960, p. 517ff), the symptoms are relatively uniform, regardless of specific etiology, although they may be colored somewhat by the child's own personality. Impulsive hyperkinesis is a primary problem, frequently combined with destructiveness and little thought for consequences. Attention seeking, extreme and unpredictable variability of mood, and explosive temper outbursts are seen. Frustration tolerance is low and attention span is short. Intellectual ability need not be affected, but undue anxiety may restrict the child's ability to work up to his potential.

Kanner (1957) notes the presence of antisocial behavior in many children with posttraumatic chronic behavior disorder; he cites irritability, tantrums, fighting and general unmanageableness, stealing, lying, deviant sexual behavior, and truancy as examples of symptoms. Depressive features also may appear. Although this disorder is often similar in appearance to the postencephalitic disorders, he finds the prognosis for the latter much poorer. "Extreme self-centeredness and disregard of the welfare of others, a complete reversal of the personality, and retention of intelligence with poor scholastic performance" are common to both postencephalitic and posttraumatic child patients. Apparently, "the organic damage destroys inhibitions set up ordinarily by training and sublimation. Free range is given to the expression of hostile aggression and pleasure-seeking, in the absence of counterbalancing experience of guilt" (p. 295). Protracted inpatient treatment with "gentle firmness" is recommended, with emphasis on habit training and academic work suited to the child's capacity. "The personality changes call for the best that mental hygiene and psychotherapy can offer" (p. 311).

The following is a case study of music therapy with a disturbed child whose difficulties were compounded by posttraumatic brain damage.

M was an illegitimate child who lived in a large city with his mother, who worked, and two older half-sisters; the father had left the family. M had a history of inability to get along in the neighborhood; he reported as facts stories of sexual perversion and was believed to have set some fires. He was somewhat above average in school until shortly after he began the third grade, when he jumped or fell from a window, sustaining multiple fractures of the skull, and remained unconscious for more than a week. He was admitted to the state hospital three months later. Although some brain damage was obvious after the fall (EEG and psychological examinations revealed at least three lesions, and his physical behavior revealed temporary loss of equilibrium and considerable hyperkinesis), the examining psychologist believed that M's behavior disorder was primarily a result of emotional factors operant from some time before the accident (which may have been an attempt at suicide).

During his three years of hospitalization, M attended some of the school-type activities provided for the children. However, he received no specific treatment other than tranquilizers. He became increasingly hyperkinetic and continued to express as fact his fantasies, which fell into two categories. One type, self-depreciatory in nature, extolled the abilities of his father, little sister, and cousins (all constant but fictitious characters), contrasting them with himself. ("My little sister can play every instrument in my father's music store; he taught her how. Me, I can't do nuttin'.") The other type was wishful thinking, ranging from mild lies ("At home I have a big fish this long, and I keep him in the bathtub; he likes me.") to gory feats ("Once me and my cousin went skin diving, and this shark came up; he was huge, man, and I stabbed him with my long knife, over and over. There was blood all over the place, and he almost got me. Jeeze! I'm lucky I'm still alive"). His tales usually placed him in jungles or swamps, neither of which had ever been part of his experience.

By the time he was ten years old, M had become too hyperactive and destructive to remain in the children's activity groups. He remained on his ward most of the time with older male patients. During this period, he continued to attend the weekly music activity with the other children, but his adjustment in his group was tenuous at best. Feeling very threatened, he would try to control the activity himself by creating chaos. One day he asked (as though he did not mean it) if he could learn to play the trumpet. The therapist said yes, and a few days later M was surprised and happy to learn that he had been scheduled for two private trumpet lessons weekly. He began with enthusiasm.

Although M wanted to play the trumpet and had considerable natural ability, he was afraid that he would fail. Consequently, his progress was slow; new tasks evoked anxious behavior and a severe mental and physical struggle. Once the fear was overcome, he was invariably surprised by his success, but most of his lesson time was spent in reviewing what he already knew and summoning the courage to try something else. He delayed by telling stories, tinkering with the trumpet, and dashing erratically around the room, denying that he could do the assignment. Although such hyperactivity presented a strong temptation to restrain the child, it had been observed that when others did this with M, it only provoked struggling, resentment, and more extreme hyperactivity. The therapist, therefore, remained by the music stand, waited for M to discharge some energy, and then called him back to the lesson. Much encouragement and reassurance were given; only on rare occasions was his anxiety so high that it was felt best to terminate the lesson. Usually, he could return to his task after some discharge of energy. Gradually, this need was reduced.

M learned a few simple songs that he could play with another child who was learning the piano. They enjoyed sharing some lessons and played together at several social events of the children's group. M's self-esteem increased, and he became able to control himself well enough to participate in a play and several acts of a show done by the patients. After the first year of trumpet lessons, during which time he had no other regular activities, M was allowed to rejoin the children's special classes. He continued his trumpet lessons for another year. During this time, his telling of tales decreased somewhat, his self-control increased markedly, and his social and emotional progress seemed to proceed at a good rate. He was more confident in his ability to achieve and asked to join three other boys his age in a drum class. He approached this with calm assurance and learned rapidly. His behavior was usually excellent in drum class and seemed to have a somewhat stabilizing effect on the behavior of the others, who were often mildly hyperactive.

The trumpet lessons M received assisted him in a variety of ways: As experience within structure, they required that his attention be shifted from his fantasies to the reality of the music lesson. As the lessons were private, anxiety was reduced to a minimum; the lessons could be adapted to his ability levels in terms of both physical performance and emotional control. As experience in self-organization, the lessons provided ample opportunity for social recognition, reward, and enhancement of self-esteem; his feeling of value was increased considerably when he was given parts in the patients' show. As experience in relating to others, the private lessons placed him in a situation of reduced anxiety because of lack of competition, and he was able to develop self-control and acceptable social behavior under optimal conditions. The anticipation of duet work with the other child served as an incentive in this regard, and the later realization of this goal contributed to the development of his sense of responsibility to and cooperation with others. His integration into the drum class was highly successful, and his behavior in the still larger school group was reported to have been good.

A point to be emphasized here is the choice of instrument for M's music therapy; in this case, he selected it. It is believed that a nonstandard instrument would not have been helpful. This patient saw himself as highly inadequate and worthless; to have confronted him with the usual array of simple instruments would have reinforced his belief that he was capable of managing only toys (when he told his mother he was taking trumpet lessons, she humored him, but he correctly realized that she did not believe him). The trumpet itself gave dignity to the endeavor and gave M cause to reconsider the therapist's opinion of him in light of her confidence in his ability to handle a real instrument. As he progressed, he was forced to revise his own self-concept in a positive direction.

Childhood Schizophrenia

Childhood schizophrenia is not a clear-cut diagnostic entity; opinions vary widely as to differential diagnostic criteria and etiological factors, and there is some question as to whether this disorder really is a specific, unitary entity (Goldfarb, 1961, pp. 18–22). Nevertheless, the diagnosis is being applied with increasing frequency and is considered relatively common (Bakwin and Bakwin, 1960, p. 531).

According to the *Diagnostic and Statistical Manual* on mental disorders (American Psychiatric Association, 1952, pp. 26–28), schizophrenia "represents a group of psychotic reactions characterized by fundamental disturbances in reality relationships and concept formations, with affective, behavioral and intellectual disturbances . . ." (p. 26). It is "marked by strong tendency to retreat from reality, by emotional disharmony, unpredictable disturbances in stream of thought, regressive behavior, and in some, by a tendency to 'deterioration'" (p. 26). The childhood type of schizophrenia, according to the same source, includes "those schizophrenic reactions occurring before puberty" (p. 28); the clinical manifestations may differ from those of schizophrenia in older patients, however, because of the "immaturity and plasticity" (p. 28) of the young child.

There is an initial period of normal development of at least two or three years preceding a gradual onset of the disorder. The wide variety of possible symptoms includes alternations of motor hypoactivity with hyperactivity; aimless wandering and other gross motor activity that is purposeless, repetitious, and often rhythmic; blank facial expression; delusions and hallucinations; compulsions; seclusiveness; withdrawal from reality (Bakwin and Bakwin, 1960, pp. 531, 537); panic; motor clumsiness; disorientation in time and space (Goldfarb, 1961); and numerous other general and specific manifestations. Intellectual performance is often uneven, the individual responding on a normal or advanced level at some times and a strikingly subnormal level at others; such successes and failures appear unrelated to the difficulty of the task (Bakwin and Bakwin, 1960, p. 534). In general, treatment aims are to improve the child's rapport with reality, his relationships with others, and his awareness and control of himself.

References

BAKWIN, H., and BAKWIN, RUTH M. *Clinical management of behavior disorders*. Philadelphia: Saunders, 1960.
Diagnostic and statistical manual. Washington, D.C.: American Psychiatric Association, 1952.
GOLDFARB, W. *Childhood schizophrenia*. Cambridge, Mass.: Harvard, 1961.
KANNER, L. *Child psychiatry*. Springfield, Ill.: Charles C Thomas, 1957.

16

CLINICAL EXPERIENCES WITH
EMOTIONALLY DISTURBED CHILDREN

DOROTHY BRIN CROCKER

The emotionally disturbed child, regardless of intellectual capacity, needs help in externalizing his tensions. Houck (1964) has written,

The disturbed child has a variety of needs to be met. These are needs so individual and so urgent that ordinary means have failed. Drawing upon his own resources has not been sufficient. These needs vary from child to child, as well as from time to time within an individual child (p. 1).

Musical experience for the disturbed child offers many opportunities for him to channel undesirable impulses into socially acceptable activities. There are values in music for the emotionally blunted child; for the hostile, aggressive child; for the withdrawn child; and for the child crippled by anxiety. "The music therapist, in conjunction with other therapeutic team members, can function effectively in these areas of deficit" (Houck, 1964, p. 1).

In discussing the correlation between psychotherapy and music therapy sessions, Nicholaou (1960) stated,

Because the personalities of the music therapist and the psychotherapist differ, the relationship will differ. It cannot be said, however, that the music therapist will empathize to a degree less significant than that possible for the psychiatrist, but it can and should be said that the psychiatrist will provide interpretation significantly deeper than that possible for the music therapist to provide. The observations of the music therapists, and other members of the team can be utilized by the psychiatrist in evaluating the child's needs in his environment (p. 5).

After the psychiatrist makes the diagnosis and outlines the goals of treatment, the music therapist uses these goals to structure the music therapy program; he also follows instructions as to how much and what kind of interpretation is to be made. The music therapist may try to provide situations in which participation in musical activities can arouse feelings of frustration in the child. These, in turn, may be resolved by new learning that might enable the child to modify his interpretations of his world and the people in it. Because psychotherapy often is focused on the relationship between therapist and patient, fostering such a relationship frequently is the primary aim in music therapy. However, the efficacy of the treatment is increased by the various and subtle ways music can evoke feelings.

This chapter deals with music therapy for children with various disturbances. Some of the sessions were held in a school for children with emotional and/or academic problems, and others were held in a private studio; some were group sessions, and others were individual. Children were scheduled regularly for one-half hour or an hour either once or twice a week. Extra periods were arranged, if possible, when a child was unusually upset. A record player, rhythm band instruments, drums, some band and pre-band instruments, Autoharp, guitar, piano, electric organ, song books, and tape recorder were used at various times.

Frequently, the music therapist improvised on the piano and requested that the child tell a story to the music (Crocker, 1955; Crocker, 1956). This was followed by a discussion of the music, both to develop skills in listening to music and to encourage verbalization of feelings and attitudes. When the improvisations, some of which might be named fear, anger, happiness, sadness, or other emotions, were played, the child often discussed his feelings about that emotion. (This was never done without having first secured the approval of the child's psychiatrist when treatment was started.)

Children were encouraged to use their imaginations while performing or listening to music, thus inducing a greater tendency toward fantasies. Materials, carefully selected after many trials, included music that seemed to elicit fantasy. Such practice was used in both individual and group settings. Occasionally, suggestions were made on how to listen imaginatively. There were also times when the children listened to music of their own choice for whatever catharsis or esthetic pleasure it afforded, without comment from the music therapist except in response to comment by the children.

Even though communication through music is nonthreatening, the associations it may arouse can be threatening. Asking a child to perform or to lead a discussion of the music may be a means of increasing self-esteem or giving him more status within the group. However, it may also be interpreted by the child as pressure from a figure of authority, or it may arouse feelings such as fear of failure—fear that his response might be inadequate or inaccurate. An alert music therapist will be cognizant of reactions to pressure, will understand the child's assumptions concerning authority figures, note the child's reactions to fear of failure, and observe how he handles these feelings. The music therapist will soon know what the child likes and dislikes in the music sessions, his strengths and his weaknesses.

Sharing music with another can frequently have a calming effect when the anxious child feels that something is threatening the control he needs in order to prevent himself from being immobilized or "blown apart" by his anxiety. "Anxiety can interfere with intellectual functioning, judgment and emotional stability, and distort the individual's entire personality pattern" (Berkowitz and Rothman, 1960, p. 55). Spontaneous dancing and creative movements to music can be supportive to the anxious child. The child who has difficulties in self-expression, the isolated child, or the child who is rigidly inhibited should be treated with extreme gentleness—casually invited and included, but never forced into participation. His efforts should be accepted on his expressive level without criticism. The belligerent, defiant child may test acceptance to the limits or attempt to manipulate the music therapist into rejecting him and showing disapproval of his participation, thereby reinforcing his distorted interpretation, his faulty functioning, and his "assumptive world" (Frank, 1961, pp. 20–35). Refraining from criticism and requesting the child to repeat some acceptable motions may influence his expressive level. The following case histories illustrate some of the techniques used.

Case 1. N was a twelve-year-old boy with a diagnosis of schizophrenia. His symptoms included fear of breaking things; poor emotional control; low frustration tolerance; fear of severely harming his parents; feelings of inferiority, jealousy, hostility, and suspicion; and a high incidence of griping and complaining, not manifested by physical aggression. He sucked his shirt, wiggled constantly, and wrung his hands repeatedly. His psychiatrist asked that the music therapist refuse to let the patient manipulate her into the kind of behavior that would verify his beliefs that his feelings of suspicion, distrust, and self-unworthiness were justified. She was to refuse to reassure him repeatedly that he had not broken something, to redirect his need to provoke others until they retaliated (which was his way of forming relationships, even though they were unsatisfactory), and to help him achieve some inner control.

His music sessions were centered around music appreciation—that is, listening to music and then discussing it and the composers—and learning to play the piano. He also told stories to music. N showed considerable interest in the lives of the composers and asked many questions such as Did they trust people? Were they suspicious? Did they get angry? and so on. The following story, told in response to an original composition, is an example of N's projection at a certain point of his therapy. Most of his stories were statements about his own stupidity, his anger, or his breaking something.

> The music sounds like the composer was afraid of what he might do. It got awfully angry and mad but then it got quiet and he thought maybe it would be all right if he liked someone a lot. Maybe he would have a real friend he could trust and it would be someone who would think he was a fine guy and not be afraid he would break anything. And if he had a friend he wouldn't get so upset and it would mean everybody didn't dislike him if he had a friend who wouldn't tattle on him. But when the music got loud like it was at first he knew that he was stupid and he might do something bad to someone who got after him for griping.

After nine months of treatment, N showed an increase in frustration tolerance. In music, he was able to play the piano slowly and carefully, without having an outburst of temper, wringing his hands, or sucking his shirt when he made an error. He could tolerate correction without feeling threatened and rejected. Restless movements subsided somewhat, and anxiety lessened. The content of his stories or statements to music altered, and his attitude changed from a desire to tell stories to one of indifference. This was interpreted as an indication that his need for special attention, which the individual sessions provided, was lessened as better integrative functioning was accomplished.

Case 2. Y was diagnosed at age nine as having a schizoid personality. Earlier, it had been noted that her behavior frequently was bizarre and hallucinatory. When she was angered, she attacked, both verbally and physically, the person provoking the anger. This happened with siblings and neighborhood children, but at the public school she was quiet and withdrawn in class and played alone on the playground. She had no friends and viewed all adults as "mean and hateful," saying, "My mother and daddy hate me—so does my teacher."

Because of her apparent musical ability, Y was referred to the music therapist. It was hoped that kind, firm, consistent behavior on the part of a friendly adult would enable her to form a satisfactory relationship, thereby altering her assumption that all adults hated her. In addition, her doctor felt that learning to play the piano would provide an intellectual challenge, afford group recognition, and provide an emotional outlet.

Y studied piano, taking lessons twice a week for five years. She attended her lessons regularly with the exception of a vacation of two months every summer. The first six months were devoted primarily to developing a good relationship and learning the fundamentals of music. She attempted constantly to manipulate the therapist into criticizing and rejecting her by saying, "I don't care if my arms are too low, and I like seeing my joints break." The therapist would comment casually, "It is easier to play if your shoulders and arms are free and in a comfortable position. You can hold them that way and when you want to, you will."

Y began to play with other children, and she was reportedly a little less shy at school by the end of the first year. She was warm and friendly to the music therapist and took pride in playing the simple pieces she had memorized. The second year resulted in a continuation of the supportive relationship, with progress in music as a secondary aim. Outbursts of anger began to show up during the third year, which probably resulted, according to her doctor, from her mother's illness and irritable, inconsistent discipline. There was more tension in the home because of a rebellious teen-age sister. The home conditions were more aggravating during the fourth year, and the need for "team communication" was especially evident on one occasion. When Y said "I did it—I got the butcher knife and went in her room and was going to kill my mean old mother, but I didn't," the music therapist replied confidently, "No, and you never will. If you start to do anything like that, you will always stop yourself." Without further conversation, the music lesson was resumed, and Y played wildly, loudly, and inaccurately, with exaggerated dynamics. When she finished, she shrugged her shoulders and left without saying goodbye, only to return in a moment, hug the therapist, and say softly, "I love you—you are good to me." Then she left abruptly. The therapist reported immediately to Y's psychiatrist. The destructive feelings of the child toward her mother were handled subsequently in psychotherapy.

Y ultimately learned to play well. She received praise for her performances in recitals and school programs during the time she studied piano. According to her parents, when she was upset she frequently played until the music relaxed her.

In conclusion, musical experiences for the disturbed child can supplement his psychotherapy program by affording him a unique outlet for some of his unacceptable impulses. The immediate and long-range therapeutic goals established by the therapist guide the music sessions. The establishment of a therapeutic relationship and a warm emotional climate determine the effectiveness of the music therapy for any maladjusted child. The disturbed child needs esthetic expression (Masserman, 1955, pp. 431–433; Gaston, 1958, p. 294), and music offers esthetic experiences in a special way.

References

BERKOWITZ, PEARL H., and ROTHMAN, ESTHER P. *The disturbed child*. New York: New York University Press, 1960.

CROCKER, DOROTHY B. The responses of child patients to piano improvisation. In E. T. Gaston (Ed.), *Music therapy 1954*. Lawrence, Kan.: Allen Press, 1955. Pp. 110–112.

CROCKER, DOROTHY B. Music as a projective technique. In E. T. Gaston (Ed.), *Music therapy 1955*. Lawrence, Kan.: Allen Press, 1956. Pp. 86–97.

FRANK, J. D. *Persuasion and healing*. New York: Schocken Books, 1961.

GASTON, E. T. Functional music. In N. Henry (Ed.), *Basic concepts in music education*. Chicago: The University of Chicago Press, 1958. Pp. 292–309.

HOUCK, FRANCES COLTHARP. Personal communication, 1964.

MASSERMAN, J. H. *The practice of dynamic psychiatry*. Philadelphia: Saunders, 1955.

NICHOLAOU, G. T. The correlation between psychotherapy and music therapy. Unpublished manuscript, Dallas, Tex., 1960.

17

MUSIC THERAPY IN A CHILDREN'S HOME

DORIS E. ROBISON

In this chapter is described a project in play therapy in which many facets of music were employed to help deprived and rejected children. The setting was a church-sponsored home in the Middle West, a cottage-type institution of six units that housed an average child population of seventy-five. Beside the usual administrative and maintenance personnel, house-parent couples for each unit, and recreation workers, the staff included professionally trained social workers and a group-work director, an educational director, a music therapist, a registered nurse, a pediatrician on call, and a child psychiatrist who acted as consultant and assisted with in-service training. Whenever possible, children attended the village grade school. The institution's program was child-centered, and a team approach involved frequent conferences and staff meetings. The music therapist had regular individual conferences with caseworkers and housemothers. She had access to the case records of children and contributed to them her reports of each child's progress, or lack of it, as evidenced in music therapy contacts.

Almost all these children came from homes broken by separation and divorce. Many had suffered traumatic experiences during family quarrels and often had been beaten and abused. Neglected and unloved, emotional needs common to all children had been unfulfilled. Many had lived in a succession of foster homes, attending one school after another. They were physically, emotionally, and culturally deprived. Their problems were those of the uprooted—confusion, fear, loneliness, insecurity, and aggressive or withdrawing reactions. Case records of many adult mental patients describe backgrounds similar to theirs. From time to time, efforts were made to transfer certain children to treatment centers for the emotionally disturbed, but this was seldom possible because of the long waiting lists in the few facilities available.

The music therapist worked intensively and individually with boys and girls selected by the staff as the most disturbed, but he reached all the children through group activities. Although participation was voluntary, every one of the children helped plan the program, and they came eagerly to unit sings, rhythm bands, and music-listening groups. Later they performed in very popular shows as soloists or dancers, in singing or instrumental groups, and in tableaux (Robison, 1957). In the music room, the most popular pieces of equipment were an enormous bass drum with a large brass cymbal hanging from the attached standard, a small xylophone, a record player, and the tape recorder through which a child could hear his own performance. Rhythm, pre-band, and "grown-up" instruments were also available. During music periods specific problems could be observed (Robison, 1966) and worked through. Two hundred children, ranging in age from four through sixteen, participated in the play-music program during its seven years.

General goals were to promote emotional health and development; to provide acceptable ways of expressing hostility and aggression; to offer opportunities for displaying skills and accomplishments; to encourage better posture and grooming; and to introduce the beauty in music and the joy that can be realized through active participation in rhythms, songs, and the playing of musical instruments.

Goals for the more disturbed children were set by treatment teams, which might include a caseworker, the houseparents, and the music therapist, with the psychiatrist available for consultation as needed. Specific individual goals might be to form that important one-to-one relationship; to help a regressed child become aware, make up for deficits in his past, and resume emotional growth; to stimulate the unmotivated; to relax a tense, rigid child; to give ego support and build up self-confidence; and to aid in socialization. The case reports that follow suggest means used in working toward some of these goals.

Case 1. *In a psychiatric evaluation made when he was ten and one-half years old, K was described as a "driven, anxious child confused about origin and family relationships; without stimulus to learn; in need of much ego support." His psychological report indicated a mental age of ten years and three months, an IQ of 98, and a restricted range of interests and added that he would provoke punishment to get attention.*

The fourth of five children, K spent his first year with his parents, his second year in an institution while they were being divorced, and the next four years either with his very immature mother or in a series of boarding homes. At six he was admitted to the children's home and remained there for eight years. He was small for his age, smiling and mischievous, hyperactive, and a clown or show-off in a group. There were behavior problems at school and in his unit. His predominant characteristic was a "don't care" attitude. When he had to repeat two school grades, even though he had been tutored in reading and mathematics, he showed no apparent concern. His speech was almost unintelligible. Both initial and final consonants were omitted, as well as many word endings. When offered help by the speech therapist at school, he made no effort to improve, but seemed to take pleasure in, and laugh at, his babyish manner of speaking.

In music therapy this child participated in rhythm bands, music games, and singing groups. He was given an opportunity to show off in socially acceptable ways as he conducted a rhythm group or acted out the part of Mr. Rabbit while others sang.

When K was eleven, a series of crises occurred in his life. It was decided to offer him individual music periods in order to emphasize the stability of his relationship with the music therapist, with the hope that this might become more meaningful and stimulate his emotional development. Goals were to build up his ego through music activities of his choice and to work toward improvement in his speech.

K accepted the offer of music periods eagerly; he wanted very much to play a guitar. Because his hands were too small to manage the chords, he was taught to pick out the melody of "Taps" and later learned a couple of simple chords using three or four strings. He agreed to work on speech, commenting that his grade school teacher had told him to practice his r's. During the first few periods, he cooperated fairly well, and it was evident that he could sing consonants more easily than he could speak them and that his articulation was much better when he really made an effort to speak correctly. He was decidedly less hyperactive in the music room than in his unit, although sometimes it seemed that his hands, feet, and tongue were constantly in motion.

One evening, when K almost missed his individual session and arrived upset and tearful, the period became very productive. He chose a note game (Note-O) and, while playing it, talked on and on, confiding his unhappiness that he was so short, that his hands were too small to finger the guitar properly, that boys younger than himself were moving to the older unit, that "the boys get mad at me, and they say, 'You don't even know how to talk.'" After winning the note game, he proceeded to work diligently on speech-articulation drills.

From this time on, K's "don't care" attitude gradually disappeared. He studied harder at school and with his tutor. New houseparents found his ways engaging rather than irritating and were able to help him accept responsibility. He not only remembered his own music periods but reminded other boys to go promptly. Although he sometimes grew tired of speech drills and was eager to beat the drum loud and fast or sing his favorite songs, he perservered and showed steady improvement in all areas.

The second report concerns a tense, rigid, overconscientious girl who had never learned to relax and have fun. It illustrates the use of music with a child suffering from anxiety and emotional dependence. Experience in self-organization and experience in relating to others are focal points in the music therapy process.

Case 2. Z's father died when she was six years old. Her mother, who was described as extremely neurotic, found employment in another city and left the child with her maternal grandparents. At the age of nine, Z came to the home, and was placed in a unit under the direction of a rigid and overprotective housemother.

When the play-music program began, Z was twelve and one-half years old and in the seventh grade. Dark and intense, a perfectionist with a great fear of making mistakes, she showed many evidences of extreme tension. This girl seldom joined in group activities and considered herself unattractive and unpopular. When she was given an individual music period, the goals were to promote fun and relaxation, to strengthen her self-confidence, to relieve her shyness and moodiness, and to aid socialization.

Z had taken piano lessons for two years and played cello in the grade school orchestra. She stared incredulously when the music therapist consulted her about plans for the play-music program, finding it difficult to believe that her opinion was really desired. Asked what she would especially like to do, she wondered doubtfully if the therapist could help her with songs. Although she added quickly that, of course, she wanted to continue with piano, she never remembered to bring her second-grade book to the music room. She was hesitant and uncertain, her rhythm was jerky and uneven, and she sang a little sharply, but she worked on her songs very seriously. Favorites were "Summertime" and "You'll Never Walk Alone." The therapist helped with rhythm and melody, but was uncritical of tone quality.

Arriving early one day, Z watched through the glass door as two small girls enjoyed a rhythm band. When they left, she came to lean against the end of the piano and murmured, "I wish I were little so I could play a drum." The therapist smiled at her and suggested, "Why not try it right now?" She did so with manifest uneasiness until reassured by the offhand statement that this would be a fine way to improve her rhythm and to learn the melody of new songs. Her misgivings dispelled, she began to respond to the rhythmic beat and go along with the music. She continued to relax until in later periods she felt free to try out all the rhythm instruments and sometimes even pirouetted around the music room on light, dancing feet. Her gloomy, downcast expression lightened, and an elfin smile appeared. She sang on pitch, with added range and resonance, and developed some lovely tones. Her posture improved, too, and she gained in poise and attractiveness. Listening to her recorded voice gave her confidence that she sang well. When she began to participate in unit sings, she was pleased that the other girls wanted her to sing solos. That summer the overprotective housemother left, and new houseparents encouraged her beginning independence. In the fall she was chosen to sing in a sextette at school, the first time a girl from the home had been given this coveted opportunity.

When a family group is admitted to a home, the probability is that each of the children will be placed in a different unit. This adds to their feeling of loneliness. They may meet on the playground, and perhaps walk to school together, but the intimate closeness of family life is gone. In some cases, it is considered wise to provide a special activity for these brothers and sisters, apart from the other children. A group appointment in the music room, where they can sing together, have a rhythm band, and then perform for each other, can fulfill the need for familial unity. They may come on a Sunday afternoon when parents fail to visit, or a series of scheduled periods can be planned.

Case 3. R, T, and W came to the home soon after their harsh, brutal father had been given a prison sentence for rape. The mother, passive and inadequate, could not control her children. She placed them in the institution, divorced their father, was employed for a time, and later asked to be committed to a state hospital. The music therapist worked with all three children for a year and a half.

R, eleven years old and in the fifth grade, had been sexually attacked. She was a plump child and somewhat cross-eyed, afraid of the dentist, of tests, and of hospitals. Careless and destructive, a messy eater and a bed-wetter, she became a scapegoat in her unit. She contradicted everyone, was defiant, made up stories, and told unsavory details of her family history to other children. Goals were to give her an outlet for tension through music activities, to improve her speech and help her achieve through singing, to provide added incentive for control of bedwetting through the support of an accepting person, and to guide her toward truthfulness, mannerliness, and better posture and grooming.

Eighteen months later, she had become physically more attractive. Her singing and enunciation had improved, and there was less meaningless giggling. However, the psychiatrist told her caseworker that no basic improvement could be expected without long-term psychiatric treatment.

T, ten years old, was also in the fifth grade. Psychological testing rated his intelligence as superior. He had been picked up by the sheriff and held in jail at his mother's request for running away, stealing, and setting fires. She had told him, "You're no good, just like your father." He was hostile and aggressive, a behavior problem in the unit.

As preparation for playing in rhythm bands, he was given instruction on how to use drums and other rhythm instruments. He came for rhythm bands every Saturday and participated enthusiastically in unit sings. When he came to the music room for a special individual appointment, the tough-boy attitude was never in evidence. He played the bass drum, relaxed, yawned, and spoke in confidential tones. The hardness in his face was replaced by a warm, satisfied expression. He was unit representative on planning committees and made helpful suggestions. His behavior on the playground and in his unit gradually improved. When the music program ended, he was a member of the confirmation class at church and planned to join its junior choir.

W, the younger boy, six years old, was very quiet, slow, and dreamy. He seldom spoke, stared at adults vacantly, and failed to answer questions. His head seemed large for his body, and his face was not childlike. A poor eater, he was often in the hospital with an upset stomach or a cold. He failed to carry out his unit duties and soiled consistently, but only while in the charge of his housemother. At school he appeared much more alert, listened, studied, and made good progress in his first-grade class.

Both his caseworker and his housemother requested an individual music period for W. He appeared very shy and began by walking around in the music room, touching the table, chairs, and rhythm instruments gently. When he came to the bass drum and the cymbal, the therapist showed him how to use a tympani stick. As he tapped softly, she began playing rather slow rhythm music on the piano. He settled down behind the drum and was soon responding to changes in tempo and dynamics, smiling, and showing more confidence in his arm movements. When it was time for him to stop, he resisted leaving, then asked if he might come every day.

In the music room, W clearly acted out his wish to be a very small child; for example, he would crawl on the floor, then climb on a low shelf and wait to be lifted down, and ask for help with coat buttons. Over a period of time, during which he explored many avenues of musical activity, he began to show progress in emotional adjustment. His housemother reported a more alert attitude and less soiling. His rhythm, singing, and speech were also improving. At one sing in the unit, he did "Jingle Bells" as a solo and later sang it in his room at school.

After the three children had been in the home for fifteen months, it was decided to experiment with a regularly scheduled family group. R and W were to continue their individual periods each week, and all three would share a one-half hour session each Saturday afternoon.

R, T, and W took part in a Christmas carol service and later sang one of their favorite spirituals at a holiday after-dinner program. An evening show was in preparation, and they were eager to sing spirituals in blackface. This was permitted when an off-duty nurses' aide volunteered to help with costumes and make-up. Their performance brought loud applause from children and staff. The group experiences of these siblings seemed to bring added benefits for each child.

The five children described in these case reports were not unique. There were boys and girls in the home who were less emotionally disturbed, but there were others whose disturbances were much more extreme. "And, for the child who is too insecure and afraid to reach out toward self-expression and happiness by himself, we must provide special help" (Robison, 1953). For all such children, music therapy has much to offer.

References

ROBISON, DORIS. The response of institutional children to a play music program. *Child Welf.*, 1953, 32, 12–16.
ROBISON, DORIS. Story from an orphanage. *Mus. Educ. J.*, 1957, 43, 42–46.
ROBISON, DORIS. Meaningful observation. *J. Mus. Ther.*, 1966, 3, 106–109.

18

ADOLESCENTS

Introduction

DONALD E. MICHEL

Adolescence and adolescents are topics of increasing concern in modern society. Many problems that begin in the earlier stages of child development come to fruition during adolescence. In the following pages, music therapists report their experiences with disturbed adolescents in various clinical settings. Even though individual work and techniques are always of great importance, group therapy seems to be better for these patients because of the acute group and social consciousness of this developmental stage and the resulting problems.

Sommer, in the next article, makes a plea for care in controlling the group and social situations in which adolescents are included, apparently having the state hospital setting (or a nonspecialized setting) in mind. She also illustrates very well how important it can be for patients to receive individual attention before group therapy situations are utilized. That is, it can be important to some individuals to gain experience in structure and, perhaps, experience in self-organization *before* they are involved in groups or other activities that result in experience in relating to others. In a subsequent article, Cavallin and Cavallin might be interpreted as advocating the reverse order of these experiences in music, at least for *some* adolescent patients. Finally, Sharpe, Werbner, and Folsom each present case studies indicating the effectiveness of music therapy with adolescents.

Individual Therapy with Adolescent Patients

DOROTHY TWENTE SOMMER

Adolescents with behavior disorders present special treatment difficulties in large public institutions, yet these patients can become a unique challenge to the music therapist. Group activities appropriate for adult patients may be unsuitable for teen-agers. The inclusion of one young person in a group of older patients is likely to have a disastrous effect on the group. It also is potentially harmful for an adolescent patient to socialize with alcoholics and psychopaths twice his age at a dance or in the canteen. Just as a short term in prison can launch a young offender into a career of crime, so can a mental hospital introduce a patient into the vicissitudes of institutional living.

Hopefully, a young patient's stay in a hospital will be brief and limited to an admission ward. Unless there are enough teen-age patients to form a special group, it generally is better to treat this patient individually. Friedenberg (1959, p. 64) says that when two people who are otherwise different from each other share skills, goals, and a common area of experience, each helps the other understand his own uniqueness. When a patient is interested or skilled in music, the music therapist is the logical person to play a major role in therapy. This does not imply that the music therapist must perform psychotherapy, which would require extensive training in specific techniques. What is needed is a warm, accepting relationship between patient and therapist, facilitated by common interests.

Effective individual therapy places certain responsibilities on both parties. The music therapist should have sufficient time for extra visits with the patient. He should allow for coffee breaks, short walks, or special trips outside the hospital grounds. The therapist also must report the patient's progress to other team members. This, of course, is essential in individual therapy with any patient, but it is vital in dealing with adolescents, because even in a normal state *the adolescent personality often arouses guilt, anxiety, and hostility in adults*. Friedenberg (1959) believes that this conflict in the adult arises from "fear of disorder and loss of control, fear of aging and envy of life not yet squandered" (p. 180). The therapist should evaluate honestly his feelings toward the patient and, when necessary, consult with a psychiatric adviser.

The situation in individual therapy must be so handled that the patient considers the music therapist a friend and teacher. If he can take the therapist into his confidence regarding his hopes, fears, goals, and plans, so much the better. The therapist should be informed, whenever possible, of any administrative decision that will affect the patient's well-being. When discharge is imminent, the therapist should be consulted as to the patient's needs outside the hospital. If necessary, arrangements should be made to continue music therapy on an outpatient basis. The following example of individual therapy with X, an adolescent patient, illustrates many of these points.

X, a fifteen-year-old with exhibitionistic tendencies, was referred to the music therapist after she had been in the hospital for six months. By this time, she had gained the reputation of being a troublemaker. It was apparent that she was using her hospital confinement to secure maximal attention. Her history listed a broken home, a series of foster homes, a very sketchy formal education, and numerous juvenile misdemeanors. She was sent by the court to the mental hospital. At this time, she was the only teen-ager on the admission ward. Her positive qualities included intelligence, warmth, and cheerfulness, and she easily won the friendship and trust of almost everyone. Occasionally, she ran off with psychopathic male patients.

At one point in her hospitalization, she had expressed an interest in the piano. The treatment team believed that playing the piano could serve as an outlet for X's exhibitionistic tendencies. It was agreed that she should spend a large portion of her activity time with the music therapist for piano lessons and informal sessions.

X needed a period of exploratory "musical scribbling" (Ruppenthal, 1965) and some immediate gratification. Initially, she was allowed to indulge her childlike curiosity in every instrument in the music room. During a typical session, she would flit from the set of drums to the Autoharp, to the guitar, and finally to the piano, experimenting briefly with each instrument. Sessions often included playing records, dancing, or listening to music.

With the piano, the therapist's goal was to give X some gratification and to increase her attention span. At first, the Play-by-Color (Wolfe, 1952) series was used. X learned this rapidly and was delighted that she could play recognizable tunes so easily. Because Play-by-Color books were available on her ward, she was able to practice there also. As her interest increased, Jorgensen's (1955) Music to Play and Sing and McGinley's (1950) Chords and Melodies were introduced. These provided the necessary rudiments for picking out folk and pop tunes and adding chords and rhythm.

The therapist spent much informal time with X. She was encouraged to help in the music department and record library and to do other odd jobs. The therapist accompanied her on shopping trips, drives, and various excursions outside the hospital. When the patient was ready to be discharged, the music therapist conferred with her psychiatrist and social worker. It was agreed that it would be desirable for X to continue her music lessons. The social worker located a foster home and arranged to have the state provide funds for additional piano lessons with a music teacher in the community. The patient left the hospital a better integrated, more responsible individual. Her relationship with the music *therapist probably had an important role in her self-discovery. The individual approach is extremely valuable in working with adolescents who have problems in establishing a stable self-identity in an adult world and should be considered whenever possible.*

Group Music Therapy
to Develop Socially Acceptable Behavior
Among Adolescent Boys and Girls

BARBARA J. CAVALLIN
H. W. CAVALLIN

In recent years, there has been a considerable increase in the rate of admissions to state hospitals of patients between the ages of sixteen and twenty-one. Because of the specific problems this age group has in developing appropriate social behavior between the sexes, it was decided to include a program to help them develop such behavior in the treatment setting. Music is a particularly effective tool for social interaction. It offers a flexible range of activities (from a passive program of listening to active participation in dancing and jam sessions) in which the degree of closeness or distance between the sexes can be controlled easily by the therapist and the patients.

Patients were selected for this program according to the level of their functioning rather than according to diagnostic categories. All those chosen were in an open ward and capable of participating in most activities with a minimum of supervision. This was the only selection criterion used, for problems in developing appropriate social behavior seem to be common to most adolescents, regardless of their diagnostic categories. The group of patients was limited in number to between fifteen and twenty.

The program was originally structured by the therapist. There was a definite time to meet (twice a week), and all members of the group were expected to attend punctually. It was agreed that refreshments could be brought to the meetings, but they were to be obtained before the scheduled meeting time. The actual structure within the allotted time was extremely flexible, and the patients were to have much of the responsibility for this structure. They were to select the music, handle the records and the record player, and also be responsible for cleaning the room after the meetings. Eventually, the patients were encouraged to select new records and organize singing and dancing groups. The therapist consistently encouraged freedom and creativity, but always stressed that freedom must be accompanied by a sense of responsibility.

The first meetings were characterized by tenseness and withdrawal.

The boys sat on one side of the room and the girls on the other. Little verbal communication occurred, and most of it took place with the therapist as a mediating agent. A general attitude of dissatisfaction was revealed by complaints, mostly about the music, which the group classified as "square" and "antiquated." Having the patients choose some new records from a catalog resulted in a decrease of complaints and a growing interest in the program. During this period, an increase in the patients' anxiety also appeared. They complained about having to attend the activity when they could be in the canteen, and said they did not see "any sense" in "all this" because they were not particularly interested in music. However, none of them would miss a session or be late, and they were unusually careful about their dress.

In a session approximately two months after the program started, two of the most active members began dancing and necking in a rather provocative way. The rest of the group became very anxious. A girl left the room, vowing she would never come back, and one of the boys turned his chair around and faced the wall. Rather than reacting in a prohibitive way, the therapist attempted to cope with this behavior by discussing the reaction of the group. In the next session, a regression to the former stage of complete segregation of the sexes occurred. Soon, however, communications seemed to improve, and the group members developed better interaction. Overt but acceptable behavior, such as holding hands and dancing closely, began to appear. The whole incident seemed to have created a more comfortable atmosphere for the group.

The patients soon began to organize their time. They divided their two music hours into an active session and a passive session. It was decided that one session would be spent in listening and dancing, and the other one would consist of special interest activities. One group of patients wanted to organize a jam session, another group wanted to learn to play instruments, and a third group chose to listen to records. Adjoining rooms were used for these activities. The therapist concentrated on the active groups, but also aided the listening group. The listening session was given more structure by the adolescents; they organized three groups and decided that a different group would be responsible for selecting the records and playing them during each session.

A few difficulties were encountered by the group. Among these problems were crushes on the therapist, fights over a girl's or a boy's attention, and occasional temper tantrums by some of the more disturbed members. However, the group managed to handle these problems without much assistance. Their major sources of strength seemed to be a sense of cohesiveness and the presence of an interested adult to help them when their impulses seemed overwhelming.

The adolescents were reassured by the presence of an adult during the process of learning socially acceptable behavior. They also communicated their need for independence by planning new creative activities. When they organized a variety show that was staged for the patients in the hospital, they were adamant about being the organizers of the show, but wanted the therapist to be their technical adviser.

The number of complaints about the program decreased. Hospital staff began to report changes in the general behavior of the adolescents. The more significant of these changes were the appearance of positive feelings in the adolescents toward the adult staff and a decrease in elopements. It is difficult to say exactly how much these changes were influenced by the music activities, but there was little doubt in the minds of those who worked closely with the group that music played a significant role in the overall treatment program. The music therapy group technique was found to be highly successful and was believed to help approximate a normal maturation process for hospitalized adolescent patients.

Case Studies

Case Report
—NORMA SHARPE

P was a plump boy, fifteen years of age. When brought to the hospital from a children's aid center in August, 1961, he was physically violent, attention-demanding, and often retreated into a life of fantasy. He was one of thirteen children, of normal intelligence (grade 8 at age fourteen), and had an emotionally deprived childhood in several foster homes since the age of eight. His diagnosis was hysterical reaction. Psychiatric treatment goals were to provide better environmental and emotional support and to prevent reinforcement of the pathological defense mechanisms.

The music therapist met P during ward music sessions, and P asked if he might learn to play an instrument. He had a postpolio weakness of the left arm and hand; he could use the hand for gross movement but not for the small finger placements necessary in playing violin, guitar, or clarinet. P expressed an interest in piano, and the music therapist decided to start him on melodica, which would approximate right-hand piano playing and also give him respiratory exercise. He had semiweekly lessons in the music room and practiced faithfully on the ward. He chose the songs to learn, and his interest in them served as practice incentive, as well as giving him a sense of pride in accomplishment. P frequently became angry when he failed to read the notes correctly or when further technique was required (breath control, phrasing). One time he left the music room in a fit of anger. No attempt was made to bring him back, and he returned the next lesson day apologizing and ready to continue.

P performed his melodica pieces at ward sings, three hospital recitals, and for a community organization made up of blind adults. The experience helped him accept his own handicaps, as he felt the others were "worse off." As secretary of the Workers' Music Club, he attended to his duties conscientiously, and offered suggestions for acquiring new patient members and improving the attendance-record system.

When the music therapy assistant left the staff to be married, P became upset but accepted the change to another music staff member. He wrote to the former music assistant, and when she discontinued answering his letters, it was explained to him that she probably wanted him to relate to other staff members. He was placed on probation in a job in a motel, but when he molested a female child, he was returned to the hospital. The music therapy staff continued to work with P, and without minimizing the seriousness of his offense, made clear that more mature behavior was expected of him. P began to work industriously on the melodica and to participate in the music program on the ward and in the music room. Working in the stores department, attending recreation dances, and participating in music therapy were his chief hospital activities.

After three home visits, he was probated to his mother in August, 1964, and officially discharged in February, 1965. At the end of probation, he was placed in a wood-refinishing course at Goodwill Industries, and has continued to work in this occupation. Music therapy provided this patient with short-term goals he could realize and the warm interpersonal relationship needed during these maturation years.

Case Reports
—NATALIE R. WERBNER

Case 1. E was an extremely obese thirteen-year-old boy. He had expressed interest in music, and it was hoped that music therapy would offer him an opportunity to achieve treatment goals in a nonthreatening and noncompetitive situation. His constant demands on his peers and on adults, along with his volatile temper and lumbering nature, made him a most unpopular person. However, he had a quick and subtle wit. His need to be wanted and praised was satisfied in a limited way in his weekly music sessions.

Originally, he had asked to learn to play the piano and read music. His approach to music was quite different from that toward his schoolwork, the quality of which was considerably below his ability. He showed that he could comprehend abstract ideas and even attempted to do some music theory papers. His interest in composition was stimulated when he browsed through a notebook of original compositions by former pupils and patients of the therapist. E wanted to compose a "long, long, long song." The repetitive adjective was typical of his requests and descriptions. The creative desire was fostered by having E improvise on the keyboard while the therapist notated the music. In spite of his lack of pianistic background, E discovered and consciously used many accepted techniques. In his music, as in his verbal output, there were many repetitive passages.

At times, when the therapist played back to him what he had composed, he excitedly accused her of changing his ideas. To help him understand that the source of difficulty was his change of mind rather than the therapist's misinterpretation of his playing, the therapist suggested that it might be helpful if she brought a tape recorder to each session so they could check accurately what had occurred. She also pointed out that the changing of an initial musical idea to one that better expressed what the composer wanted to say musically was a procedure often used in musical composition. Through use of the tape recorder, E was able to take more responsibility and to separate his thoughts and actions from those of the therapist.

After spending many weeks creating a continuous "long, long, long" piano composition, he decided to tell a story while he played. Quotes from his stories give some indication of his fantasies and his confusions.

> Once upon a time there were three little kittens and the mother said, "Where are you going, kittens?" and the three mice said, "I do not have no mittens but I still want some of the pie," and the mother said, "If you're mice I am not your mother, because I am not your mother. I am a kitten." Do you know the story of this little _____ named Dracula that gives nice little boys all his pie? Now I have you, I'm going to take you home with me and take you with me in my house to make you a little, teeny, weeny, weeny, weeny, teeny, weeny, little, idiotic baby boy . . . and oh! there's one name that I can promise and that's Lon Chaney—Lon Chaney, because he hates Dracula and Lon Chaney is Dracula so I can't call you Lon Chaney because I am Dracula, because Lon Chaney is my name and you can't have my name, so if you don't want my name, I gonna still call you Count Dracula, Lon Chaney, and the big giant.

As this material poured forth, the therapist treated it as a creative effort on E's part. But being aware of the many other ramifications of the material, she consulted the chief of social service about it. It was decided that such experience was beneficial to E and that the music therapist should continue to treat it as she had in the past, making no attempt at any interpretation on a psychological level.

E derived great pleasure from seeing his own three-ring notebook fill up with his original works. He also learned about various extended compositions, such as symphonies, sonatas, and oratorios. Added to these benefits was the incidental, but treasured, status he gained among his peers as a result of having a regular, individual music time—something highly prized by many youngsters in the hospital.

Case 2. S, a fifteen-year-old girl, entered the children's convalescent hospital in a depressed, withdrawn state, with an acute school phobia, plus minor aggravation of her rheumatoid arthritis. She professed to have lost interest in everything, and there was concern about finding something that might appeal to her. During preparations for a Christmas program, a doctor heard her singing in the chorus and recognized the fine quality of her voice. She told him that she enjoyed this activity, and he immediately passed the information on to the social worker who was seeing her on an intensive, individual basis. The social worker, in turn, requested that S be offered an opportunity to have individual sessions with the music therapist. It was believed that these sessions might put some enjoyment in S's life and that the deep despair she was experiencing might be alleviated.

Because S found it almost intolerable to make any decisions, it was planned that the music therapist would help her as much as she could and demand as little of her as possible. S accepted the therapist's offer of weekly singing sessions, and the therapist always acted as if she expected S to respond, which she did. Although the therapist expected S to respond, her attitude included the acceptance of S's possible desire not to respond and the assurance that this desire would not be met with hostility on the part of the therapist.

Physical therapy treatments had been scheduled before the music sessions. Sometimes S returned late from physical therapy and attempted to skip breakfast in order to be on time for her music lessons. Occasionally, the music therapist kept her company for a few minutes while she ate. Through such actions, the therapist tried to show that she cared about S and wanted to help her in a variety of ways.

During nine months of music therapy, S never once refused to attend. However, it often appeared to the therapist that S wished to shut herself away from her surroundings. She would sit or lie on her bed, appearing totally dejected. However, when the therapist approached, S would get up and go with her, in spite of what appeared to be extreme physical pain in walking. On one occasion, S had spent the day in bed as a result of an acute attack of arthritis. This happened about a month prior to the patient's discharge from the hospital, and it was possible to ask that she make her own decision as to whether she felt well enough to get up. S decided to attend the session.

The therapist suggested that S make a song book. She chose one or two songs she had particularly enjoyed singing during each session, and the therapist made copies for her to put in the book. S's collection grew weekly, and it was hoped that she would continue to add to it after her discharge. After a conference with the patient's schoolteacher about the necessity of stimulating her interest in reading, the therapist began to share some of her books about music with S. These books were used in conjunction with the music in the therapy sessions, as were a varied selection of phonograph recordings.

An example of S's growth was her willingness to wear the therapist's sweater during a session when she felt cold. This probably could not have happened earlier in therapy, when S hardly believed that she really mattered or that she could trust someone without being betrayed. After seven months of sharing the therapist's songs, S made a return gift by singing a song she had learned in her classroom for the therapist.

S's last session showed still another facet of her growth. T, a teen-ager, was invited to come to the hospital for the specific purpose of singing and playing the guitar with S. When S seemed hesitant about singing in front of someone new, T spontaneously stated that she, too, had this feeling many times and was trying to overcome it. After this exchange, music was performed in a variety of ways, ranging from solos by each girl to trios that included the therapist. S seemed able to accept, integrate, and enjoy this sharing of her singing session with another person.

Case Reports

—GENEVA SCHEIHING FOLSOM

Case 1. This case history covers a year's work with a nineteen-year-old boy in a private intensive treatment center where music therapy was part of a prescribed program for each patient. J had been admitted because he had uncontrolled outbursts of hostile, destructive behavior accompanied by boastfulness and contempt for other people's opinions and rights. Coupled with this was an intense need to be accepted by the group and a longing for the affection and warmth he had never known.

For several months after admission, two attendants, chosen for their size and ability to handle this big, powerfully built young man, accompanied J to all activities. His full schedule included using a punching bag, driving tennis balls into a net, throwing the medicine ball, and so on. His therapeutic program was designed to develop control of hostility and increase gratification from interpersonal relationships. Because he played a band instrument, his doctor felt his interest in music could be used in achieving the therapeutic goals.

The psychiatrist prescribed daily piano lessons and practice with a music therapist who was a warm, motherly person. Using a combination of gentleness and firmness, the therapist was able to engage his attention for increasing periods of time. At first, he was given exercises and selections that permitted him to pound and bang on the piano, and gradually these were modified as his needs for such outlets diminished. Then he was encouraged to play duets with the therapist so that he could gain pleasure from a cooperative effort.

When his behavior was sufficiently under control, J was assigned to the patients' band. He had expressed interest in this activity some time earlier, but his behavior had been too aggressive. When he finally was allowed to join, there were only five others in the band, so the group was suitably small. One attendant still accompanied him, but his initial behavior was so disruptive that he was told he could not remain unless he could control himself better. By working closely with him and giving him the chance to exercise leadership where his skill permitted, the music therapist helped him overcome these initial difficulties. As his behavior improved, the other band members became more friendly and expressed admiration of his musical ability. Meanwhile, he discussed and worked out his problems with his psychiatrist. But it was through the activity with the music group that he began to comprehend the relationship between the control of hostility and the gratification to be experienced from personal contacts. The recognition he received for genuine achievement demonstrated this relationship better than mere words.

J was a proper case for referral to music therapy. Throughout the development of his illness, even when he had an acute breakdown, he maintained his interest in music, probably because he did receive gratification from it, and it was one of the few things he did that gave others a chance to praise him. He was able to utilize the piano as an outlet for his aggressiveness, and this provided another interest in addition to purely physical outlets. The opportunity to participate in the band was offered as a reward for acceptable behavior. Because he had much motivation to be accepted into the band, he made attempts to modify his behavior. The therapist worked with him individually when he was removed from the band and helped him perfect his part so that when he was able to go back into the group, he could function at an acceptable level musically. In no other activity was there this fluidity of movement between individual and group work. This patient also had some problems with masculine identification, but within the band, he could still be a he-man while enjoying an artistic pursuit. His first success in group endeavor came in the music group, and later he was able to participate in sports groups.

Case 2. This eighteen-year-old girl was a patient in a state mental hospital. Before the introduction of a new regime in the hospital treatment program, she had succeeded in manipulating the staff to her own purposes. For months, she had controlled the patient dances and community sings. She had a fairly nice voice, and she had used the community sings to show off, to organize the younger patients, to take over the sing, and to do solos and small-group work on the stage. In order to stop this acting-out behavior, the staff decided on an attitude of firm kindness.

The therapist took control of the dances and community sings, and the patient had no opportunity to sing solos or arrange for groups to sing special numbers. At the dances, the therapist selected the records or turned some of this responsibility over to patient planning groups. The patient was excluded from these. Whenever she tried to manipulate the therapist or patients, this behavior was pointed out to her. On several occasions when she was unable to control her own behavior, she was removed from the activity.

Because she needed a socially acceptable means of receiving praise, it was decided that she should be allowed to be a member of the chorus that was performing for the Christmas pageant. At the first full rehearsal, the patient talked to her neighbor, ignored directions, sang before cue, made snide, stage-whispered remarks about the therapist, and generally disrupted the entire group. The easiest way to solve this problem would have been to remove her, but the aim of her treatment program was to teach her to control her aggressive behavior and to drop her manipulative attempts. The therapist moved her into another section of the choir, where she was placed between an attendant and a nurse. After rehearsal the music therapist who, after some months of work and despite having the role of chief frustrator, had established a good relationship with the girl, visited the ward and talked with her. It was pointed out how obnoxiously she had acted and that more had been expected of her. The therapist concluded by telling the patient she could have one more chance before she was removed from the program. At the next rehearsal, she was quite cooperative and seemed to be making a real effort to conform. After the rehearsal, she came to the therapist and said, "I'm sorry I made such a fool of myself the other night." The therapist agreed that the patient had indeed made a fool of herself but accepted her apology. At the same time, she was informed that the limits were still there and that further disruptive behavior would result in dismissal from the group. The girl was highly motivated to remain in the chorus. She controlled her behavior and was able to contribute to the success of the performance. She had learned to use her voice as a means of earning praise and could feel a sense of pride for contributing cooperatively to a group effort. Part of her discharge planning included arrangements for participation in a church choir after her return home.

Case 3. Another eighteen-year-old female was admitted to a private psychiatric hospital with a long-term history of schizophrenic reaction. At the time of admission, she was decompensated, almost completely withdrawn, careless of appearance, and at times extremely hostile and aggressive. In the social history given by the family, it was stated that the patient was a proficient pianist. She evidently had used her practice time as a means of escape from threatening interpersonal relationships.

The patient was assigned to music to help reestablish her defenses and to give her socially acceptable gratification. The therapist went to the patient's room and invited her to come to the music clinic. She responded to the invitation by telling the therapist to "go to hell." Five days a week and for several weeks, this same interchange took place. The therapist would invite the patient, and the patient would give the same response and slam the door in the therapist's face. Because the attitude prescribed was passive friendliness, the therapist would retire and sit in an adjoining waiting room for the remainder of the hour assigned to the patient. Finally, the patient stuck her head out of the door and asked the therapist why she was sitting out there. She was told that it was her lesson time, and the therapist had nothing else to do. The patient told the nurses to keep the music therapist out, but the music therapist persisted.

After a period of six weeks, the patient told the therapist she would go to the music room in "self-defense." The therapist took her there, showed her where the music was filed, and stayed away from the piano while the patient sight-read and selected music she liked. During this time and for several weeks thereafter, the therapist did not intervene when the patient came to the music room. When asked for suggestions about what to practice, the therapist recommended suitable exercises and repertoire.

As the patient became more comfortable, the therapist took a slightly more active role in structuring the lesson time. The patient began working to regain her technique. She still had to be accompanied to her lesson, but was ready when the therapist called and was willing to leave when the lesson was over. The therapist was still maintaining a passive, friendly attitude, and the patient suggested some duets the therapist had taken care to place on top of a pile of music. The patient had more technical facility than the therapist, and the duets provided a situation in which the patient could excel. At first, the duets were more of a race than a musical production, but eventually the patient began to work closely with the therapist and really enjoy the cooperative effort, not only for the music but because of the relationship. By this time, the patient had begun to go to other activities and to form tentative relationships with other staff members and patients. Her peers and the staff members had begun to praise her musical accomplishments, and she played the piano occasionally in the recreation hall. These performances brought her attention and recognition.

The prescribed attitude was changed to one of active friendliness. The therapist asked the patient to be accompanist for the girls' glee club. The patients also petitioned her to help them and she accepted. This participation required the patient to be on time for rehearsals, to be able to accept firm direction, to keep up with the music, and so on. She gained recognition for her contribution to the group. As she progressed, she played for the outpatient club and was accompanist for their chorus. When she went to school, she acted as accompanist for a group.

Because this patient had been skilled in music before hospitalization, this was a promising area of therapeutic approach. The flexibility of the music program made it possible to reach the patient first through a one-to-one relationship. Later, the use of her skill as a musician in groups was a way to help her become comfortable with people and to give her the gratification she needed. And, finally, she was encouraged to use her skills in her life adjustment outside the hospital.

References

FRIEDENBERG, E. Z. *The vanishing adolescent.* New York: Dell, 1959.

JORGENSEN, ELIN. *Music to play and sing.* Lawrence, Kan.: Music Aids, 1955.

McGINLEY, E. *Chords and melodies* (piano arranging series). Delaware Water Gap, Pa.: Shawnee Press, 1950.

RUPPENTHAL, W., Scribbling in music therapy. *J. Mus. Ther.,* 1965, 2, 8–10.

WOLFE, S. *Play-by-color* (Book 1, 2, Hymns, Carols, Stephen Foster). Milburn, N.J.: S. Wolfe, 1952.

Part V
MUSIC THERAPY FOR ADULTS WITH BEHAVIOR DISORDERS

Robert F. Unkefer

*I*n this section, more than the others, it is difficult to refrain from etio- logical terms. This is partly because many of them have become common in everyday speech, even if incorrectly used much of the time. So many doctrines of causation have been advanced, and many of them with so little proof, that the music therapist is tempted to adopt a theory and to cease the arduous task of observing and reporting behavior. This is often an easy way out, but more often a poor way, because the music therapist is primarily concerned with behavior. It is true that often he is a member of a therapeutic team and is asked for his opinion or recommendation as to the best treatment procedure and that, of course, he gives it in the light of his experience and observation. But the young therapist should not adopt an intricate and complex psychological theory so emotionally that the adoption has all the earmarks of a religious conversion. Nothing is more scientific than to observe well and report accurately. And this the music therapist can learn to do. This is the shortest way to expertness and the wisdom to make good decisions.

19

ADULT BEHAVIOR DISORDERS

ROBERT F. UNKEFER

Adult behavior disorders manifest themselves in so many and varied patterns that their systematic description must be left to those scientists especially concerned with behavior disorders and who have contributed several sets of diagnostic categories—the psychiatrists. However, even for them the field is so broad that they, perhaps more than any other specialists, may define their task simply as one of helping people. A further barrier to detailed description is that the geneses of behavior disorders, in a number of instances, have been explained differently, the several explanations being at some variance with each other. Eschewing specifics, then, some general observations may be made concerning adult behavior disorders.

Behavior disorders have been "variously described as abnormal, subnormal, undesirable, inappropriate, maladaptive, or maladjusted—that are not compatible with the norms and expectations of the patient's social and cultural system" (Redlich and Freedman, 1966, p. 1). People suffering from behavior disorders are not able to take their places in life in the manner dictated or prescribed by their culture. Their behavior according to their culture is not correctly "ordered." The appropriateness of an individual's functioning is in terms of his society. His disorder is known by his behavior.

The behavior disorders are generally classified under four or five broad and traditional headings: (1) The *psychoses* are severe disorders with impaired behavior, inability to deal with inner and outer reality, and inadequate social response. (2) The *neuroses* are most often characterized by anxiety, unadaptive behavior, and less than adequate function. (3) *Psychosomatic ailments* are evidenced by organic dysfunction, real or imagined. (4) *Mental deficiences,* the fourth classification of behavior disorders, are discussed in Part II; often the *sociopaths* are included as a fifth classification.

The music therapist in his research and clinical practice will be endeavoring in an effective manner to induce, elicit, or persuade better

[231]

behavior patterns. The patient, through proper treatment, will be persuaded to discard or substitute for better behavior those objectionable patterns of behavior that necessitated his treatment. Whether directly or indirectly by means of music, the chief aim of the music therapist is *change of behavior* in his patients.

Research

All hospital researchers have depended largely on clinical method and relatively little on experimentation. So it would be expected that music therapists would have equal or greater difficulty in carrying on research. Laboratory procedures are impossible with most patients, and rarely does good experimental control coincide even in small degree with long-term clinical practice. Because of the youth of music therapy, few of its practitioners have qualified themselves to do research through the necessary graduate study. As in all other areas of activity therapy, then, research in music therapy related to adult psychiatric treatment is still in an incipient stage of development. "Incipient" is an appropriate word, for it is meant to imply the beginning of effective research. The direction is yet insufficiently focused. Newer techniques of measurement need to be applied in laboratory research, and more precise methods of observation need to be used in clinical research. Nevertheless, some valuable and carefully conducted work exists. This research should be influential in clinical practice.

Much of the literature published in professional and pseudoprofessional journals deals with operational practices in hospital music departments. The techniques that are described are often directly related to the particular music skills of the music therapist who is reporting. It is possible to accept these articles as low-order research reports because they frequently include careful observations of patient behavior and changes in behavior that are apparently connected with experience in music and music activities.

The problem of clinical research in music therapy is the same as in all areas of clinical research. It is very difficult to assess how much, if any, of the patient's improvement is directly due to a single part of his treatment. This is true in all medical practice. Most patients get better, some get worse; just why or how is often not clearly understood. Recognition of the unsolved problems related to clinical research should not prohibit such research, nor should more descriptions of clinical work be discouraged. The case presentations in Chapters 20 and 21 support theoretical constructs. Some of the techniques can be duplicated by other music therapists; some probably cannot.

Listings and descriptions of research have appeared in two issues of the *Journal of Music Therapy*. Sears and Sears (1964) abstracted 170 research studies and clinical reports and made qualitative judgments about the research procedures of these studies. E. H. Schneider (1964) listed almost 800 titles with complete source information; all bear directly on music therapy. Examples of clinical studies are cited in the section that follows.

Clinical Studies

Michel (1960) surveyed the case reports of 375 patients, each of whom had participated in a music therapy program in a Veterans' Administration hospital at some time during a six-year period. Fifty cases were intensively studied using follow-up data obtained from questionnaires. Two hundred psychiatrists who had had experience with music therapy also were questioned. This study was considerably more objective than the usual case reports and substantiated the uses of music as therapy by quantitative as well as qualitative measurement. Perhaps the most important finding was that in a majority of cases, the greater the communication between psychiatrist and music therapist, the better the progress of the patient.

Darbes and Shrift (1957) evaluated the effects of group music therapy on three groups of hospitalized psychiatric patients. A control group had no music therapy experiences, whereas one of the experimental groups was concerned primarily with music listening and the other with singing. The results of several measures of behavior show that the control group regressed, the listening group remained the same, and there was improvement in the singing group. The authors concluded that,

. . . the experience of music therapy in a group does have the following effects: (1) it increases and improves the quality of the self-image of the patient, (2) it stabilizes the behavior patterns in the group and on the ward, and (3) it lays a secure foundation which facilitates the patient's chances of leaving the hospital. In all these areas, the experimental groups of patients demonstrated their superiority over the control group of patients (p. 8).

Several studies have been concerned with the use of music in the hospital setting to increase group conversational frequency. Dollins (1956) set up two conditions of music and no music with three groups to determine whether conversation increased with music. Of the three groups (A—least normal; B—midrange; C—most normal), group B patients showed a significant increase in conversation. Groups A and C increased in conversation but not significantly. Sommer (1958) found a significant difference in increase in conversation in an experimental group but no increase in the control group. Shatin and Zimet (1958) showed that background music caused a statistically significant alteration in the frequency and quality of verbal interaction of patients during group psychotherapy. A unique feature of this study was the qualitative judgment of the verbal responses.

A number of music therapists have tested the rhythmic responses of patients. The obvious lack of coordination and the arhythmic motor responses of withdrawn schizophrenic patients attracted the attention of these experimenters. The results of a study by Graham (1958) showed that patients responded more willingly and enthusiastically to regular and unchanging rhythm than to rhythm that fluctuated. Schneider (1961) studied the *simple reaction time* of sixteen male schizophrenic patients. With intervening Dalcroze eurhythmics (four hours a week for nine weeks) between a pretest and posttest, he found a significant improvement. The results of Shatin's (1958) study indicated that patterned, rhythmic drumbeats significantly stimulate an organismic response (pulse rate and motor activity) in chronic, deteriorated schizophrenics who have been hospitalized for many years, in spite of varying rhythmic beat frequencies. In general, these studies give good descriptive material on the motor and rhythmic responses of certain types of patients and some careful judgments of how rhythmic music activities can be used.

Selection of particular patients for music therapy, a most important research area, has begun to receive attention from contemporary investigators. The need to determine more precise methods of selecting patients for music therapy based on objective predictions for success has been recognized. Selection to date has been based for the most part on observations of the patient's apparent interest in music activity or by trial and error. Bean and Moore (1966) cited data supporting the hypothesis that hospitalized schizophrenics tend more toward *auditory* predominance in fantasy than a control group of Air Force men and college students. This data led to a project in which an attempt was made to answer the following question: Will auditory-predominant schizophrenic patients show a significantly better response to passive and active participation in a planned program of musical experiences than will a matched group of visual-predominant patients? Eye-minded and ear-minded patients were selected by administering both visual and auditory projective tests. Results were not conclusive; the population sample was small. The study technique, however, is of definite value, and should attract other investigators.

The clinical research literature is lacking in what may well be the most significant area for careful study. When the literature is reviewed, it must be concluded that music therapists and other activity therapists have not yet been willing to look at themselves and their colleagues with a deliberate, premeditated plan to assess their effectiveness with patients.

This kind of literature is noticeably lacking from medical and paramedical disciplines. The study of the therapists' techniques is most difficult and elusive, but of profound importance. Most therapists have been taught that they should become objective about themselves, that they should be aware of their own needs and how to fulfill them in their day-to-day work with patients. For example, some patients may have been kept from recovery because of the therapist's succorance need. The strong need to keep people dependent is easily identified in the private music studio outside the hospital; it is, without doubt, in many cases a serious problem in the hospital.

Laboratory Studies

Research in music, conducted outside the hospital setting, has given guidance to clinical efforts. Some basic research studies that contain direct implications for clinical work have centered on showing the type and strength of physiological changes in the human organism that can be manifested by changes in musical stimuli. Such studies are not new. In the middle 1930s, after reviewing the experimental literature concerning the effects of music on physiological processes, Diserens and Fine (1939) said,

Music: (1) Increases bodily metabolism. . . . (2) Increases or decreases muscular energy. . . . (3) Accelerates respiration and decreases its regularity. . . . (4) Produces marked but variable effect on volume, pulse and blood pressure (5) Lowers the threshold for sensory stimuli of different modes. (6) . . . influences the internal secretions . . . (p. 253).

More recent studies have extended the early reports, and experimentation is continuing in this area. In the 1950s, numerous studies were completed that provide noteworthy examples of systematic, carefully controlled experimental work. Each of these studies fits into a total picture that, when viewed as a whole, leads to the conclusion that music per se can effect predictable physiological changes in the human organism.

Changes in galvanic skin response (GSR) seem to have received the most attention from the experimenters. Weidenfeller and Zimny (1962) conducted two experiments, one using eighteen depressive patients and the other using eighteen schizophrenic patients, to test the hypothesis that calming music produces an increase and exciting music a decrease in GSR. In both experiments, two musical pieces judged by college students to be exciting and calming were played for six minutes. Measures of GSR obtained for every one of the six minutes confirmed the hypothesis in each experiment. Gray (1955) studied the pilomotor reflex and found that hospitalized mentally disturbed patients were significantly more responsive to music than nonhospitalized patients and that musicians were significantly more responsive than nonmusicians. No significant differences were found between male and female subjects or between subjects tested in groups and those tested individually. Ellis and Brighouse (1952) studied the effects of music on respiration and heart rate and found that (1) all three compositions (Hall's "Blue Interval," Debussy's *Prelude to the Afternoon of a Faun,* and Liszt's *Hungarian Rhapsody #2*) caused significant increase in respiration rate; (2) *Hungarian Rhapsody #2* caused more significant increases in respiration than the other two; and (3) none of the music caused a significant change in heart rate. Sears (1954) studied vascular changes in capillaries as effected by music. Her results indicated that changes in the movement of blood in capillaries did occur when music was played, although no difference was noted between sedative and stimulative music. Sears (1958) reported a very detailed examination of the effects of music on muscle tonus. Considering the responses of all the subjects as a group, Sears concluded that "music stimuli does evoke changes in the muscle tonus of listeners, and the evoked effects of increased or decreased tonus correspond closely with what is implied by the terms stimulative and sedative music" (p. 204). It was noted that sedative music reduced the tension level 99 percent of the time and that stimulative music was less effective in increasing tension levels. Furthermore, "changes in tonus were more effectively produced in nonmusicians than in musicians, and in female subjects than in male" (Sears, 1958, p. 204). Wilson (1957) studied variations in gastric motility caused by musical stimuli: "Generally, all of the subjects responded with stronger contractions to the sedative music. However, the most striking effect which happened without exception was the cessation of activity which occurred when the subject was displeased with the music played" (p. 62). Of particular value is Sears' (1951) unique study of postural responses to recorded music. Verified and consistent changes in the posture of his subjects were induced by changes in musical stimuli.

References

BEAN, K. L., and MOORE, J. R. Responses to sound effects and pictures as predictors of participation in music therapy. Unpublished manuscript, Univer. of Iowa, April, 1966.

DARBES, A., and SHRIFT, D. The effect of music therapy on three groups of hospitalized psychiatric patients as measured by some clinical and observational methods. *Bull. NAMT,* 1957, 6, 7–8.

DISERENS, C. M., and FINE, H. A *psychology of music.* Cincinnati, Ohio: Authors, 1939.

DOLLINS, C. N. The use of background music in a psychiatric hospital to increase group conversational frequency. Unpublished master's thesis, Univer. of Kansas, 1956.

ELLIS, D. S., and BRIGHOUSE, G. Effects of music on respiration and heart rate. *Amer. J. Psychol.*, 1952, 65, 39–47.

GRAHAM, R. M. Suggested procedures for conducting rhythm activities on wards of chronic and regressed mental patients. Unpublished master's thesis, Univer. of Kansas, 1958.

GRAY, R. M. The pilomotor reflex in response to music. Unpublished master's thesis, Univer. of Kansas, 1955.

MICHEL, D. E. A survey of three hundred seventy-five cases in music therapy. In E. H. Schneider (Ed.), *Music therapy 1959.* Lawrence, Kan.: Allen Press, 1960. Pp. 137–152.

REDLICH, F. C., and FREEDMAN, D. X. (Eds.), *The theory and practice of psychiatry.* New York: Basic Books, Inc., Publishers, 1966.

SCHNEIDER, C. The effects of Dalcroze eurhythmics upon the motor processes of schizophrenics. In E. H. Schneider (Ed.), *Music therapy 1960.* Lawrence, Kan.: Allen Press, 1961. Pp. 132–140.

SCHNEIDER, E. H. Selected articles and research studies relating to music therapy. *J. Mus. Ther.*, 1964, 1, 83–111.

SEARS, MARGARET S. Study of the vascular changes in the capillaries as effected by music. Unpublished master's thesis, Univer. of Kansas, 1954.

SEARS, MARGARET S., and SEARS, W. W. Abstracts of research in music therapy. *J. Mus. Ther.*, 1964, 1, 1–60.

SEARS, W. W. Postural responses to recorded music. Unpublished master's thesis, Univer. of Kansas, 1951.

SEARS, W. W. The effects of music on muscle tonus. In E. T. Gaston (Ed.), *Music therapy 1957.* Lawrence, Kan.: Allen Press, 1958. Pp. 199–205.

SHATIN, L. The application of rhythmic music stimuli to long-term schizophrenic patients. In E. T. Gaston (Ed.), *Music therapy 1957.* Lawrence, Kan.: Allen Press, 1958. Pp. 169–178.

SHATIN, L., and ZIMET, C. The influence of music upon verbal participation in group psychotherapy. *Dis. nerv. System.*, 1958, 19, 66–72.

SOMMER, DOROTHY TWENTE. The effect of background music on frequency of interaction in group psychotherapy. In E. T. Gaston (Ed.), *Music therapy 1957.* Lawrence, Kan.: Allen Press, 1958. Pp. 167–168.

WEIDENFELLER, E. W., and ZIMNY, G. H. Effects of music upon GSR of depressives and schizophrenics. *J. abnorm. soc. Psychol.*, 1962, 64, 307–312.

WILSON, VIRGINIA M. Variations in gastric motility due to music stimuli. Unpublished master's thesis, Univer. of Kansas, 1957.

20

CLINICAL PRACTICES

Introduction

ROBERT F. UNKEFER

Support for the introductory remarks and examples of clinical work discussed in Chapter 19 can be found in the reports that follow. Their authors have been concerned with developing treatment techniques and specific goals for music therapy and have sought objectivity in their work and reports. Slaughter supports and clarifies the expressed position of music therapy in psychiatric practice. He includes several case studies characteristic of his work with individual patients in a state hospital and in a private psychiatric hospital. Ruppenthal, Spry, Gray, Glover, Goldsmith, and Collins provide studies describing a variety of treatment goals and the manner in which music and music activities were used to attain them. Thompson has directed a music and creative arts therapy unit in a county psychiatric hospital for many years. In Chapter 21 she identifies goals for several types of patients and presents the practice of music therapy in a large hospital.

Approaches to the Use of Music Therapy

FORREST SLAUGHTER

During the past few years, concepts in the mental health profession have undergone continuous and dramatic changes (Blasko, 1962; Glover, 1962). Music therapy also is changing, and its concepts, procedures, and practices need constant reevaluation in order to meet new concepts of psychiatric treatment.

Although much research in the potentials of music therapy remains to be done, it is evident that music can play an important role in the rehabilitative process. Music can and does influence human behavior, but it is not a cure-all. It can rarely accomplish treatment aims and goals by itself. In order to be most useful and therapeutic in the hospital setting, music is subordinated to an overall treatment plan designed to meet the specific needs of the patient as prescribed by a physician (DesLauriers, 1958; Levine, 1960). Music is administered by a music therapist who, through his personality, knowledge of his medium, skills, examples, and attitudes, provides the experiences necessary to achieve therapeutic results (Wolberg, 1954, pp. 317–322; Fromm-Reichman, 1952, pp. 7–31; W. C. Menninger, 1936). The therapist uses music as a tool in assisting each patient to reorganize his disorganized and inappropriate patterns of behavior into more acceptable ways of dealing with life's problems (Des-Lauriers, 1958; K. A. Menninger, 1963, p. 297; Wrobel, 1963). In this way, both the therapist and the music contribute to the positive growth and development of the patient.

The following cases from a large Middle Western state hospital and a small private hospital illustrate how music can be used to provide therapeutic experiences for the patient.

Case 1. *This case study reveals how a fairly rigid schedule of study and practice provided the opportunity for a patient to gain gratification from acceptable behavior. This is a specific example of experience in structure. As the patient progressed, she was given support by the music therapist and provided with the opportunity for experience in self-organization. She was able to take responsibility for self-imposed tasks.* *

A young lady was admitted to the hospital because of her promiscuous acting-out and irresponsible delinquent behavior. She had no plans for productive living and was an expert at manipulating and playing people against each other. She had had some background in music but was never quite successful in using it. She needed to develop better interests and controls through a structured program and gain gratification through socially acceptable behavior.

Her previous experience in music provided one of the treatment approaches. She was scheduled for two 30-minute individual lessons with five 30-minute practice periods each week in piano and violin. She also was scheduled for beginning band rehearsal for one hour, three times a week, and mixed chorus for one hour, twice a week. The first scheduled sessions in all music programs went well, with the patient expressing interest and delight in being able to do something constructive. While attendance and interest in the group activities remained fairly high, her attendance at the individual lessons and practice began to diminish and become erratic. On those occasions when the patient was tardy or failed to come for either a lesson or practice time, she would bring a gift, made in occupational

* Preliminary comments on a number of the cases reported in this chapter are by Robert F. Unkefer.

therapy or manual arts, as a peace offering. The therapist refused to accept the gifts and firmly insisted that she attend scheduled meetings regularly and on time. Gradually, she did improve in attendance at individual sessions with a corresponding improvement in musical performance, for which she was complimented. On several occasions, the patient mentioned that she thought she was doing a better job of controlling and carrying through her playing on both instruments. What was meant by "carrying through" was that, although the patient would start each piece or exercise, she rarely finished it properly. During these episodes, the therapist would stop the patient and insist that the section be done over as proficiently as the rest of the piece.

In the meantime, she continued to progress in the group activities. She volunteered to help some of the slower members in the band. Her improvement in sight reading, timing, and dynamics gave her the security she needed to help others. A step forward in her treatment was made when she was elected vice president and librarian by the members of the mixed chorus. As librarian, her duties included arriving a little before the others so she could have the music passed out and ready. She also collected the music after rehearsals and kept it neatly arranged on the music cabinet. Because she had had choral experience, she was instrumental in helping the group decide on some of the music they performed. The patient chaired, along with the therapist, a small committee chosen by the other members for the purpose of gathering information concerning new robes to be worn during concerts.

Further progress was made in the patient's treatment when she was scheduled to catalog approximately five hundred new records for the music department. The weekly patient newspaper devoted several columns to her and the job she had done to help improve the system of record checkouts. The activities in music had offered the patient new, structured interests through which gratification could be gained in a socially acceptable way.

Case 2. This case is included for two reasons: First, it supports the validity of individual work in music in a short-term treatment plan; second, it illustrates how music study can be used for therapeutic gain with a patient who had little previous music study. It should be noted that by the sixth lesson on a thrice-weekly basis, the patient had progressed to a level of acceptable piano playing. Such a rate of progress is not unusual. This type of music study provides the opportunity for gratification from a new learning experience and is one of the most direct means for the patient to gain pride in self. Hobby formation has not been championed as a reason to provide new activities for psychiatric patients because the emphasis has been on the hospital treatment of the moment. The shift to shorter periods of hospitalization will bring more programing of activities that will help the patient bridge the gap between hospital and community living.

A successful businessman in his middle fifties was admitted to the hospital because he was losing interest in his business, friends, organizations, and most of his previous hobbies. It was decided that he needed to develop new interests and hobbies. One of his secret ambitions through the years had been to play the piano for his own enjoyment, but he had never found time for it because he was always striving for success in business. His doctor prescribed piano lessons as a part of his total treatment plan. At first, the patient was hesitant because he thought that his age was against his learning. Furthermore, he had no particular ability for playing by ear, and he wondered how he could accomplish anything. The therapist agreed with him up to a point but assured him that although age could affect learning, it depended on what and how he wanted to play and the amount of interest, time, and willingness he was able to put forth. The patient wanted to play simple, older tunes that were familiar to him and stated that he would not mind being able to play some of the newer tunes if they were simple. Both patient and therapist agreed to give the lessons a trial.

The patient was scheduled for three individual lessons a week without practice time. The therapist started him in an adult book, and progress was fairly rapid. By the third lesson, he had become acquainted with the basic notes, timing, and fingering, and by the sixth lesson, he was playing traditional tunes, arranged with single notes in both hands. He continued to progress until he could use three-note chords.

Gradually, the patient improved to the point that a group of patients asked him to play at a small social function. He asked the therapist whether he should play and stated that his doctor had left the decision up to him. The patient wanted to try but was not sure he could do a good job. The therapist reminded him that he was taking the lessons to learn to play for his own enjoyment, but if he felt comfortable playing for others, he could. He eventually decided not to play, but told the other patients that he might be interested on another occasion.

Before the patient was discharged a short time later, he asked about continuing lessons after he returned home. The therapist encouraged him but suggested he look for a teacher who would understand his purpose in taking the lessons. Within a few days and before he had left the hospital, the patient's family had started to search for the proper music teacher.

Case 3. One shy, intelligent patient was an accomplished instrumentalist with broad professional experience in both classical and jazz music.

After a frightening occurrence, he began having difficulty in controlling himself. His social life became restricted. Fearing error and blame, he was unable to make decisions and wanted others to make them for him. If they did, he was dissatisfied and uncomfortable. Whatever the situation, he felt trapped. After the initial interviews and observations, it was decided that he needed to rediscover his prebreakdown adjustments and use the patterns that had made him a good musician prior to his illness.

The doctor and music therapist decided that the patient should be given individual lessons twice a week. The first sessions were uneventful and progressed appropriately, the patient being able to accept the one-to-one relationship. Occasionally, he attempted to minimize his music ability and accused the therapist of giving insincere compliments. The therapist's reassurances were met with doubt, and the patient would launch into an explanation of why his tone, fingering, or other techniques kept him from performing well. Then he would state sadly that he did not know whether he should continue playing. Sometimes the patient would weigh the question of continuing a musical career and again enumerate his physical complaints. The therapist tried to convey that he understood how the patient felt in not being able to make such decisions, then encouraged him to attend to the lesson at hand.

Later, as the individual sessions progressed, the patient expressed interest in ensemble work. After various discussions involving the therapist, patient, and doctor, it was agreed that whether or not to play in the ensemble must be the patient's decision. He decided to enter a small group and profited from his experience. During one of the meetings in which plans were made for a performance, the patient misunderstood a remark that passed between the therapist and another member of the group. The patient became upset, loud, and abusive, and all attempts by the therapist to control his actions were met with hostile accusations. Finally, the patient was ordered firmly to stop this behavior or leave the group. This resulted in more hostile abuse and a threat to quit the ensemble. The therapist remained quiet, as did the other ensemble members, until the patient finished. By this time the hour was up for the session. The other members left the room, but the patient continued to pace the floor, casting angry glances at the therapist, who said he would be looking forward to seeing the patient at the next session. The patient attempted to speak but could not, cleared his throat, turned away from the therapist, and hastily walked out of the room. He was present and contributing to the group at the following session.

On one other occasion, after the ensemble had been incorporated into the concert band, plans were made and completed for a band concert. The patient had cooperated in preparing for the event. However, a few days before the concert, he approached the therapist and stated that he did not know whether he would play in the concert. The therapist listened to the patient's explanations and encouraged him to discuss this decision with his doctor. Later the patient repeated that he did not know whether he would play but emphasized not playing. Again the therapist referred him to his doctor. Finally the patient talked to his doctor who, in turn, did not make the decision for him but referred him back to the therapist. In the meantime, the therapist and the doctor had met for a conference, and it was agreed that neither would decide for the patient but would encourage him to make up his own mind. Finally, the day before the concert, he decided not to play. In doing so, he had made another forward step in his recovery by making his own decision and surmounting his fear of being wrong and being blamed for it.

Case 4. A young adult was admitted to the hospital because of strange withdrawal behavior and loss of interest in his personal appearance and former hobbies of art, fishing, and golfing. He was confused and had threatened bodily harm to his family on several occasions. He needed to learn self-control and to express his destructive impulses in a socially acceptable way. Because he had shown some interest in music, he was scheduled for drum lessons twice a week. At first, the lessons were fairly unstructured, and the patient was allowed to sit at the drums and pound away. There was very little verbal communication between patient and therapist except "hello," "goodbye," and a casual "go ahead" from the therapist, permitting the patient to beat the drums at will. Occasionally, the therapist would step to the piano and attempt to join the patient in a jazz duet. This was impossible because the patient banged away arhythmically.

This continued until the therapist began playing records containing jazz drum solos just about the time the patient was due for his session. One day, as the patient arrived, he stated that he wished he could play like the "guys on the records." The therapist discussed this possibility with him and asked him to think about it; if he decided he would like to learn, they would try to work it out together. When the patient decided he would like to play the drums, the first structured lessons progressed well. On several occasions, when the lessons in hand and foot coordination were difficult, he became upset and wanted to return to pounding again. After consulting his doctor, it was decided that he should be encouraged to continue his lessons. In a few weeks he began to show considerable progress, and individual practice time was added to his schedule. Further progress was shown in his treatment when he was able to ask the therapist to play the piano with him in simple ·duets. As the patient continued to progress, he was able to cope with his hostile feelings and enjoy learning to play the drums. He eventually enrolled in high school classes and in due time received his diploma.

The foregoing illustrations are not intended to be all-inclusive or to suggest any final or rigid approach to the use of music in the hospital setting. They do not imply that music was the only activity used with the patient. In many cases, occupational, recreational, and educational activities were also scheduled. Nor are these examples meant to show that all attempts with music in the clinical setting are successful in achieving treatment aims and goals. However, they do serve to give some understanding of ways in which music can be used in the psychiatric setting.

Case Studies

Case Report
—WAYNE RUPPENTHAL

Because of the drawling speech that came from this tall, angular, twenty-six-year-old man, it seemed appropriate and natural to call him "Tex," as he requested. The apparent difficulty was that Tex could not walk. He first came to the music therapy clinic in a wheelchair when his doctor was showing him the various adjunctive therapies in the hope of finding something that would kindle a spark of interest. At the staff conference, his paralyzed legs had been of central concern, for in none of the many tests and examinations he had been given was there any organic explanation for the paralysis.

Tex talked of many things he had done. In the recreation therapy clinic, he was reminded of his various spectacular participations in football and basketball and of how he had been a cowboy and a rodeo star. In the woodworking shop, he was reminded of some construction work he had done. In the bowling alleys, he was sad because his paralyzed legs would never again allow him to carry a bowling team to a decisive league victory.

In the music therapy clinic, he was attracted almost immediately to a string bass that was in the group room and remarked to the music therapist that he had played bull fiddle with Tommy Dorsey's orchestra. The instrument was brought over to his wheelchair and set in a position that would enable Tex to play it. At that point, it became apparent that he had probably never had his hands on such an instrument before. But the doctor and the music therapist both accepted his excuse that he was "out of shape" because he had not played for several years and agreed that "no one could play the instrument in a wheelchair." But would he like to come to the clinic to "fool around" with it a little each day? Tex said that he would.

Tex wheeled himself into the clinic daily for several weeks to "fool around" with the bull fiddle and, although it was now a certainty in the minds of the staff that he had had no previous musical training or experience, his efforts were accepted and no one attempted to teach him. The only comments that were made were on the order of, "It sounds like you're beginning to get back in shape, Tex."

The dance combo consisted of six patients with an instrumentation of three saxophones, piano, guitar, and drums, with the music therapist playing the trumpet. Their rehearsal hour preceded the time when Tex came to the clinic, and the therapist noticed that after once arriving early enough to hear the last few minutes of the combo rehearsal, Tex consistently came early and, in a far corner of the large room, attempted to pluck the bass along with the combo.

After several days of this, the therapist remarked to Tex that it was a shame he could not stand up and play, for the combo surely needed a bass to fill out the rhythm section; but, of course, this was not practical unless some way could be found to get him supported in an upright position. The next week Tex ventured the suggestion that maybe if he had crutches, he could be supported by them, lean against the grand piano, and thus join the combo. The crutches were provided, and Tex became a member of the group.

Fortunately, Tex began to develop a fair rhythmic sense, but even his relatively good ear for pitch discrimination did not fully compensate for the fact that he could not read music. He had never dropped the façade that had been erected by his Tommy Dorsey story, and the staff felt it would be unwise to confront him. The impasse was broken one day when the chief music therapist, who was known by Tex to be an excellent violinist, was putting his violin in its case; he remarked that he was going to take a violin lesson. Tex said it seemed odd for someone so expert to be taking a lesson. The reply was, "You and I know that each of us needs to go back occasionally and refresh himself on the basic fundamentals of his instrument." The next day Tex asked the therapist if he would have time to "take me back through a review of the basic fundamentals, because we're both string players." The day arrived when Tex came to the clinic on crutches, and later he was able to discard them entirely.

The patient who had been playing bass drum in the concert band left the hospital, and Tex accepted the role of bass drummer with no hesitation. Rehearsals went well for several days, and then, suddenly, in the few moments between numbers, Tex groaned loudly and fainted. Tex revived—the center of the group's attention. The next day he fainted again, and the music therapist noticed that, as before, he had fallen into a large, cushioned chair. This time, although there was evidence of group concern, the therapist went on with the rehearsal; when Tex "came to," he got shakily to his feet and went back to the drum.

After the rehearsal, the therapist talked with Tex and suggested that he speak to his doctor about these fainting spells because, if they continued, another bass drummer would have to be found. "We will be playing for quite a few things before an audience in the near future, and we just can't take the chance of having a concert disrupted by a fainting spell." He never fainted again at rehearsal or concert.

Tex was ultimately discharged from the hospital, able to make a satisfactory readjustment to society. He had learned to satisfy his tremendous need for attention by earning it rather than using his former devices—paralysis, fainting, and grandiose fabrications about his past accomplishments. Many people in the hospital had a part in his treatment, but among the most effective were his doctor, who first detected his interest in music, and the music therapists, who *accepted Tex at his level of functioning* and helped him supplant his inappropriate attention-getting devices with behavior patterns that *earned* the gratification he needed.

Case Report
—GERALD K. SPRY

The patient was a thirty-two-year-old unmarried male. He was admitted in 1964 of his own accord because he felt that part of himself was in another world trying to solve some undefinable problem. He complained of listlessness and chronic fatigue and constantly had feelings of inadequacy. He seemed to be very introspective, preferring books to human contact. The patient had two dreams that bothered him. In the first one, he was confronted with two paths. He always took the wrong path and ran into a crowd, whereupon he was attacked by a vicious dog. In the second dream, he found himself partially clothed in a crowd and tried to escape without being seen.

The patient's relationship with people seemed confused. He liked them but at the same time felt uncomfortable and uneasy. When with females, he was especially uncomfortable. The patient requested music therapy with specific emphasis on drum lessons. His referral sheet listed his diagnosis as early schizoid. The specific objectives of music therapy were to offer structured tasks and maintain interpersonal distance. It was also requested that tasks be structured so that the patient had to make decisions. A situation was set up that required him to decide between taking lessons on the snare drum only or on the complete trap set. It was carefully pointed out that he could later reverse his decision with no adverse consequences. Then four different lesson times were offered to him. Here again, he had to decide which time to take his lessons. Then the patient picked out a practice time for each day. He was told that he must attend these lessons and practice periods at the designated time.

The patient decided to take lessons on the trap set. During his first lesson, a very simple rhythmic pattern was presented, in which the snare drum was played with brushes on the first and third beats with the bass drum coming in on the same beats. He practiced this alone and then with records. In his first week of practice, the patient was able to accomplish this rhythmic pattern, thus achieving the short-term goal of immediate ego support. In each succeeding week, a simple situation was set up to give him the support he needed.

The goal now became that of helping the patient make decisions on his own, while continuing the development of ego support and directing him in his relationships with other people. These relationships were greatly improved through participation in the hospital choir. Eventually, his feelings of uneasiness lessened to the extent that he was quite comfortable in a group situation.

Even though no extensive musical ability was required, a great deal of initiative was necessary in order to continue his daily lessons and practice. The musical goal on the drums was to play four different rhythmic patterns simultaneously. As each pattern was introduced, more mental concentration and physical coordination were needed. The patient had a difficult time maintaining a schedule. It was pointed out to him that he only deprived himself when he was late for his lessons or did not appear at all. In order to make the patient attend to the situation at hand, more and more of the environment was structured. Gradually, more concentration was required of him.

The opportunity for creativity was available. By composing his own drum solos and rhythmic patterns, the patient gained much needed support. Eventually, his progress was sufficient to enable him to join the hospital dance band. Many times the patient came to his lesson expressing hostility and aggression because of some incident that had taken place earlier in the day. While concentrating on his lesson, he released this energy in a socially acceptable manner.

The value of this program to the patient after dismissal from the hospital could be good, not in monetary terms, but in ego support. The therapist encouraged him to continue his music after his release from the hospital.

From the start of the therapy program, the therapist had as little contact with the patient as possible. Decision making and initiative were left to him, although he was encouraged to develop and try many things. It was important for the therapist to structure situations so the patient would receive the desired support and, at the same time, achieve this support through his own motivation. In consequence, the therapist, after conferring with the doctors, set up a situation in which the patient achieved only failure. The purpose was to show that failure or a wrong decision would produce not disastrous results but only temporary setbacks.

Eventually, it was decided to announce to the patient that he was going to be discharged in two weeks. Observations of his reactions were recorded over the two-week period. Within one week, he regressed into an almost catatonic stupor, but finally eloped from the hospital.

Case Reports
—RICHARD M. GRAY

Case 1. This case shows clearly how an error in clinical practice can be averted. The patient was not allowed to spend his time strumming the guitar, thereby holding people away from him by marginal acceptable behavior. His assigned time in music activities was structured to promote a close relationship with the therapist. Even though the structure was resisted by the patient, it did provide the framework for learning and forced him to accept contact with the therapist. Random, unstructured, and repetitive activity in music is frequently viewed as acceptable behavior. All too often it is a simple, convenient way for the patient to buffer himself from other people. When this occurs, the pattern must be broken. G was a thirty-seven-year-old male who exhibited a dissociative reaction. He never really knew his parents. When he was a very small child, his father expelled him and his mother from their home, and his mother died when he was five. He feels he never had any real home, because he spent his childhood with a very strict grandmother. When he was in high school, he lived with an aunt and uncle who were frequently brutal to him. During World War II, he joined the Navy and was assigned to submarine duty. He was married while in the service. In 1944, he became depressed, drank poison, and was hospitalized until his discharge in 1945. He was divorced from his first wife about a year after his discharge from the service.

Following his discharge from service, G complained of blackout spells. There were some periods of irritability, depression, and nervousness, which precipitated considerable drinking. According to the patient, when he stopped drinking for three years, the blackout spells increased in number. Another marriage of short duration (two weeks) was followed by a third, which is in the process of dissolution at the present time. The patient has been hospitalized six times with intervening periods characterized by marital discord, nervousness, amnesia, and alcoholism.

The purpose of music therapy with this patient was to develop interpersonal relationships. During the immediately preceding hospitalization, he was referred to music therapy, the hospital radio station, and manual arts therapy (woodworking). Although he worked only sporadically in the radio station and in music, he gave obvious evidence of his flair for entertainment. He played some of his country-western compositions for the music therapists and sought their criticisms. In woodworking, he made a combination electric guitar and bass, which he played well.

During the most recent hospitalization, his physician specifically requested that demands be made on the patient to improve his guitar technique. The necessity of playing in the hospital instrumental group, which read music, was explained to the patient, who had previously played only by ear. This was done for the following reasons: The physician felt that strumming for the patient's own pleasure was contraindicated and that learning to read chord symbols and increasing knowledge of chord fingerings would make other types of instrumental groups available to the patient when he was discharged from the hospital.

The patient was expected to keep his appointments for lessons, private practice, and band rehearsals. When he was absent, the ward was called, and the physician was notified. Although the patient resisted this structure, he made musical progress, and the therapist was able to establish a good relationship with him.

Case 2. This case report shows how the patient could accept attention from other people within the structure of a safe, pleasant activity. D was a thirty-year-old man who worked as a farm hand. His early life was described as normal. He played guitar, sang at social events, and enjoyed teaching children to play. D's illness began in 1953 while he was in the armed forces. At that time, he was assigned to clerical work. He began withdrawing, showing feelings of inferiority, and at a station hospital, was found to be hallucinating and smiling inappropriately. His illness did not respond to electroconvulsive treatment. The diagnosis was severe chronic catatonic schizophrenia.

Following three months of hospitalization, however, it was possible for him to make a marginal adjustment at home. After five years with his family, he was readmitted to this hospital for reevaluation and treatment recommendations. There was no apparent change in his condition. It was during this more recent admission that he was referred to music therapy. Treatment aims were to provide closely supervised activities, encourage conversation, and activate friendliness. The patient was initially given guitar lessons from a music therapy trainee.

D came to lessons accompanied by the nurse or nursing assistant who participated in order to provide additional encouragement for him. He was allowed to take the instruction book back to his ward so he could practice there. During lessons, D played the chords of familiar songs while the therapist played chords and sang the melody. He declined to join a group of other guitar students, saying that he was not proficient enough. Efforts to interest him in music fundamentals proved fruitless.

Several weeks after music therapy was initiated, he began to speak more clearly and express definite likes and dislikes. When the music therapy intern's training period ended, the staff therapist took over the lessons and met regularly with D. Gradually, increasing demands were made on his ability. He now played chords while the therapist played only the melody. He was invited to play duets with the therapist in patient recitals and was able to do so.

The patient has left the hospital and at last report was making a marginal adjustment at home.

Case Reports
—RAY G. GLOVER

Case 1. This example seems to show that the patient is not yet able to profit from the structure of the music activities. She has not made great gains from the experience to encourage self-organization; she does not accept self-imposed tasks. Her continued superficial contacts with other people indicate that she remains quite unable to accept responsibilities in relationships. A reevaluation of goals is in order to determine if the particular music activities are encouraging the patient to continue a pattern of immature relationships. If this is determined, the activity program should be changed or the structure of the music activity should become more demanding. The patient was a thirty-three-year-old female, a divorced former stenographer. She was admitted to the hospital because of confusion, disorientation, and depersonalization. The second of four siblings in a family of moderate economic means, her history showed no unusual problems during infancy or childhood. Her school life was described as having been lively, active, and friendly. She completed two years of college but stopped after being married. She was extremely interested in music and played the electric organ. The husband believed that his wife's mental illness started five years before her admission to the hospital, although he did not recognize the symptoms at the time.

The following is a summary of her psychological examination. The patient is a frail and polished looking young woman who seems somewhat preoccupied, withdrawn, and seclusive. She appears hypoalert and well oriented in all spheres, although preoccupied to the extent of occasional inaccessibility. She seems to be within the average range of intelligence with a fund of knowledge adequate and corresponding to her education. She has a good memory for both recent and remote events. Her thought processes are predominantly relevant, coherent, and understandable, although some regressions, looseness, syncretism, and autism are noticeable. The patient periodically mutters to herself, interpolating in the middle of an answer. She also uses clichés, irrelevant and somewhat disjointed proverbs, and jokes to fill in some of her semioriented answers. She is excessively preoccupied with somatic hallucinations and expresses concern about her cheekbones drawing together, her right arm shrinking, and her toes expanding. Affectively, the patient is rather bland. There are marked signs of regression in thinking, behavior, and affect.

The patient was started on a compulsive regime of activities consisting of cooking, ward occupational therapy, piano instruction, and choir. Group psychotherapy was recommended for a later date; it was inaugurated about a year later with poor results. She was also placed on a chemotherapy regime. Her activity-therapy prescription indicated the need for "alleviation of feelings of inadequacy and confusion and improvement of self-esteem." The attitude toward her was to be kind firmness. The following are excerpts from the music therapist's progress reports: She practices the piano once or twice a week and is happy and cooperative. She is regular in attendance at choir and socializes fairly well. She is very talkative about trivial things. She has sung several solos quite adequately. She seems to "block" occasionally while playing the piano; otherwise, she plays well.

A later report stated: The patient seems to "block" when making up her own piano arrangements. She is assigned duet work in an effort to give her something concrete to follow and to make it necessary that she play what is written. She does this satisfactorily. For the most part, our personal relationship has been a happy one. However, when I clamp down and make her play correctly, I'm not too sure how well this is received; sometimes she seems to think she was right all the time. She is regular in attendance in choir, socializes fairly well, but tells a lot of pointless stories, seemingly as a result of her nervousness. She does not face reality.

Six months later the therapist reported: She enjoys playing duets most when she is not corrected. Usually she does not remember the correction the following day and plays in the same way as before. She generally feels she is right about the music and can do no wrong. However, I think that perhaps a little progress has been made. She has not been so flighty in choir the past few months. She gets along well with the group and seems more outgoing. She stopped telling her pointless stories for a while, but occasionally tells one now.

At a progress-evaluation meeting, it was reported that the patient's husband had no interest in her and was considering a divorce. The patient was not willing to face this fact and still maintained that her marriage was a wonderful thing and life was a bed of roses. One day as she entered the music clinic, a record by a popular female singer was being played. One of the songs, "It's the Talk of the Town," included the phrase "Everybody says you've left me." This song visibly disturbed her. The next song was "He's Funny That Way." After the phrase "I've got a man crazy for me," she screamed, "Liar! Liar!" and became more disturbed. Halfway through the third song, "Say It Isn't So," the patient ran out the door. As soon as she was in the hall, however, she assumed the façade that everything was wonderful and thanked the therapist for the music. It was believed that the words of the songs made her realize the truth of the situation between her husband and herself.

At the time of this writing, the patient appears more stable although she still suffers from occasional delusions. She sings in the female vocal group and the choir and seems to get satisfaction by serving occasionally as accompanist for the group. Her piano playing is satisfactory as long as she uses written music.

Case 2. The patient was an obese, thirty-three-year-old male whose occupation was listed as laborer. He was a veteran, single, and a high school graduate. He was transferred to this hospital, after spending one and one-half years in another state hospital, because he was considered a trouble-maker and potentially dangerous and should be hospitalized in a maximum security building. This was done, but after a year he was transferred to an open ward.

The patient was the older of two children. When he was sixteen years old, his father died of cancer. It is said that he felt quite close to his father. He never got along well with his mother because she "worried too much about little things such as what time he would come in at night." He said he had pretty much his own way at home until his brother was born. He believed that his brother was the cause of considerable friction between them. He spent most of his time with his father, assisting him with his work and joining him in recreational activities, whereas his brother spent most of his time with their mother.

During his high school days, he was frequently truant. Finally, he was sent to a military school for a year, where he found the restrictions irksome. During his early years, he was regarded as a fat boy by his schoolmates and suffered considerable teasing. He states that when he was around fourteen years of age, he suffered a head injury, after which he was frequently dizzy for a few weeks. About a year later, he began to suffer from headaches, which have become increasingly worse during recent years. He worked at many jobs after he left school, but always quit because of the restrictions of regular hours or because of his headaches. He was inducted into the Army but was given a medical discharge after three months because of migraine headaches and his refusal to have an operation for a hernia.

The patient first began to admit to himself that he was having difficulty in his social adjustment after he was involved in the fatal shooting of a lifelong friend. He stated that while visiting his friend, they both drank considerably. During the evening, the friend attacked him physically several times, and when he attempted to leave, his friend interfered. The patient drew a target pistol and fired at him. The bullet struck the friend, causing his death. He was given a six months' sentence in the county jail, but was granted a special parole in order to seek medical treatment.

After his transfer to this hospital, he made a good adjustment and his headaches subsided. The patient's first contact with the music department concerned the repair and upkeep of the record players and other electronic equipment. He insisted that this was one of his jobs, and that no one was to interfere. It was later learned that the patient had once played clarinet, although he could not be considered an accomplished musician. He became interested in a small combo that was being formed and was assigned to participate in it. The patient was arrogant, self-righteous, and at times uncooperative. He would not admit mistakes when confronted with them. He played louder than anyone else in the group and with a very harsh tone. This was tolerated. As time went on, the patient refined his playing so that it was more acceptable. He purchased a saxophone from a local music store, and his playing improved. Finally, he was able to accept his mistakes and was willing to correct them. He became interested in arranging and transcribing music for his instrument and in adding harmony lines. Instead of playing the melody himself, he relinquished this to others at appropriate times and played the second or third part.

It is believed that this patient was helped greatly by subtle pressures from the group and from the therapist. He received praise for appropriate responses and encouragement in acceptable areas until he became aware of the situation and decided to change. The patient was dismissed from the hospital and is reportedly doing well.

Case Reports
—HERBERT P. GOLDSMITH

Case 1. D, thirty-three years old, was hospitalized in 1959. She was divorced and had one child who lived in another state. She was committed to the hospital by her parents. In February, 1963, she was placed in an intensive-treatment program, and music therapy was included in this schedule. In March, 1964, it was determined that D was not benefiting from the intensive-psychotherapy program. At this time, she was dropped from group therapy but continued in music therapy. Specific goals prescribed were to heighten her affect, which was flattened, and to provide an opportunity for resocialization.

In April, 1964, the music therapist suggested to the patient that she begin lessons in an effort to develop her pleasant singing voice. She was exceedingly reluctant to undertake voice lessons, yet was obviously flattered by the therapist's opinion of her ability. She finally consented, and sessions were begun on a weekly basis. The patient advanced quickly. She learned Italian diction and mastered a group of Italian songs. At present, when the patient begins the study of an Italian art song, she translates it herself with the aid of an Italian dictionary. This enables her to understand, interpret, and communicate the meaning of the song she sings.

When the patient began studying voice, she was preoccupied and distant, often stopping in the middle of sentences and constantly wringing her hands. Her eyes were frequently downcast and her brow furrowed; she appeared to have little confidence in herself or in her vocal ability. Six months later, the patient's appearance and attitude were changed. She looked younger and prettier, having taken an interest in her personal appearance. Her conversation was lively and interesting. She had gained a great deal of self-confidence and had made a marked adjustment to her environment. A full-length recital was planned. She looked forward eagerly to this performance. In a recent staff conference, the patient's doctor indicated plans to furlough her soon after she completes this recital, because she has improved so markedly during the past six months.

The praise the patient has received from people who have heard her sing has convinced her that she does have a relatively good voice. She feels that she has accomplished something meaningful and that her talent will allow her to make a worthwhile contribution to her community when she returns.

Case 2. This eighteen-year-old female, first admitted to the hospital in March, 1961, is the daughter of a deceased dentist who was once a member of the hospital staff. The patient had been living with her mother and her eighty-year-old grandmother. A long-term authority complex, beginning with her relationship with the father and continuing with her relationship with the mother, constitutes the significant background of her past and present behavior disorders. The patient has acted out against authority and authority figures in various ways—by running away, truancy, promiscuous sexual acting out, hostility, and violence. Her self-control has been further weakened by chronic brain syndrome (CBS) associated with psychomotor epilepsy. She actively resents authority and often reacts against it by aggression or through epileptic seizures. At the time of admission, the patient's adjustment had deteriorated to a psychotic level, and it was found that she was difficult to manage on the ward, being both obstructive and destructive. She associated with other girls who had similar backgrounds and who expressed their conflicts and impulses in similar ways.

The music therapy treatment goals were to help satisfy, in a non-threatening, nonprovoking way, some of the patient's dependency needs, including her need to relate to parental figures and find an acceptable source of authority. The patient was assigned to individual therapy and several forms of group activity. The individual therapy provided the therapist with an opportunity to develop rapport on a nonauthoritative level and also provided for dependency development. The choir became a real testing ground for acceptance of the authority figure. Her assigned job of choir librarian offered her a feeling of closer relationship to the therapist, yet she had to follow his directions and fulfill the demands made on her in a socially acceptable manner. A folk dance group provided an opportunity to teach her acceptable ways of acting out frustrations and aggressiveness while continuing to accept the authority figure. A music appreciation class provided an area for supplying satisfaction of dependency needs while developing personal relationships and finding acceptance of her ideas and concepts within the patient group.

Because the patient had previous experience playing clarinet, it was decided to assign her to one of the instrumental groups. After several months in these activities, an evaluation by the psychiatrist showed that she had made marked improvement, adjusted to her environment, and was much more amenable to authority figures.

Even though acts of extreme violence have occurred from time to time on the ward (including exhibitions of jujitsu in which several doctors were victims), the patient never resorted to this form of acting out in music therapy. At times, she attempted to provoke the therapist into rejecting her, but in the main, there has been decided improvement in her adjustment. Seizures, violent acting out, and aggressiveness have diminished greatly. At present, the patient is being considered for placement in the hospital school program, because it is believed that her adjustment warrents this further step in her rehabilitation.

Case 3. A thirty-two-year-old divorced patient was a voluntary admission to the hospital in March, 1963. At the time of admission, he was very confused and stated that he had come to the hospital because he had lost his ability to concentrate and had ideas of self-destruction. He had guilt feelings about a previous marriage and believed that they contributed much to his illness. His intelligence quotient was found to be 144. The patient had nearly completed four different undergraduate degrees. He stated that he wished to attain high goals in life, but at the same time appeared not to have exerted himself in college work. In the past, he has been hallucinatory and delusional. At present, he denies any hallucinations, but it is believed that he still continues with some type of autistic thought. He is an accomplished musician, his principal instrument being the French horn.

Since September, 1963, the patient has been in intensive psychoanalysis. He was assigned to music therapy by the psychiatrist, the goals being to develop ego strength, to provide supportive therapy, to improve socialization, and to provide intellectual stimuli.

Initially, the patient was apprehensive and very reluctant to participate in music therapy activities. He was finally persuaded to join an advanced instrumental group on a trial basis. Gradually, he overcame his anxiety and began to be cognizant of his place and importance in this performing group. The second significant step in the patient's progress was made possible through the formation of a chamber music ensemble. This ensemble was comprised of five patients, all of them highly intelligent and musically proficient. As a member of the ensemble, the patient had more opportunity for individuality, and the importance of his role within this status group increased. Also, he was continually stimulated and challenged in a learning situation appropriate to his intellectual capacity.

Following several appearances in the hospital and before community groups, the patient's anxiety regarding performing in public diminished to the extent that he requested solo work whenever possible. His first solo was a performance of special music for a chapel service. Some anxiety appeared at this time, but subsequent solo performances lessened this reaction.

The patient has been participating in music therapy activities for approximately a year. During this period, his interests have branched into other music therapy and hospital areas. He appears to be enjoying these new activities. There is a marked improvement in both his personality and his musical ability. He appears to be less confused and better able to concentrate. His willingness to undertake responsibility and contribute in an individual manner is evidence of his improvement. It has been recommended that this patient continue in programed music therapy activities during the remainder of his hospitalization.

Case Report
—CAROL M. COLLINS

This case report is a short description of a rather common experience of many music therapists. Frequently it is possible to establish contact with a patient through a simple music experience rather than through a verbal invitation. Apparently the patient feels that she can choose to play along or sing along because it is predictably safe to do so.

B was referred from a "total-push" treatment ward for long-hospitalized women. She was receiving electroshock and activity treatments. It was difficult to communicate with her because of her hebephrenic chattering. When the doctor heard her playing chords on the piano, he turned to the music therapist saying, "I don't know what she will do; she might run away or anything, but I'll be responsible."

The therapist first took the patient for a walk during which the conversation was completely unproductive. In desperation, the music therapist stopped by the recreation hall and sat down at the piano. When she began to play, the patient ad-libbed an obligato in the treble to the accompaniment of "Chopsticks." B played at least a dozen improvisations. During exploratory sessions, the therapist discovered that the patient not only played the piano and danced, but could imitate any song style desired and could sometimes make up her own words, depending on how well she was in contact with reality at the time.

When B was scheduled to sing and dance in a variety show, her ward attendants did not believe that it was possible. She seemed almost as "far out" as she always had, but upon hearing her introduction, she stepped on the stage and performed like a seasoned veteran. As the therapist became acquainted with B's behavior, she was able to understand not only B's moods but some of the verbalizations from her hebephrenic chatter. The patient became more dependable, performed with the dance band, and became a member of the choir.

References

BLASKO, J. J. New directions in general hospital psychiatric facilities. *Hosp.*, 1962, 36, 45.

DESLAURIERS, A. M. What is therapy in music therapy. In E. T. Gaston

(Ed.), *Music therapy 1956*. Lawrence, Kan.: Allen Press, 1957. Pp. 29–53.

FROMM-REICHMAN, FRIEDA. *Principles of intensive psychotherapy*. Chicago: The University of Chicago Press, 1952.

GLOVER, R. New concepts in psychiatric treatment. In E. H. Schneider (Ed.), *Music therapy 1961*. Lawrence, Kan.: Allen Press, 1962. Pp. 48–49.

LEVINE, D. Music therapy as part of the total hospital program. *Bull. NAMT*, 1960, 9, 7–8, 11.

MENNINGER, K. A. *The vital balance*. New York: Viking, 1963.

MENNINGER, W. C. Individualization in the prescription for nursing care of the psychotic patient. *J. Amer. Med. Assoc.*, 1936, 106, 756–761.

WOLBERG, L. R. *The technique of psychotherapy*. New York: Grune & Stratton, 1954.

WROBEL, A. M. Roles of the music therapist in the open institution. In E. H. Schneider (Ed.), *Music therapy 1962*. Lawrence, Kan.: Allen Press, 1963. Pp. 43–49.

21

MUSIC AND CREATIVE ART THERAPIES
IN A HOSPITAL SETTING

MYRTLE FISH THOMPSON

This report outlines the main divisions of a music therapy program in a hospital setting and the broad concepts on which it is based. Case histories are then presented. Work done in the clinical center (music therapy workshops) stresses participation in individual lessons and practice, in small ensembles (coached and uncoached), and in large choral and instrumental groups. The purposes are to stimulate the interest of patients in music as a meaningful cultural activity and to direct their energies into making music for enjoyment, satisfaction, and growth toward health. Socialization values lie in the pleasure of being together, doing things together, and learning to share esthetic experiences with others. A sense of achievement and feelings of self-worth fortify the ego, whereas the discipline of belonging to a group requires personal organization and the recognition and acceptance of reality goals.

Music activities carried on elsewhere in the hospital involve performances by patients and personnel. These are used for entertainment on the wards, parties, and community sings and dances in the auditorium. Background music is supplied for administrative functions and meetings of various professional departments. Suitable music is provided for weekly religious services. Such out-of-clinic activities serve to enhance the prestige of the patients who perform and tend to broaden their interests.

Demonstration programs of music workshop activities are used frequently as an orientation for professional trainee groups in the hospital. These demonstrations describe the program—its goals and its problems —and participation in them affords patients considerable pride. When patients are taken into the community to entertain, they are almost invariably a credit to the hospital in behavior and performance. They illustrate to many kinds of club and church groups that patients are people. Sharing in the social hours at the meetings of these groups increases the patients' ease and security in functioning outside the hospital.

Large group performances for holidays, special patient events, and an annual music and art department show are used to involve patients of many types and levels of skill in music and allied arts (scenery, dancing, dramatics, and management). Patients work with staff personnel in planning and coaching these shows. By-products of these activities, both in and out of the workshop, frequently include reduction of bitterness and brooding, improved concentration, better attitudes, a feeling of relationship with other patients in the hospital, and participation in activities typical of the world outside the hospital. The shows serve as a bridge for returning to the community and afford a richer way of life for those who must remain hospitalized.

Case Histories

CATEGORY I

Talented patients with professional training and experience who have little hope of discharge. Principle: *Use what is healthy in each individual to maintain his best level of behavior and enjoyment.*

Case 1. F and B, both males past middle age, are excellent pianists. F, divorced, had switched from clerical work to selling and eventually to entertaining in a night club. In 1937 his father committed him with a problem of acute alcoholism. Discharged in 1942, he was unable to keep from drinking and returned voluntarily in 1947, with gradual onset of Korsakoff's psychosis. He has adjusted well to hospital routine and seems to find his greatest pleasure in playing for patients.

B entered the hospital as a voluntary patient in 1947 and has remained as a committed patient since 1949. His original diagnosis of psychoneurosis, mixed type, was changed in 1956 to manic-depressive reaction. His brother, the dean of men at a small teachers college, visited the patient frequently at first and tried to help him reestablish himself outside, but now he seldom visits. B had been a fairly successful musician, secretary of his local chapter of the musicians' union, and well known in the entertainment field. He carried on other business with some success —first as a clerical worker for a trust company and later with a real estate concern. Subsequently, he free-lanced in real estate but not successfully. Prior to hospitalization, B had a history of constant somatic complaints. These complaints have continued, although careful examination has not substantiated any physical cause. It was believed that an unsuccessful common-law marriage left B with strong feelings of guilt and inadequacy, leading to two reported attempts at suicide.

F and B form an excellent two-piano team that is acclaimed throughout the hospital. They play for community singing, are the backbone of the dance orchestra, and serve in innumerable ways for the entertainment of patients and personnel. Both patients thrive on this recognition. Patient F maintains a fair degree of acceptance of hospital life as long as he is allowed to play the piano. However, there has been a gradual increase in the symptoms of his malady. Patient B has suffered consistently recurring cycles of deep depression and what he reports as agonizing pain.

Here, then, are two long-term patients with unusual musical talent: F is lyric and very facile in arpeggio and broken-chord patterns; B has a strong rhythmic thrust, full of originality. Each has failed in facing the world outside, but each has gained recognition in the hospital community and finds genuine pleasure and satisfaction in serving it.

Case 2. Patients C and D are middle-aged women and are capable pianists. Although they prefer classical and serious concert music, both improvise well and each has her own style. C has been diagnosed as having schizophrenic reaction, catatonic type. She has been in private hospitals several times and has been a patient in this hospital since the early 1940s. She came to the music department in 1948 as a volunteer worker on outpatient status and was assigned to assist with ward programs. Her outpatient status did not last, because of promiscuous sexual involvement that led to bizarre, destructive behavior. During many months, she was confined to the continued treatment wards. After being transferred to an active-treatment ward, she was reassigned to music therapy. She took part enthusiastically in the music program, practiced, played in piano ensembles, sang in the church choir, and occasionally played the organ and entertained on the wards under supervision. In the late 1950s, a volunteer teacher helped in rebuilding her self-esteem by taking her to play in local music clubs where she was able, with the help of tranquilizers, to maintain a graceful and dignified composure. She played in New York City for the National Association for Music Therapy. During the last fifteen years, this patient has shown an increasingly short attention span and a growing tendency to be self-centered. Although she still plays well technically, she has lost her earlier sensitivity. Nevertheless, C's music is one vital asset in which she finds comfort after her periods of disturbance.

D has retained her style, her good grooming, and a consistent interest in music, dance, and dramatics. Her illness is an affective reaction in which she has seemingly reached a nonpsychotic plateau. In spite of age and some deafness, she remains sensitive in musical taste and has intellectual curiosity in all the arts. She plays in small ensembles and occasionally for creative-dance groups. She is able to catch and match mood swings of soloists she is accompanying and has worked with foreign patients, helping them express themselves in their own folk music. She is invaluable in theater productions, both in acting and coaching.

In 1957 and 1958, she was considered for employment in the music therapy department. In each instance, she went into a manic episode when the time arrived for administrative action to be taken. The physicians believe that the idea of a job was too threatening for her to handle. She has many privileges and enough money and family to have pleasant times outside the hospital. She is consistently quiet and reserved and seems to be accepting her role as a long-term patient.

CATEGORY II

Learners at various levels who will probably be long-term patients. Principles: *Keep patients alert and develop new horizons of interest that will build healthy attitudes.*

Case 3. E is a male patient, single, and in his early thirties. He is diagnosed as having schizophrenic reaction, undifferentiated, with some birth injury suspected. His intelligence is normal. After two previous commitments in private institutions, he was transferred to this public hospital. He is eccentric in behavior and appearance. He stammers and is easily excited to argument, at which time he is suspicious, repetitious, and resistant to reasoning. His father is dead. His mother is neurotic and presently lives on the West Coast; she rarely contacts the patient.

E began xylophone lessons in 1955 at his own request. He came to lessons regularly, practiced earnestly, and learned to play several familiar melodies. He refused wrist-loosening exercises and ultimately dropped the activity when his mental and physical rigidity kept him from progressing. He took part in several shows but was usually disgruntled because the parts he could handle were not important enough. He attended music appreciation sessions and turned in several well-written reports. He started violin lessons in 1962 and has continued them. He is attentive and open to suggestions. An earlier exaggerated dread of physical contact, such as is necessary to teach beginners to handle an instrument, has lessened considerably. He is working with less tension and more concentration and is able to respond to occasional bits of humor. However, his antisocial behavior, although less bizarre, still continues. Because it is likely that he will be a long-term patient, it is planned to prepare him to take part with others in music activities. This is something constructive for him to do and should give him some sense of belonging.

Case 4. Z is a middle-aged married woman who has little chance of leaving the hospital. Her diagnosis when committed was schizophrenic reaction with paranoid trends. She is friendly and loquacious except that she is constantly arguing with the hospital staff about their not "letting" her go home. After several years of hospitalization, it is obvious that her husband intends to leave her here. Married children send her nice clothing, but their visits are increasingly more rare and she dwells constantly on the "injustice" of her commitment. She entered the hospital ten years ago with paranoid ideas and hallucinations reported by her family. She was assigned to the music department, sang with the choir and in show choruses, and has taken part in many dance activities.

Z also enjoys play acting, speech-dynamics classes, and oil painting. Although she had not had previous training, she has turned out canvases prolifically since the art classes started in 1956. They are acceptable enough to be framed and hung in several places in the hospital. Although they are all copies, they show her own mark of individuality. She works fast, with concentration, and takes instruction well. She is inclined to be possessive about her work and to hoard it rather than have it displayed. But once she has acquiesced to its display, she is proud and pleased. She is sometimes secretive about signing her canvases. She consistently directs recognition of her skill in painting to the focus of "going home," however unsuitable the occasion for discussing it.

Z is a valued ward worker and is always willing to help in any department project. Presently, she is quite proud of being the choir secretary, a job in which she is very efficient. Even though none of these activities compensates enough to keep her happy about having to remain in the hospital, they fill her time in constructive ways. She seems to exist in a fairly contented manner as long as she is active.

Case 5. G is a fifty-five-year-old single male with schizophrenic reaction, undifferentiated type, who has consistently been an introvert since he left college during his freshman year. He lived alone for years, rarely bothering to dress. However, at some time he learned to play the violin fairly well. When he was assigned to music early in 1958, he was very confused, would tolerate no conversation, and preferred playing alone, without accompaniment. As he lost fearfulness, he began to enjoy weekly sessions of duets with an elderly male volunteer violinist. Through this, he was first drawn into small ensembles and later into orchestra. By 1960, he would play violin duets with other violinists in the department. The biggest musical hurdle, beyond his reticence, was a tendency to race tempo and skip measures and entire sections in a frenzied way. Constant efforts by staff members plus the experience of playing with groups helped him develop steadiness. He has participated in many programs. Gradually, he began to respond to, and occasionally even initiate, conversation; he has also developed the ability to make choices.

G has a strong will. When he refuses to take part in some activity, nothing will move him. Occasionally, he has accepted an invitation to join folk dancing, but he has refused every other form of dance movement, even morning relaxation exercises. He seems at home now in the department, although he continues to be seclusive. He absolutely refuses to leave the hospital grounds to do programs.

CATEGORY III

Short-term patients with talent and professional experience who have been helped toward discharge by music activities while in the hospital. Principle: *Help develop skills that either will assist patients avocationally when they return to the community or lessen their anxiety through gratifying activity while they are hospitalized.*

Case 6. J, a thirty-three-year-old Negro, was admitted in 1958 with paranoid personality characteristics and a drinking problem. He was placed on convalescent leave after eight months' hospitalization and was discharged in absentia in 1959. He was separated from his wife who had returned to France with their three children. He played saxophone, flute, trumpet, and piano, and organized, led, and managed professional popular combo groups. He had some success making recordings abroad but did not succeed well in the United States. J reported that his wife took little notice of the pressures on him and his resultant fatigue. He also reported that their problems, caused by racial differences, became acute in this country. Debts increased, as did his nervous restlessness, drinking, and depression.

At the hospital, J regained self-esteem. He was active and helpful as an entertainer and stimulated other patients to participate in jam sessions. Although inclined to be a little arrogant and demanding at first, he overcame this type of behavior as he earned recognition for his talents. Besides helping himself, he helped many other patients.

J did composing and arranging while in the music clinic. He wrote a suite and was able to accept guidance in transcribing from piano to score. He recorded this composition while on pass from the hospital. Later, on longer leave, he kept in touch with the department, came to play his record for friends in the clinic, and also brought his band to give an auditorium concert. At that time, his doctor reported that he had adjusted well and had not been drinking and that no paranoid ideas could be elicited from him. The medical comment on his discharge mentioned the considerable help J had found in using music facilities to rehabilitate himself.

Case 7. K was an attractive, blonde, twenty-seven-year-old single girl who worked in the music and art department of the hospital for five years after a short previous commitment in a state hospital. Her parents were divorced, and the patient lived with her mother and stepfather. The stepfather was good to her but died the year before her hospitalization. The patient's mother was unstable, highly neurotic, and immature. K was shallow, childish, vain, aggressive, and quick-tempered. Diagnosed as schizophrenic, chronic undifferentiated type, she spent two periods in the hospital. During the first, she had a series of electroshock treatments and, later, insulin-coma therapy but was reported to have shown little improvement. A lobotomy in 1955 was apparently successful, although her emotional controls remained obviously weak.

In addition to being physically attractive, she had unusual talents, which had been exploited by her mother when she was a child, as both a dancer and singer. She was used in several hospital shows, although often in secondary parts to help control her tendency toward prima-donna behavior. She sang in the church choir. K received extended passes and became increasingly irregular in attending music activities. She stopped her vocal lessons and was not inclined to be involved with performance obligations on the wards. However, she came frequently to visit the music department while on pass. She was discharged in 1956 after a series of extended passes. She was readmitted in 1957 after having lost a premature baby. She remained hospitalized until she received an extended pass in 1961.

This discharge had better results. As she became absorbed in the community, her freedom from the hospital seemed to give her a healthy independence. She lived away from her mother and was given support by volunteers who had heard her sing both at the hospital and on programs presented in the community by the hospital music department. Through these contacts, she was hired as a paid church soloist. In 1962, she married; she now seems to be secure within her family and community.

Case 8. Patient L, fifty-four, was an avocational violinist of professional caliber who was employed by the state in mimeophotostatic work. He remained in the hospital for only a few months in 1956. He had been married for twenty years and was devoted to his wife who had had three manic-depressive episodes. The wife also suffered from Parkinson's disease. There were no children.

L was never very interested in his work but enjoyed his music activities. He played regularly with two symphony orchestras, taught violin at home, and played wherever possible in small chamber groups. On admission, he was euphoric, showed flights of ideas, and was delusional and overactive. After electroshock treatments, he was assigned to the music department, where he was allowed to participate in all the music activities he enjoyed. He was particularly grateful for the atmosphere of interest in cultural things. His hours in music were devoid of the pressures of his wife's illness and the job in which he was not interested. Through his acknowledgment of the talent of others, his own euphoric tendencies came into more realistic focus. He organized his time, his activitiy was structured, and there was sufficient goal demand to keep him alert.

CATEGORY IV

Short-term patients who were learners at various levels and who felt they were helped toward recovery by music activities. Principles: *Stimulate avocational interests, fortify self-esteem, establish good work habits, and provide socialization.*

Case 9. M was in his early thirties; his diagnosis was schizophrenic reaction, chronic undifferentiated type. He had several short periods of hospitalization, during which he showed marked, though gradual, progress. In his first hospitalization, he was tense, anxious, confused, and slow in responses and did not exhibit feelings of self-worth. He froze when confronted with problems. Although he stated that he wanted to learn music and was conscientious in practice, he was slow because of his nervousness and self-abnegation. He was helped by a second, longer hospitalization, so that he was able to participate in several activities with ease. He has become interested in music fundamentals and theory and has learned to play the saxophone well enough to perform solos. In piano, he is at the grade-2 level.

M has used the activities of music and art to good advantage in developing a sense of security. His tenseness seems to have disappeared in a relaxed, friendly acceptance of his rightful place in activities and in the friendships he has formed. His self-assurance seems to be well established. Presently, he is on a long pass preliminary to discharge.

Case 10. N, in his late twenties, has no psychosis but is a drug addict. He is neat, pleasant, and well poised. His reserved manner, at times, makes him seem seclusive. N began drugs as an escape from depression over the onset of tuberculosis, which is now arrested. His present health is listed as good.

N entered the hospital voluntarily early in 1960, remaining only a few weeks. When out on pass, he reverted to his addiction and returned in May, 1960, evincing a sincere intention to conquer his habit. He was certain that his remission was caused by leaving the hospital too soon. N accomplished an amazing amount of learning while in the hospital. He began guitar lessons and practiced diligently. He became skillful enough to play with a group after three months. In piano, his therapist found him to be an eager and rapid learner.

N also took bassoon lessons. He is reported to have been persevering, able to practice independently, amenable to guidance, and ambitious. All his therapists remarked about his tendency to work quietly, but they felt there was no reticence when he needed to communicate about his lessons. His questions were always good. He expressed apprecation of the music skills he had acquired, stating that they would help avoid further trouble with his addiction after his discharge.

Part VI

MUSIC THERAPY
FOR GERIATRIC PATIENTS

Ruth Boxberger
Vance W. Cotter

The music therapist must play different roles from time to time with different patients, but his proper role with geriatric patients, in most cases, will be to act as an affectionate and respectful son or daughter. This is because geriatric patients, perhaps more than any others, suffer the loss of prestige and status they once had. The social position of the elderly is greatly changed today and is often resented because the elderly remember that they, in their younger days, did not place their aged relatives in institutions; they personally took care of them. Music and attention can bring much gratification and sense of worth to the old. The music of their youth and rhythmical participation are highly restorative and satisfactory and help the old once again to take a larger and more functional role in life.

22

THE GERIATRIC PATIENT

RUTH BOXBERGER
VANCE W. COTTER

Introduction

The status and disposition of the aged in the United States has changed significantly in the last several generations. Increase in medical knowledge and skill in treatment have kept alive many who would have died previously. Antibiotics and the more efficient handling of vascular diseases are two common examples of these advances. Two medical terms —*gerontology* and *geriatrics*—rarely heard in the past are now well known even by laymen.

There have also been social changes in our society directly concerning the aged. In times past, these aged—the *grand*parents—were sources of knowledge and advice. Less and less is this so. Knowledge increases so rapidly that much of the information and know-how of the old is useless, and modern man must look to other sources. This loss of status is keenly felt by old people who remember the respect accorded the elderly in their own younger days. Such loss of status is often damaging to their outlook on life, with consequent behavior changes.

Not so long ago, most American families would have felt disgraced had they placed their elderly relatives in the care of strangers. Many families would never have done it under any circumstances. This feeling of profound disgrace or lack of decent filial obligation has changed in marked degree. For one thing, houses are no longer two-family homes—there is room for only one family. And, anyway, the rest home provides better care—more professional care—than the children or grandchildren can give. Nevertheless, many elderly people cannot help but remember the care and respect for the aged seen in their childhood and young adulthood.

Thus, social changes and, often, lack of knowledge have so affected the lives of many old people that they are overcome by feelings of worthlessness, not being wanted, not being loved, and resentment. Their problems, in such cases, seem to be more psychological than physiological.

Many times, there is a complex of the psychological and the physiological. In any event, the music therapist will most often be successful sincerely playing the role of a respectful and affectionate son or daughter.

With the increase in the proportion of older people in our population, there is a growing awareness of the problems of aging. This awareness is evident at local, state, and national levels. At the local level, there are rest homes and similar domiciles and an increasing number of community health centers; at the state level, there are geriatric wards and like provisions. Growing concern at the national level in the problems of the aged is shown clearly by the White House Conference on Aging in 1961, the revised Kerr-Mills act, and the social security amendments of 1965, more commonly known as the Medicare program.

Statistical projections indicate 1975 as the date when persons over sixty-five will represent 9.3 percent of the population of the United States or approximately twenty million people (Landsman, 1965). The phenomenon of an aging population has produced a need for intensive study in the areas of gerontology and geriatrics. Barron (1961) defines the former as the "systematic multidisciplinary study of the patterns and meanings of aging," and the latter as "those techniques that aim to control and reduce its problem aspects" (p. 269). According to the 1960 census, 24 percent of the total first admissions to mental hospitals in the United States were patients sixty-five years of age and older. At the end of 1960, persons in this age group comprised about 30 percent of the total public mental-hospital patient population. The rate of admissions of persons sixty-five and older has been decreasing at a time when the number of persons of this age in the general population has been increasing (Landsman, 1965). The rapid development of nursing-home beds during the past ten years may have played a significant part in the reduction in the admission of older patients (Davis, 1963).

The Aging

True old age takes place when the individual loses the resources for self-maintenance in his society and the ability to carry out his socioeconomic functioning (Goldfarb, 1961; Ford, 1962). Beard (1959) reported that recent research findings in the fields of biology, medicine, nutrition, psychology, and sociology raise doubts about some earlier assumptions regarding old age. Economic, social, and psychological factors also can determine the appearance and change of symptoms of senescence. The opinion that old age is a period of inactivity until death (because of organic damage) is considered now to be invalid. The decline and deterioration of life functions originally were believed to be mainly organic, but

Meerloo (1953) and Kruzen (1954) have indicated that there is a close relationship between psychological functions and environmental influences in the production of symptoms in the geriatric patient. "Society doesn't invest in the older person because he has no future. Each older person as a member of civilization naturally has this same attitude. As he grows older, he begins to feel depreciated—and actually to depreciate as a result" (Weinberg, 1961, p. 19).

The adjustments that older persons make are related to the patterns of living they have developed in the past. Weinberg (1961) has made it clear that

. . . mental illness in aged persons is not hopeless any more than at any other time of life. And whether an aged person's mental disease is organic or functional, his behavior during his illness will be determined by his character throughout life. If he has emotional difficulties throughout life, they will be multiplied by advancing years (p. 17).

Wolff (1957) seemed to be in complete agreement when he stated:

The person who has always had emotional equilibrium will tend to retain it in old age. The person who has had only superficial control of his aggressive and destructive drives will suffer more emotional disturbance when the powers of emotional control break down in old age. . . . The life pattern of the individual will be important in determining whether his reaction to stress will be withdrawal, suspicion, irritability, hostility, depression, and rage, or one of the more adaptive defenses (p. 103).

Individuals' roles in life become so much a part of them that they break down when faced with the erosion, as they grow older, of the roles that have previously satisfied them. They may be too rigid to be able to transfer their energies to a new mode of functioning because they are vague as to the roles they should play.

However, it is quite certain that organic deterioration will alter the physical and verbal behavior of the geriatric patient. General arteriosclerosis, cerebral arteriosclerosis, and senile brain disease are conditions that play an important part in the production of symptoms. All organs and tissues are weakened or damaged to a certain extent because of the variation or partial cessation of the circulation of the blood supply (Wolff, 1957). Behavioral symptoms such as disorientation in one or more spheres (time, person, place), memory loss for recent events, impairment of sight and hearing, defective judgment, and lowered efficiency in performance resulting from brain damage were described by Wolff (1957) and Ginzburg (1953). Weinberg (1961) said that "personal habits decline, . . . attention wavers often," and the individual "may become irritable or jealous or even engage in violent acts. Sleeplessness and restlessness also are frequent" (p. 18).

"Emotional instability" and a "diminished rapport with reality" are expressions often used to describe the behavior of the geriatric patient. Research by Vinson (1961) demonstrated that there was no significant difference in the psychological test scores of geriatric patients with and those without organic brain disease. Rorschach-test results show the patients to be capable of testing reality although they are emotionally labile. Barad, Altshuler, and Goldfarb (1961), in a survey of dreams of older persons, reported that "the findings leave little doubt that the aged person is capable of sensitive emotional response even in the presence of organic brain damage" (p. 42). The ability to learn certain types of material also appears to decline with old age. Experimental and industrial studies indicate that older people are helped by the activity method of learning. Rigidity in thought and behavior also is apparent (Crown and Heron, 1964).

From an intensive study of admissions to a large metropolitan hospital, the following patterns emerged. The basis for admission was the exhibition of behavior described as excited, noisy, depressed, restless, suicidal, delusory or hallucinatory. About 27.5 percent had moderate to severe physical disabilities. Only about 15 percent conformed to the general stereotype of the elderly psychiatric patient who manifests confusion, memory loss, or incoherence. Approximately 60 percent displayed some form of chronic brain syndrome (cerebral arteriosclerosis, senile brain disease, and so forth), whereas about 32 percent suffered from functional disorders. Many of the patients who were admitted had histories of prior mental disturbance. About one-third of these first admissions were returned to the community, about one-third died within three months, and about one-third received prolonged care for an average period of less than five years (Stratton and Barton, 1964).

Reports on the rehabilitation of elderly patients are in agreement that comprehensive planning is required if optimum results are to be secured in meeting their needs. Some form of psychotherapy, group or individual, is recommended, but the treatment goals and techniques are different for older people. Reconstruction therapy cannot be expected to succeed with aged patients, but the ventilation of pent-up feelings, the overcoming of a sense of isolation, and the reevaluation of previous goals can be achieved (Freedman and Bressler, 1963). Therapy for the aged is supportive therapy (Kastenbaum, 1963).

A comprehensive treatment program for the aged should be based on both somatic and dynamic motivational factors. Individual therapy, group therapy, and pharmacology should be employed (Wolff, 1963; Kent, 1963), and desirable activity should be encouraged, as well as retraining for increased self-care (Kent, 1963; Eaton and Wittion, 1962). Goals of treatment include reeducation to bolster the patient's skills and assets, improving his self-concept by increasing memory span and ability to concentrate, and adding to his self-esteem and feeling of dignity through the establishment of good interpersonal relationships. "The recognition and the application of the therapeutic use of self is one of the most important factors in treatment, especially with aged persons" (Goldfarb, 1961, p. 19).

It is of great importance for trained personnel to recognize that aged people, although esteeming the filial attitude of the therapists, may at times regard them as parental figures, rejecting or benevolent; teachers, providing information and developing skills; friends and allies, initiating activities of interest; or advocates, planning for increased pleasure and comfort in their surroundings (Freedman and Bressler, 1963; Goldfarb, 1963). There is some evidence that volunteers such as college students are particularly suited to helping rehabilitate chronic patients (Cohen, 1963). Older people are most secure when a mutually supportive and intermingled relationship is established between old and young (Kaplan, 1962). The dutiful son or daughter role is most often effective.

A geriatric patient is considered rehabilitated when he is discharged from the hospital with some of his emotional needs fulfilled and a program planned for his personal growth and development that will strengthen his inhibited, scattered, or underdeveloped creative powers (Wolff, 1964). A nursing home may serve as a facility for patients discharged from a mental institution or as a place to go to initially, instead of a mental hospital. With the emphasis on community health centers rather than on secluded public mental hospitals, the nursing home will, no doubt, play an increasingly important role in the treatment and care of aged psychiatric patients.

The present trend of thought emphasizes the desirability of treatment for old people who are emotionally unstable or who demonstrate a diminished rapport with reality, even though organic impairment does exist. Experimental evidence reinforces this trend. Music has proved to be very useful in the treatment of the geriatric patient.

The Use of Music with Geriatric Patients

Music is well suited to the treatment of geriatric patients because of the gratification and socialization that may result from creative experiences with it. The nonverbal stimulus of simple rhythm is very effective with patients who have a diminished rapport with reality. Andrus (1955), after an eleven-month study, stated,

Rhythmics, an essential part of the program, was designed to reactivate enjoyment of bodily movement, to provide remedial work for the skeleto-muscular problems so frequent in old age, and to effect reconditioning in motor functions. It also provides an avenue of expression on the nonverbal level (p. 433).

There are differences in rhythmical response at different age levels. Roth (1961) presented evidence of a significant difference in the performance of a psychomotor task (tapping) by an older group (aged sixty to seventy-five) as compared to a younger group (aged thirty to thirty-five). The older group proved to be less flexible in following deviations from their habitual tapping speed. Wells (1954) has placed special emphasis on the value of rhythm bands for geriatric patients, reporting marked improvements. The patients seemed more alert, were less incontinent, increased in mobility, and improved in personal appearance.

In addition to rhythm, singing, and listening, other activities should be employed to encourage individualistic responses by the patients. "Music therapy should be used as an outlet for the creative impulses of older people" (Donahue, 1954, p. 125). Wallin (1962) stressed the need for individualization in the psychological, educational, and social adjustment of the aged because of the great individual differences among them. Interesting and creative activities that are rewarding may result in a rejuvenation and re-creation of behavior.

Music is essentially a group phenomenon, even during individual participation; it has sociocultural overtones that cannot be escaped. Taking part in a musical activity generally expresses a willingness to participate as an equal. Consequently, isolation and hostility are either not present, or at a minimum. Music is nonverbal in its expression; it links but does not divide. These are the qualities in music that make it an ideal agent for social integration (Dreikurs, 1954, p. 19).

When group singing has been used with senile psychotic patients, the patients seemed to enjoy most those folk songs with which they were acquainted. Because of the patients' short attention spans, music used occasionally and for only a short time was most effective. It was concluded that the activity was a pleasurable experience and resulted in increasing group cohesiveness. A positive atmosphere of sociability and entertainment was noted, and the cleanliness, morale, and general behavior of the patients seemed to improve.

Hall (1957) reported on a six-week ward program involving twenty-five ambulatory female patients. Musical activities included singing, dancing, rhythm band, and listening to recorded music. Some patients who had exhibited indifference, hostility, and resentment to people and objects pertaining to the ward situation showed positive behavioral changes during the series of music sessions. The entertainment aspect, personal attention, and anticipation of the daily music sessions were considered to be responsible for the behavioral changes. It was suggested that the psychological and physical needs of the patients were met and that frequent contact and communication with the therapist were necessary for best results.

Altshuler (1960) described a therapeutic procedure that placed hyperactive patients in one group and hypoactive patients in another. Musical activities used were singing, walking, dancing, and mild gymnastics to music. The treatment goals in each session were to establish a setting in which an atmosphere of warmth, acceptance, calmness, and tenderness was present and in which nearly total participation and engendered spontaneity led to enjoyment. All behavior that was appropriate to the musical situation was recognized promptly and positively reinforced with encouragement. The main musical rhythm used with the geriatric patients was steady, simple, and direct. Syncopated rhythm was avoided. A test, in which each patient's normal walking speed was recorded, was utilized to establish a mean tempo. Largo, adagio, andante, and moderato were the tempi most welcome on the geriatric ward. The tone color of stringed instruments was preferred to that of brass and percussion. Favorable listening response was observed when the music was soft, melodious, and familiar and the selections not too long.

Hart (1960) utilized a variety of music activities in a nursing home. Treatment goals were to promote creativity, self-esteem, group interest, and cooperation. Increased interest was inferred from the anticipation, participation, and enjoyment evident in the patients' behavior.

Four 45-minute music sessions were scheduled each week for nine weeks. Activities initiated were group singing, rhythm band, group listening, and guest entertainment. Group singing was the most difficult activity to establish. Perhaps because of past experiences, the only songs the patients wanted to sing were hymns. Four sessions were held before they began to request songs and participate freely in the singing. Although the rhythm-band activity was not expected to be looked on with favor, the response was enthusiastic. To some extent, this may have been because the instruments were constructed by the patients with the help of some junior high school volunteers.

Group listening was always well received, and there were numerous requests. The music appeared to stimulate conversation because of past associations with familiar melodies. This activity was especially valuable to the patients because spontaneity of conversation broke down the stereotyped behavior and topics of conversation that had persisted for so long a time. Guest entertainers came to the home once each week. During these visits, the patients tried to look their best and extended a warm reception to their guests. They considered two programs outstanding: first, that of a student who did chalk drawings interpreting the music that was played; and second, that provided by a girl from Hawaii who played the ukulele and sang songs from the Islands.

No important changes in the patients were reported, although the manager and staff said that the patients looked forward to the musical activities and enjoyed participating in them. During a follow-up visit six months later, the music therapist discovered that patients who had not participated in the activities commented about them (Chachere, 1966).

Studies by Cotter (1960), Griffin (1959), and Kurz (1960) demonstrated that planned recorded music and participation in music activities had a beneficial effect on the behavior of geriatric patients. From the data, which were statistically evaluated, the following results were noted: an increase in appropriate behavior, reduced aggression, less physical and verbal reaction to hallucination, reduction of frequency in incontinency, greater interest in musical activities, improvement in personal appearance, and a lowering of the level of undesirable patient noise. Ward personnel commented favorably on music activities for the patients.

Although the role of the music therapist with a geriatric patient may be somewhat different from his role with other patients and the techniques must fit the individual patient, the broad aim of music therapy must still be to help the patient change his behavior so he once more takes a real role in life to his fullest potential. He needs to be persuaded and assisted to develop a more creative life, cultivate new interests, engage in new activities, and reestablish the necessary bonds with society. In such a creative life resides the greatest contentment. Geriatric patients need assistance *to learn* (in the best sense) *to grow old instead of merely becoming old.*

References

ALTSHULER, I. M. The value of music in geriatrics. In E. H. Schneider (Ed.), *Music therapy 1959.* Lawrence, Kan.: Allen Press, 1960. Pp. 109–115.

ANDRUS, RUTH. Personality change in an older group. *Geriatrics*, 1955, *10*, 432–435.

BARAD, M., ALTSHULER, K., and GOLDFARB, A. I. A survey of dreams in aged persons. *Arch. gen. Psychiat.*, 1961, *4*, 4, 19–62.

BARRON, M. L. *The aging American: an introduction to social gerontology and geriatrics.* New York: Crowell, 1961.

BEARD, BELLE B. The relation of sociological to biological research in gerontology. *Geriatrics*, 1959, *14*, 655–657.

CHACHERE, ANN HART. Personal communication, 1966.

COHEN, E. S. Nursing homes, state hospitals, and the aged mentally ill. *Geriatrics*, 1963, *18*, 871–872.

COTTER, V. W. Effects of the use of music on the behavior of geriatric patients. Unpublished master's thesis, Univer. of Kansas, 1960.

CROWN, SHEILA M., and HERON, A. Psychological aspects of aging in man. *Ann. Rev. Psychol.*, 1964, *15*, 417–441.

DAVIS, J. E. Evaluation and planning for the elderly psychiatric patient. *Geriatrics*, 1963, *18*, 238–241.

DONAHUE, WILMA. The challenge of growing older. In Mariana Bing (Ed.), *Music therapy 1953*. Lawrence, Kan.: Allen Press, 1954. Pp. 119–126.

DREIKURS, R. The dynamics of music therapy. In Mariana Bing (Ed.), *Music therapy 1953*. Lawrence, Kan.: Allen Press, 1954. Pp. 15–23.

EATON, M. T., and WITTION, C. L. Treatment of aged psychiatric patients: resignation versus restoration. *Geriatrics*, 1962, *17*, 229–234.

FORD, H. How to approach a geriatric patient. *Geriatrics*, 1962, *17*, 110–115.

FREEDMAN, J. H., and BRESSLER, D. M. A general hospital's geriatrics outpatient clinic. *Ment. Hosp.*, 1963, *14*, 328–330.

GINZBERG, R. Geriatric ward psychiatry. *Amer. J. Psychiat.*, 1953, *110*, 296–300.

GOLDFARB, A. I. Patient relationships in the treatment of aged persons. *Geriatrics*, 1961, *16*, 18–23.

GOLDFARB, A. I. Our goals for older patients—vitality or survival. *Ment. Hosp.*, 1963, *14*, 151–153.

GRIFFIN, J. E. The effects of a planned music program on habits of incontinency and interest in music activities of geriatric patients. Unpublished master's thesis, Univer. of Kansas, 1959.

HALL, DOROTHY. Music activity for the older patient. In E. T. Gaston (Ed.), *Music therapy 1956*. Lawrence, Kan.: Allen Press, 1957. Pp. 115–118.

HART, ANN. The development of a music therapy program in a convalescent home. In E. H. Schneider (Ed.), *Music therapy 1959*. Lawrence, Kan.: Allen Press, 1960. Pp. 116–120.

KAPLAN, J. New theories affecting geriatrics in social institutions. *Geriatrics*, 1962, *17*, 169–174.

KASTENBAUM, R. The reluctant therapist. *Geriatrics*, 1963, *18*, 296–301.

KENT, E. A. Role of admission stress in adaptation of older patients. *Geriatrics*, 1963, *18*, 133–138.

KRUZEN, F. H. Physical medicine and rehabilitation for the chronically ill. *J. Amer. Geriat. Soc.*, 1954, *2*, 75–85.

KURZ, C. E. The effects of a planned music program on the day hall sound level and personal appearance of geriatric patients. Unpublished master's thesis, Univer. of Kansas, 1960.

LANDSMAN, G. The role of research in community mental health planning for the aged. *Comm. ment. Hlth J.*, 1965, *1*, 144–148.

MEERLOO, J. D. M. Contributions of psychoanalysis to the problems of the aged. In M. Heiman (Ed.), *Psychoanalysis and social work*. New York: International Universities Press, Inc., 1953. Pp. 321–337.

ROTH, E. Lernen in verschiedenen altersstufen [Learning at different age levels]. *Z. exp. angew. Psychol.*, 1961, *8*, 409–417.

STRATTON, D., and BARTON, W. E. The geriatric patient in the public mental hospital. *Geriatrics*, 1964, *19*, 55–60.

VINSON, D. Objectivity in the assessment of psychobiologic decline. *Vita. Hum.*, 1961, *4*, 134–142.

WALLIN, J. E. W. The psychological, educational, and social problems of the aging as viewed by a mid-octogenarian. *J. genet. Psychol.*, 1962, *100*, 41–46.

WEINBERG, J. Reality altered. In Judy Bonner (Ed.), *The word is hope*. Austin, Tex.: Hogg Foundation, 1961. Pp. 17–19.

WELLS, A. Rhythmic activities on wards of senile patients. In Mariana Bing (Ed.), *Music therapy 1953*. Lawrence, Kan.: Allen Press, 1954. Pp. 127–132.

WOLFF, K. Definition of the geriatric patient. *Geriatrics*, 1957, *12*, 102–106.

WOLFF, K. Occupational therapy for the geriatric patient. *Geriatrics*, 1963, *18*, 247–250.

WOLFF, K. When is a geriatrics patient rehabilitated? *Ment. Hosp.*, 1964, *15*, 250–252.

23

MUSIC AS A MEANS TOWARD REVITALIZATION

Musical Activities for Geriatric Patients

MARY RYDER TOOMBS

Many different musical activities have been found useful in music therapy for geriatric patients. Listening to music on the wards effects a favorable response, particularly when the music is familiar or has a special meaning for the patients. Some of the best liked music includes standard Protestant hymns, Strauss waltzes, polkas, and songs such as those written by Stephen Foster. Patients appear to enjoy music most when it is played at a moderately low intensity level. Recordings are highly acceptable, and patients seem to like piano and guitar music more than that of other instruments.

Group singing is frequently used with these patients. Placing a single song on a sheet of stiff paper with the words printed in large type has proved to be very helpful; the single sheets keep patients from becoming confused and losing the place, as they do with a book of songs.

Another music activity used frequently with geriatric patients is the dance. The simplest forms of dance activity, that is, exercise dance movements within a circle formation, can be used with older persons. The dance movements usually consist of slow, swinging, or circular movements of the arms, legs, head, hands, or feet. More active geriatric patients, such as those in a manic stage, have been included in square dancing with other psychiatric patients. (Their physical condition had been ascertained prior to the activity.) On several occasions, different geriatric male patients responded to recorded waltzes by arising spontaneously from what appeared to be a dozing position to waltz with the therapist or a nearby female aide. Frequently they would sit down as soon as the music stopped. But sometimes the dancing of the waltz served as an icebreaker, and the patients would then converse freely with the music therapist or the aide with whom they had danced.

To offer variety, a rhythm band can be utilized. The rhythm band could be the activity for one session, group singing for the next (two days later), and dancing for the third (again, two days later). This approach—using rhythm instruments alternately with other kinds of group participation in music—was believed to be the best means of meeting the needs of a ward of low-functioning men. If geriatric patients are physically able to play rhythm sticks, bells, drums, and so on, they usually enjoy this activity. If they cannot handle the instruments readily, a rhythm band may be only another frustrating and defeating experience unless careful, gentle aid is given. When rhythm-band experience is mixed with other music activities, patients who meet defeat or frustration in one frequently find rewarding satisfaction in another. Also, the pleasure gained in one activity may be great enough to transfer to another, until gradually a majority of the geriatric patients is at least making an effort to participate in all activities.

Trained or talented musicians have been discovered in psychiatric hospitals, even among chronic, long-term schizophrenic patients and institutionalized geriatric patients, male and female. Many of these older people function at their highest level in a performing group or ensemble. Two of the following case reports describe benefits to the trained musician. The other cases are typical of the use of music therapy with geriatric patients in general.

Case 1. *An elderly, depressed male patient in a state hospital was referred to music therapy on an individual or small-group basis. In the referral, the physician indicated that the patient had played the violin very well and had studied enough to sight-read music readily. Because this man was preoccupied with suicidal thoughts and guilt feelings about his wife's recent death, the therapist spent many sessions taking the violin to his bedside, talking with him about his interests, his family, and music. Gently but persistently, he was encouraged to play the violin again. Finally, the patient played a few strains, then some longer phrases. Eventually, he agreed to walk across the hospital grounds to the music therapy area to join three other male patients who also were violinists. The ensemble formed by these four violinists performed in church and on two other programs. Because of the advanced age of this particular patient and his heart condition, only antidepressant drugs, milieu therapy, and music therapy were prescribed for him. Music was a means of establishing rapport with this patient and assisting him to overcome his depression for a few hours each week.*

Case 2. *A geriatric patient described as manic-depressive was on industrial assignment to the music therapy department of a state hospital. In* addition to keeping the music department clean, he helped carry instruments and music stands to other areas of the hospital. He sang bass in the barbershop quartet, played baritone horn in the band, and sang in the church choir each Sunday. Even though his high energy level often was difficult for the music therapy staff to tolerate, he appeared to benefit greatly from his daily musical experiences and, in turn, contributed to the entire music therapy program.

Case 3. A geriatric patient on the admission ward of a Veterans' Administration hospital was referred for individual music therapy because he believed that if he worked on singing again, it would relieve some of his depressed feelings and help him gain better control of his emotions. Because he held strong religious beliefs, he was assigned to sing only spirituals or art songs with a spiritual theme. His breath control and tone quality were not as good as formerly because of his age, but he still sang with artistry. He often grew emotional while studying his songs; however, this behavior was accepted, and he was encouraged to resume singing when he felt like it. Frequently, he was critical of his singing and was eager for assistance from the therapist. At the close of his music lesson, he always expressed his appreciation for her help. He was hospitalized for only a short period and, therefore, was not asked to join any groups or give any performances. He was encouraged to rejoin his church choir when he returned home.

Case 4. A resident in psychiatry in a state hospital suggested an experimental listening project for a woman in her eighties who appeared very fragile and evidenced paranoid tendencies. Many different methods of treatment had been tried and failed. In some way, the psychiatrist had learned that the patient enjoyed Protestant hymns, and he requested the music therapist to work with the patient daily in a passive music listening session as a last-resort effort to make contact. The patient's primary symptoms were a preoccupation with thoughts of death and the constant reference to "being fed my children by those people on the ward." She had refused to feed herself for several months and was being forced to eat. A great deal of difficulty was encountered in bringing the patient to the music department and engaging her in the activity while she was there. Behavior during the music sessions included placing her fingers in her ears, mumbling about "trying to feed me my children," and wanting to leave before the period was over. During the music sessions, choral and instrumental versions of hymns were played on the phonograph. After several weeks of one-half hour sessions each day, she relaxed sufficiently to sit quietly and voluntarily in the music therapy listening room. Although she never *told the music therapist that she liked the music, she explained to ward aides that she had been to the music room to listen to hymns. When asked if she liked the music, she said yes. This was about a month after the sessions began. By this time, she was ready to go to the music room when the therapist arrived. Also, she had begun to eat regularly again and no longer expressed paranoid delusions about her food being her children.*

The music therapist probably needs to be more flexible in the approach used with geriatric patients than with psychiatric patients in any other age group. There is much that is unknown or uncertain about their behavior, and it cannot be predicted. Each new day may bring biological and emotional changes for the patients, and the speed at which these changes occur varies markedly. However, some general principles are suggested for the therapist who deals with geriatric patients.

1. Use gentle persuasion rather than firm insistence in getting them to join groups.
2. Use music that is familiar to, and liked by, the patients, in spite of the fact that it may seem monotonous or boring to the therapist.
3. Be as aware of the patients' physical and mental limitations as possible.
4. Modify music activities to meet the patients' limitations, and keep music periods short enough to maintain their attention. Allow the patients to take a catnap during listening sessions, but engage them in conversation when it is appropriate and they seem to want to talk.
5. Be firm with hyperactive patients for their own protection and for the general well-being of the group.
6. Expect and accept some lability or inconsistency in the patients' responses.

The applicable treatment goals listed below are vitally important in improving the health of geriatric patients.

1. *Socialization.* Through the influence of music in a group activity, the therapist can offer interaction with a staff member, another patient, or patients.
2. *Exercise.* Through simple body movement to music, one can help the patient maintain good circulation and muscle tone. These simple movements allow active patients the healthy exercise necessary for the dissipation of undue energy.
3. *Gratification.* Creative activity produces behavior that, when reinforced properly, may lead to a feeling of self-esteem.

4. *Contact with reality.* Music helps patients to either maintain contact with reality or make brief contacts with reality during the music sessions.
5. *Relief of self-concern.* During music sessions, the patients extinguish self-pity and concentration on somatic complaints.
6. *Development of group feeling.* Patients derive satisfaction and a sense of well-being from once more belonging to a group.

A Structured Music Therapy Program in Geriatrics

HERMINA EISELE BROWNE
RICHARD WINKELMAYER

This report describes a type of music therapy program for geriatric patients that has been developed at two different state institutions during the past sixteen years. Structured music therapy programs in these institutions were conducted on the wards and also in the music therapy building. Female and male patients were housed in separate quarters, as were ambulatory and nonambulatory patients. Music therapy sessions on the wards were held in day rooms that were well ventilated, comfortable, and pleasant. Some ambulatory patients participated in individual and group activities in the music therapy building.

Objectives were in keeping with the age and physical condition of the patients, and were similar to those of other therapeutic programs: to stimulate activity, relieve boredom, tranquilize the overactive, encourage self-help, provide an outlet for energy or frustration, and in general, raise the morale of the entire unit.

In both institutions, the format of these structured music therapy programs was quite similar. The activities were conducted at least once a week, and twice weekly when time and additional personnel were available. Each session started with group singing of selected familiar hymns, after which the patients were allowed to choose their favorites. All patients participated in this hymn sing, and various responses were observed—singing, humming, rocking, foot tapping, and handclapping. Next in favor came old ballads, some by Victor Herbert, others by Gilbert and Sullivan. A portable organ was used for accompaniment. The organ seemed far more effective than a piano for use with geriatric patients.

After the singing, the group listened to recordings. Music by Beethoven, Mozart, Mendelssohn, and Schubert appeared to elicit the most pleasurable responses. Complicated rhythms and structure were too much of a strain for sustained listening. Next came a rhythm session when some patients danced and others played rhythm instruments. If a patient showed no response, the therapist tried to induce some form of activity by offering him a rhythm instrument. The final part of the session—the singing of favorite songs—was designed to reduce the general level of excitement.

Patients were assigned to individual or small-group activities in order to stimulate their interests or to give them a sense of satisfaction in achievement. Frequently, patients requested an activity because of a special interest. The physician recommended or approved all assignments. A few geriatric patients were assigned to the music department for small-group activities such as rhythm band and choir. In both institutions, these elderly patients were regular in attendance and provided the nucleus of each group. Short-term patients also were assigned to these activities, but they came and left according to their treatment programs. This meant that the music used for the choir and rhythm band varied from time to time in accordance with ability, number, and interests of the group. Rehearsals were held in the music rooms of the department. The choir sang for church services in the auditorium and on wards at Easter and Christmas; the rhythm band presented programs for patients on various wards.

Individuals participating in music programs on the wards usually did so at their own request or with some prompting from fellow patients or personnel. Solo vocalists nearly always received a rousing reception even though their voices left much to be desired musically. Sometimes they forgot words and supplied their own, which provided much amusement for the group. Solo pianists were, in general, much better musicians, but they could only play music learned prior to their hospitalization and most of it was stereotyped and repetitious. While the vocalists sang, the ward group listened attentively; when pianists performed, they began to lose interest, talk among themselves, or do other things.

Ambulatory geriatric patients also attended music-appreciation sessions in the workshop, and many of them took part in the actual program. The group was composed of young and elderly patients with varying types and degrees of illness. A patient would be asked to read about a selected composer and then present the material at the next weekly meeting. Others would be asked, or might offer, to present some composition by this composer at that time. If necessary, patients were aided in their preparations so they might feel comfortable about appearing. These sessions began with group singing of familiar requests. Next, the speaker talked about the background and life of the composer, interpolating suitable musical selections at appropriate times. If necessary, the therapist added information at the conclusion of the talk. Then the group listened to selected recordings, followed by a general discussion of the music. Sessions were concluded with a short group sing. Older patients participated in the discussions more frequently and to a greater degree; the younger ones took part more often by singing or playing selected works. In some instances, the composer's affliction was discussed, as well as his way of overcoming it or even making it an asset. Attendance was voluntary.

The following cases are examples of individual participation in the music therapy program.

Case 1. A patient who was able to play "The Bluebells of Scotland" very beautifully was assigned by her physician for individual sessions in the music therapy department. At the time the assignment was made, she appeared disheveled and unclean (except when the aides bathed her). She was mute, listless, and inactive on the ward and ate little. It was necessary to escort her to and from the music therapy workshop. Lessons were brief at first, with no conversation by the patient. However, after two months with two lessons each week, she showed some progress in behavior, that is, she was neat and clean, usually ready to go with the therapist, began to converse, and asked pertinent questions about the music. Musically, there was no improvement beyond the first-grade level. However, she lost her apathy, talked about her home and family, mentioned other interests, and displayed a keen sense of humor. After two years, it was necessary to drop this patient from individual sessions because the department lacked a therapist. She took an assignment with the housekeeping department and has continued her progress toward more normal living. She also has made frequent visits to her home.

Case 2. J was first assigned to the music therapy department for small-group activities (choir and rhythm) and individual vocal lessons. Finally, he was assigned to music on a full-time basis so that he could be usefully occupied. He received no drugs or other treatment, and the music therapy department seemed the most likely place for therapeutic contact. Despite a state of confusion, irrelevant discourse, slouchy posture, and ambling gait, he was gentlemanly, neat and clean in appearance, and well spoken. He developed a keen interest in the work and was a staunch supporter of chorus, choir, and music appreciation. He accepted secondary roles in operettas and other musical shows. After watching a professional, he also learned how to repair piano keys and mechanisms. Because he was not permitted to use metal tools, he made the ones he needed out of wood, under supervision in the woodwork shop. When it appeared to him that most of the repair work was completed, he slyly and deliberately broke hammers and bridle straps so he could have something to do. It was explained to him that other patients damaged the pianos frequently and he would have plenty of work for some time to come. After this, there was no further need to check on him, and he continued this service for six or seven years.

In the structured-mood group, J was among the most helpful of the patients assigned to assist severely disturbed patients who were mute and uncooperative. He found the right pages in their song books and was gentle in helping them move their arms in the expressive-movement session. Months later, when the group was able to dance, he helped those who were fearful, hesitant, or rejected by others.

His paranoid tendencies became less marked and were evident only when he thought he was being neglected or left on the sidelines. Then he clowned, sang wrong notes, pitched his voice so low it was a grumble and no longer a tone, or began to discuss his former activities on the outside, such as being an important owner-manager of an umbrella factory or playing the violin. However, he could not play the violin, and no mention of a factory was made in his case history. J was placed on family care at the age of seventy-three. The therapist visited him in his new surroundings on several occasions and found that he had made a very good adjustment. The most recent visit, during his seventy-eighth year, found him in excellent health.

Case 3. L was a voluntary patient for the second time. Her first hospitalization was at age thirty-nine, and the second at age forty-three. On admission, however, her personality made her seem so much older than her chronological age that she was considered a geriatric case. She was classified both times as a schizophrenic, paranoid reaction. Hesitantly and anxiously she expressed a great desire to be accepted as a vocal student. "All my life I wanted to sing and never could be a member of a chorus because I had no proper clothes. We were too poor." She wanted lessons now in order to join the choir and chorus. A daily twenty-minute period was arranged, with the approval of the clinical director. Concurrently, she was also assigned to the commissary and occupational therapy.

L was told that the therapist could tell her what to do and show her how to do it, but that she would have to use much effort in order to learn to sing. She was a very apt pupil. The first job was to develop proper tone production; scales for pitch and breath control came a little later. For three months, she worked on the middle voice and then was allowed to sing alto with the choir. Her response was most gratifying. "This is the happiest day of my life, singing with a group." Continuing her instruction and participation in the choir, she gradually developed her true soprano voice and was then placed in the soprano section of choir and chorus. During the time L was in music therapy, she reverted to normal behavior for her age. She made tremendous strides in her rehabilitation efforts.

When it became time for her to plan for discharge, she discussed the possibility of having a vocal teacher in her local community. This was arranged, and appropriate plans were made for her to join a community chorus. After her discharge, she made immediate contact with the teacher and the chorus and began a series of readjustments toward normal living. For the chorus concerts she was required to wear evening gowns. She attended a course in dressmaking at the YWCA in order to save her brothers the expense of purchasing these gowns and, thereafter, made all her own clothes. Her brothers, feeling that she was making a special effort toward readjustment, decided to pay for her lessons on a twice-weekly basis.

Case Report

SALLY HENNEMAN BAIRD

S was a seventy-eight-year-old cardiac patient with occasional seizures, who had resided in the hospital for approximately thirty-five years. He did much grimacing, was often combative, and would yell and flail his arms at anyone who came too close to him. He was considered to be out of contact most of the time and was the only truly custodial case on a ward of elderly, chronic, regressed schizophrenic patients.

Group-singing sessions were conducted on the ward once a week for six months by the music therapist. When the ward sings first began, S would not participate but sat at the opposite end of the day hall. When invited to join the group, he either would begin to yell or would walk away. After approximately six weeks, S joined the group. He did not sing but sat with his head down during the entire hour. When given a song book, he threw it on the floor. As time went on, he consented to hold the song book but would participate in no other way. This behavior continued for the next few months.

The therapist, believing that a closer relationship with the patient might help modify his behavior during the group singing, frequently visited him in his ward. At first, S would not acknowledge her presence. Later, he would glance at her when she asked him to and finally would shake hands. Although S related in a negative and hostile manner, the fact remained that he did relate to another individual, and this was considered an improvement. At the end of the six months, he would walk up and down the day hall with the therapist.

After the group had met for approximately three months, the therapist observed the patient smiling while the group was singing "School Days." This song was included in each session thereafter, and the patient continued to smile each time it was sung. The entire group began to look forward to this time in the hour, would join the therapist in telling S they were singing the song for him, and would encourage him to sing with them. Finally, after nearly five months, S did sing "School Days." The younger and more alert patients cheered and clapped. This momentarily frightened S, but he continued to sing the song each week and would sometimes join in singing "Let Me Call You Sweetheart." Eventually he shared a song book with another patient, and only very rarely did he exhibit inappropriate behavior such as yelling or hitting.

The obvious treatment goal in this case was to encourage S to respond appropriately to his immediate environment. The group music situation itself, the special individual attention from the therapist, the permissive and matter-of-fact attitude, and the support given to S by other members of the group provided a nondemanding, nonthreatening atmosphere in which the patient acted in a socially acceptable manner.

Part VII

MUSIC THERAPY
AND MUSIC EDUCATION

E. Thayer Gaston

*M*usic therapy and music education are much more a part of each other than is commonly realized. Certainly the good music educator follows many of the principles and processes of music therapy stated in Part I, even though he may not have realized them completely. And just as certainly the good music therapist follows many of the practices of music education. Perhaps music therapy and music education can best be distinguished by the fact that the music therapist is chiefly concerned with eliciting changes in behavior, not with perfecting musical endeavor. The opposite is true of the music educator. Characteristics of patients nearly always differ significantly from those of students. The music therapist is more sensitive to the nonmusical behavior of the child, the music educator to the musical behavior of the child. Even so, music therapy and music education have much in common.

24

MUSIC IN THE
TREATMENT AND EDUCATION OF
EMOTIONALLY DISTURBED CHILDREN

ANNAMARY E. WILSON

Introduction

In the past few years, there has been a greater focus of interest by educators on the emotionally disturbed child. Emotionally disturbed children are those who have, in greater or lesser degree, serious problems with other people, particularly peers and authority figures such as parents and teachers. These children are unhappy and unable to apply themselves in a manner commensurate with their abilities and interests (Cohen, 1966). In order *to both treat and educate these children,* programs are expanding and developing at an increased rate. At the present time, this is largely a pioneer endeavor, comparable to the efforts begun toward education of the retarded child a few years ago. Reliable data in this field are scarce; research is inadequate; and we can only look to occasional pilot studies for the clarification of techniques. Thus far, little has been verified beyond the recognition that these children need a particular kind of environment in which to recover and learn. They need selected and regulated sets of experiences in order to assume or reassume healthy responsibility and, at the same time, learn more effectively.

Settings for the education of disturbed children range from hospital or residential schools that heavily emphasize psychotherapy to special classes within the public schools that emphasize an instructional, or achievement-centered approach. Some settings are concerned with elementary children, some with adolescents, and some attempt to combine age levels. It often happens, then, that teachers find themselves caught in a dichotomous situation—that of instruction versus therapy. This dilemma may present itself in terms of hospital versus school administration and/or in classroom structure—permissiveness (student-directed) versus structure (teacher-directed). Unfortunately, the concern over these controversial philosophies has, to a great extent, impeded the growth of programs that attempt to fulfill the needs of children with learning and behavior disorders. It may be that disciplines such as music therapy will be the best media to dissipate these dichotomous situations. The music therapist with music education experience becomes indispensable because he can successfully integrate therapeutic and instructional techniques.

This chapter is concerned with a presentation of concepts that seem to be representative of the most successful settings and management devices used in educating and treating emotionally disturbed children. These concepts, arising from study and experience in public schools, mental hospitals, and the specially structured school, are presented in order to delineate a clear-cut philosophical basis of operation so essential for success. Programs incorporating these concepts differ in origin from residential centers and public schools. Finally, the role of the music therapist in a unique setting will be examined. It is, perhaps, the highest test of our discipline, which does not align itself with either side of the dichotomy, to come into full knowledge that *education constitutes social and emotional growth and that this growth constitutes education.*

The Educational Setting

Clinical, as well as educational, research is pointing more and more to the value of a structured concept of classroom environment for disturbed children. The kind of structure represented here has emerged from the following basic needs of these children:

1. The need for acceptance and success in a process of self-actualization. Activities and instruction must be directed in such a way that these needs can, *in reality*, be fulfilled.
2. The need to *participate.* The disturbed child needs an environment that can offer him the opportunity to participate in the educational process *at his own readiness level.*
3. The need for a security agent. The disturbed child must have a security agent (the teacher) to assist him in developing and maintaining effective inner controls. Lack of structure or order in his life is often the basis of his problem; his treatment setting must offer an opportunity to grow toward these controls.

Consideration of these basic needs shows clearly the demands placed on a teacher in this setting: to foster a healthy identification through acceptance; to meet education needs in such a way that participation and success can be realistically obtained; and to present an atmosphere of order and control as an authority figure, without being rigid and punitive.

We shall now examine briefly more specific structural concepts to support these needs. The setting should be a scientifically organized classroom structure that is reality-oriented, embracing concern for related treatment disciplines as well as procedures that provide maximum educational benefit. Effective learning is important for obvious scholastic reasons; it is also important for classroom management of behavior problems, growth of attitudes, and emotional well-being. The child is placed in a setting that is purposefully *instructional*; with psychological support, his problems and behavior are directed toward acceptable channels through the teacher. Some physical considerations are

1. Classrooms should physically represent the public school classroom and and should be part of a special education program.
2. Facilities, particularly furniture, should be as indestructible as possible to counteract the *failure orientation* of the children.
3. Class load should not exceed eight or nine students per teacher in order to provide individualized guidance. Realistic functioning of group dynamics cannot occur with fewer than five students. A grade differential of more than three or four years is usually unwise, particularly with high school groups. Obviously, the groups must be carefully constructed in the light of social and emotional factors.
4. Tutoring rooms should be available when needed for use in isolating a child for instructional or adjustment reasons. Disturbed children *cannot wait*.
5. Facilities should be available to handle a child if removal from school is indicated.

Control and Management

The primary conflicts that rise in working with disturbed children center around control techniques. We view concepts of these control areas in terms of three categories—classroom control techniques that involve interference and intervention; verbal control techniques of teacher-student interaction; and behavior-consequence tools.

Classroom Control Techniques

The teacher must first thoroughly analyze individual needs in terms of social and emotional growth. When possible, psychological help in this determination is desirable. In case this help is minimal or not available at all, the following general groupings in terms of approach to life are suggested by Borelli (1965).

1. *Confused:* The student cannot understand what life is about and sees little or no place for himself in the world.
   a. The confused student needs to have things explained to him, usually again and again.
   b. He needs encouragement for his own efforts.
   c. He needs to feel that life is somewhat orderly and that he can learn to cope with it.
2. *Hostile:* The student feels life is a constant threat and he must fight to survive.
   a. The hostile child needs to feel that no one wants to hurt him physically or emotionally.
   b. He needs to know that his hostility does not frighten anyone.
   c. He needs to find ways to channel his energy into more positive directions.
   d. He needs to learn how to produce friendliness rather than hostility in the people with whom he associates.
3. *Demanding:* The demanding student feels that the world is "up for grabs" and he must have his share and often much more.
   a. The demanding student needs to have consistent limits set for him.
   b. He needs to know that some people cannot be badgered, cajoled, or manipulated into relaxing their controls or making bargains.
   c. He needs to develop some ways to control his demands in a realistic way by himself, rather than depending on other people to say "no" to him.
   d. He needs to know that sharing is as important as getting and frequently more important.
4. *Resistant:* The resistant student feels everyone wants to exploit him, and he defends himself against deep relationships with anyone.
   a. The resistant student needs to have genuine concern shown for what he is, *not for his talents or worldly possessions.*
   b. He needs to feel that others care about what happens to him in the long run, not just in their individual relationships with him today.
   c. He needs to find ways of becoming more aggressive and demanding in socially acceptable ways.
   d. He needs to know that his life has meaning.

Obviously, there are no clear-cut groups; a child may fall into any or all of them. However, one characteristic is usually outstanding, and the approach to the child is based on this one.

An equally thorough analysis must be made of the child's educational needs. Ability to perform must be determined in the light of existing emotional problems; information about the grade level of the child, his performance IQ, and his remedial needs are vital if we are to ensure his educational success. In many programs, these areas are determined by a battery of psychological tests administered by a school counselor or psychologist. If this service is not available, the teacher must make the effort. The music therapist may see this task as primarily academic and one that does not involve his discipline, but may become involved in it for two specific reasons.

1. He probably will have to teach more than music in the program, because of the emphasis on small class loads. Unless accreditation is accomplished, success for the child is considerably diminished; therefore, each teacher may have to carry a two- or three-subject load.
2. Knowledge of achievement level prevents failure in areas of music requiring cognitive skills. Cognitive skills are undeveloped in many disturbed children and often are unrecognized by teachers in special areas such as art, music, physical education, and industrial arts. This concept is extremely important if we are to effect change from a failure orientation to a success orientation in the child.

Techniques of interference and intervention demand on-the-spot skills of the teacher or therapist, based on knowledge of the needs in the areas just discussed. When a child escapes a limit set for him, an attempt must be made to forestall events in the future that will give him a chance to repeat the same behavior; this is the method of *interference*. An *intervention* may occur at the academic level, or it may occur at an adjustment level. Acting-out behavior occurs in the child who faces excessive fear and anxiety, which may lie in either the academic or the adjustment area or *both*. Interventions may include

1. Reduced or accelerated stimuli
2. Reduced or accelerated social activity
3. Shortened, concise work assignments
4. Greater diversity of teaching techniques to counteract hyperactivity
5. Individualization when possible
6. Curriculum geared to readiness levels
7. Empathetic response to problem situations
8. Ample use of expression media
9. Use of differential treatment in determining individual limits

The teacher may view this concept of classroom control technique as *preventive discipline,* the first and most important goal in maintaining a setting for disturbed children.

Verbal Control Techniques

It goes without saying that every teacher of disturbed children would like to have the ability to say the right thing at the right time. Because this is impossible, the following concepts are presented to assist the teacher in achieving more effective verbal control.

In order to deal effectively with any disturbed child, two things must be communicated to each student: (1) "I care about you" and (2) "I will set limits for you until you can set them for yourself." One without the other is meaningless and tends to confuse students. If we are able to communicate both, we can provide the climate for healthy growth. Ways in which we might communicate these two feelings to students are explained by Baruch (1949) and can be summarized as follows:

1. *Mirroring feelings* means the process of trying to understand how the child feels and then putting his feelings into words for him. This promotes more understanding between teacher and child during the time that he must be disciplined. Understanding this need and verbalizing it correctly to the child takes the "sting" out of punishment, and it says that we are not fighting *against* him, but *with* him.
2. Using restriction in a calm, firm manner, without loss of personal control. The ability to do this determines the success or failure of a teacher with disturbed children.
3. Helping the child find the *true hurt* and the source of the anger, rather than blocking the anger itself.
4. Aiming toward restriction of acts *not feelings.* Releasing and draining the feeling is a therapeutic need; to *fix* it at an anger level is to block emotional growth.
5. Expressing praise and appreciation verbally in such a way that good feelings, rather than bribes or promises, are the reward.
6. Avoiding verbal clashes and unnecessary threats and demands by adopting the following pattern to obtain obedience:
   a. Good patterns in yourself for the child to imitate.
   b. Simple suggestions, without employing overaggression on your part to suggest counteraggression from him.
   c. Minimal demands, rules, and regulations.
   d. Consideration of his feelings.
7. Learning to recognize and control verbal manipulations on the part of

disturbed children. These are usually well hidden, and the acute sensitivity of disturbed children makes them difficult to deal with objectively. Many teachers, as well as therapists, can easily become involved in a pseudotherapeutic verbal process, in which supportive discussion will crystalize actual resistance.

8. Being cognizant of the fact that disturbed children are truly children who cannot wait. They need immediate restriction, immediate gratification, and immediate intervention. When this immediacy is not possible, we can expect them to act out feelings of fear and insecurity.

Behavior-Consequence Tools

Emotionally disturbed children present the teacher with an array of antisocial acts. These are to be expected during the course of a child's treatment, and consequence tools must be determined, to some extent, prior to these acts. To ignore or tolerate the acts is to break a reality structure; it means entering the child's system of adjustment and becoming entangled in it. In many cases, it means being manipulated and controlled by the child, with resulting failure for the teacher. *It is neither helpful nor therapeutic to the child to accept all his actions passively.* As his personality organization begins to break down in stressful situations, he becomes extremely frightened over his lack of inner controls and fears that his destructive impulses will be realized. When a child can no longer accept controls and predetermined limits, on the basis of his needs, by the teacher, he should be removed from the setting. When intervention and verbal techniques have been employed by the teacher to the best of her ability and have failed, a system of consequence tools, which must be part of each setting, should be utilized.

1. *Quiet or isolation rooms:* To be used if the teacher feels that control may be regained in a relatively short period of time; never to be used as a punitive action.
2. *Counseling services* (principal, school counselors, child-care workers, psychologist, psychiatrist, or social worker): May provide additional help to the child in clarifying his source of anger and in releasing feeling. The use of these services must be handled judiciously and *cannot* replace the function of the teacher or the classroom setting as a therapeutic tool.
3. *School removal:* Existing facilities should include a way to return the child to his home, cottage, or ward setting.
4. *Curriculum flexibility:* May be used for short periods of time in assisting with adjustment to school problems. However, this technique

must be used sparingly in an effort to retain a realistic school structure.

5. *Corporal punishment and suspension:* Even though these two areas can be worthwhile in individual cases, extreme caution must be used. They should be utilized only as indicated by psychiatric consultation.

When children deliberately act out in order to obtain one of the consequences listed, especially over a prolonged period of time, the effectiveness of the consequence should be questioned. Is the subject matter too difficult or too easy? Is the child facing repeated failure in peer relationships or teacher relationship? Does he find a counseling situation to be one in which he is able to further manipulate and entangle the counselor? Finally, does he need medication, or is he overreacting to medication? Removal itself constitutes pain for the child and is punishment sufficient unto itself, regardless of the defense mechanisms he may employ to deny this.

Successful teachers of disturbed children are able to *see* how a child feels, *accept* how he feels, *reflect* how he feels, help him *express* how he feels, and *guide* his actions toward a realistic success value. The skill of a teacher in establishing such a relationship is the core of his success. Constant, firm, and kind discipline, the skillful application of subject matter, and the ability to absorb hostility without retaliation are the indispensable tools with which the teacher works. Presented below are a group of *evaluation questions,* designed to assist the teacher in an evaluation of success—his own, as well as his students'.

I. What is the student's problem?

A. Attitude:
1. What kind of a world does he see?
2. What kind of people live in his world?
3. What kind of person does he consider himself to be?
4. What kind of person would he like to be?

B. Behavior—how well is he able to:
1. Control his own actions
2. Take orders
3. Follow directions
4. Solve problems on his own
5. Cooperate with others
6. Compete with others fairly
7. Make intelligent judgments
8. Operate independently
9. Express his feelings
10. Set goals and work toward them

C. Academic:
1. Is the child learning academic material presented to him?

2. How well does he achieve?
3. What does he need to learn next?
4. What are the inhibiting factors?

II. What can be done about the problem?

A. Attitude:
1. Does his present behavior need to be controlled or encouraged?
2. Does he need to discuss things or should discussions with him be avoided?
3. Does he need to feel wanted or does he use relationships to exploit others?
4. Does he need to be told what to do, or should his independence be encouraged?
5. Does he need to be encouraged to share, or does he give away too much?
6. Does he need encouragement to ask for more, or does he ask for too much?

B. Behavior:
1. Does one need to treat whatever he says as important, or can he be kidded along?
2. Does he need to be criticized in the presence of others, or should he be called aside?
3. Should he be prodded to perform, or should he be allowed to succeed or fail on his own?

C. Academic:
1. Has one used subject matter that triggers disturbance?
2. Has one adjusted subject matter to the child's readiness level?
3. Has one provided necessary stimulation in subject matter presentation?
4. Is it desirable to remove inhibitory influences on learning or to teach around them? (Borelli, 1965, pp. 1–4)

The kind of structure suggested in this section is, at best, not easy to maintain. It is difficult to keep a proper balance between a rigid, punitive structure and a permissive, therapy-laden program that short-cuts educational value. In the final analysis, it is the operational philosophy of the teacher that determines the direction. He is all the experts rolled into one, once the door is closed and class begins.

Music in the Curriculum

Concepts concerning the use of music in a structured school for emotionally disturbed children were derived from the experience of the author, a music teacher with a background in music therapy. Table 4 presents music activities in this school along with goals specifically directed toward combined therapy-educational techniques.

TABLE 4

Musical Activities and Goals in the Experimental School

Activity	Goal
Elementary chorus	To provide an activity designed primarily for relaxation, enjoyment, and socialization
	To provide an activity of choice in which students can accept more responsibility for behavior
	To promote a concept of teamwork, thereby instituting a less verbal form of control
	To familiarize the children with standard song literature for the elementary grades, to introduce rhythmical concepts through the use of rhythm band, and to teach helpful vocal techniques
Secondary chorus	To introduce standard vocal techniques, part-singing in particular
	To provide a variety of musical material and to aid students in learning some of the basic elements of music, using physical movement, percussion and string instruments, and visual aids
	To provide an activity of choice for advanced-level students in an effort to strengthen ego defenses
	To introduce the idea of a school choir to be used for special programs and assemblies
	To provide a medium for children to use to some extent in acting-out behavior
Music-appreciation classes	To introduce musical elements in a simple, basic form for the development of appreciation and enjoyment of music
	To provide a nonacademic activity in an effort to find new avenues of motivation
	To provide an activity that promotes relaxation, enjoyment, and close teacher-pupil relationship
Special instrumental lessons (such as guitar and drum)	To promote an individualized program for students who are promising and gifted
	To accommodate special cases in which the student needs to work in a one-to-one relationship, at least temporarily
	Beginning band instruction
Band	To provide for a group instrumental project in which goals are student-oriented (dance band)
Drama (combined with music)	To provide activity that can channel hostility and serve as an acceptable acting-out device
	To provide an avenue for close observation of habits, attitudes, and feelings through play-acting
	To provide gratification through performance

Students involved in these activities, which included the entire population of eighty-five children, ranged from first- to twelfth-grade level. They were grouped, for the most part, according to the wishes of the music therapist, who also taught English and dramatics to students of grades seven through twelve. To demonstrate the interaction of therapeutic, instructional, and control techniques, examples of activity are presented and analyzed.

Case 1—Elementary Chorus. A special music class was organized for the elementary children. It was presented to them as a volunteer activity, hopefully eliminating the feeling that they were being forced to attend. Most of them (about twenty-five) appeared. Knowing that this was too large a group for children of this age, the teacher immediately placed firm limits on behavior; most forms of acting out were pronounced unacceptable. During the first three weeks, from five to ten students had to be removed from the group every time it met. The children would fight over anything possible, sing in odd ways, belittle any type of activity offered. In short, anything was done that could ruin the class or prevent the teacher from teaching. With the help of a child-care worker, offenders were removed quickly and returned to their classrooms before their behavior could spread to others not yet involved. The instructor then made it a point to see each misbehaver individually after class, explaining that his actions were unacceptable. The child was invited to return to the next session if he was willing to attempt firmer control of himself.

At the end of the first month, no one had dropped music permanently, and the number of children who had to be sent out steadily decreased until some sessions would occur with no removals. Techniques employed by the children to escape the responsibility of control in the large group were skillful, but they gradually assumed control even with the introduction of increased stimuli.

The instructional techniques with this group were fairly standard. Simple echo songs were popular, as well as work with rhythm band instruments. Spirituals and patriotic songs particularly were appealing; occasionally hymns were requested. Folk dancing was not used to any extent because the group was too large; however, with the help of a resource teacher, the children were divided into smaller groups and taught folk games successfully. It was a new experience for these children to work in such a large group, and it produced much anxiety in the beginning until they realized that they could always return to the small classroom when they could no longer tolerate a large group. Demonstrating growth in self-control became somewhat of a status symbol. For the most part, the group had to be told exactly what to do. If choice was employed more than just occasionally, it had to be between only two things, otherwise chaos would quickly occur and the anxiety induced would be too great. Flexibility in choice (whether in choosing songs or activities) took a long period of time to achieve and had to be employed cautiously.

Outstanding in this group of children was the desire to fight one another and the teacher through music. Often they would sing off-key deliberately and try to sing against, not with, the rest of the chorus. Sometimes interventions came through the careful selection of music; for example, patriotic songs seemed to elicit positive group patterns. Sessions were much more successful if they began and ended with more sedative forms of music, reserving fast, rhythmical music for the highlight of the session. The use of a tape recorder stimulated interest in teamwork and concentration on blending voices so that vocal techniques and rhythmical concepts could be introduced.

Creativity often presented itself in negative forms with this group. One popular misdeed was singing made-up words with vulgar connotations to familiar tunes. Another was playing bongos and snare drums out of rhythm with the music or in a destructive manner. Channeling these actions consisted of clearly pointing out to the child what he was doing and then placing a definite limit on the action, while at the same time attempting to find another way to give him attention and recognition. Some talents could be used in a positive manner in planning creative productions for other classmates. Many in this group were aggressive and exhibitionistic and easily became motivated through performance rewards. Performance also provided enough motivation so that areas of instruction in note and rhythm concepts were easily utilized.

The group progressed rather well. Other staff members commented on its progress toward group cohesion over the period of a year. Improvement was especially noted after performances, when the children received praise for a group accomplishment. When the chorus had reached this point of pride in its ability, group performance was used occasionally as a restrictive tool in other areas; for example, children found the activity withheld if classwork was not completed. This technique obviously can get out of control if the entire staff uses it as a punitive action; however, it came about in a useful way, and the children were able to develop more control because of its use.

Case 2—Instrumental Group. A group of 10 fifteen- to eighteen-year-old boys had displayed some interest in instrumental music and had discussed it with the music teacher at various times individually. She had given some thought to the organization of a small band but felt that the boys were too antisocial to handle the situation. By accident, they organized a band themselves. One day the boys were in English class, working on an assignment, when the teacher was called out of the room. She returned to find the entire group involved in playing instruments together. Because they had no music, several of them were improvising to the rhythm of the guitarist, who had memorized some tunes. Although they were not skillful at the task, what they were doing held promise musically. Consequently, they were immediately assigned a time later in the day to organize a small dance band, which was taught by the teacher.

Socially, the group learned to laugh a great deal and to tolerate teasing. They were able to grasp enough instruction so they could read notes and play together. The teacher helped them to improve their improvisation skills. It is very unusual for such a group of sick boys (most of them with personality disorders) to progress to the point where they are able to organize positive group patterns. These incidents occur in their own good time and can be supported but not forced by the instructor. They are preceded by an atmosphere of security and respect for others. This was an extremely significant incident to the teacher because of its implications toward socialization. From this point on, meaningful strides were taken with the group in areas other than the music room. Support had to remain —there were times when the teacher said, "Yes, you have to," and the group did. This kind of overt progress is not often seen when dealing with disturbed children.

Case 3—Secondary Chorus. A senior chorus was organized as an elective for junior and senior high school students. About fifteen children volunteered for the group. Their skills in vocal music were poor and they did not particularly like music, but chorus appeared to be the top choice of several undesirable activities. The instructor was faced with problems similar to those with the elementary chorus, although expressions of hostility were more subtle in nature. Many students generally refused to sing; but if they did sing, they attempted to destroy the class by singing in a grotesque manner or too softly. The group demanded rock 'n' roll but immediately became dissatisfied when it was used. They refused to sing anything unfamiliar, although they knew a very limited number of songs. Singing incorrectly was done constantly; they fought all attempts on the part of the instructor to introduce vocal techniques. They complained about everything presented to them and refused to try anything new.

As with the elementary chorus, the group was placed under a definite program of instruction, with removal from class of the students who refused to participate. The following general outline was used:

Ten minutes—instruction in vocal technique
Fifteen minutes—concentration on specific music involving two-part singing and rounds
Fifteen minutes—opportunities for choice in singing; opportunity to play the drum set with records or piano improvisations; occasional dancing

As this chorus progressed, there were only two students who had to be dropped. The group became fond of patriotic music and lively spirituals and rejected rock 'n' roll by choice. Of particular interest to the teacher was the fact that they liked to sing songs that reminded them of school experiences prior to their entrance into this school. They usually related positive experiences in connection with such music, which was their beginning point. The songs seemed to provide them with pleasant memories of the community school, in spite of evidence that past experiences had not been pleasurable. Many times a suggestion would be preceded with, "Back at my old school, we sang it this way."

When the teacher did not express disapproval of requests for rock 'n' roll music, the students had no more use for it. Had it been deliberately rejected by the teacher, the group would probably have used it repeatedly as a measure of resistance. Performance was used in this group also as motivation. A teamwork approach was adopted in preparation for programs. Although the group remained poor in musical skills by any standard, there was ample evidence of improvement.

Case 4—Uses of Background Music. Music, both stimulative and sedative, was used quite frequently by teachers in other classes. Sometimes, they used musical recordings as a reward technique; occasionally it was reported that some quiet music made the children less restless and hostile. An interesting incident proved to the therapist that the adolescent defines stimulative and sedative music in terms different from those of the adult.

A large English class of adolescents requested that the teacher play music while they completed grammar assignments. The request was granted, but the therapist attempted to play rather slow, semiclassical music for the group, assuming that it would have a sedative effect on them. They began to appear restless and agitated; finally, one brave soul suggested that they did not like old-fashioned music. The teacher substituted some jazz, expecting them to react in a hyperactive manner. Instead, they reacted physically with some movement of hands and feet, but actually seemed to be more satisfied and appeared to be concentrating better on the work assignment. The students explained later that most of them were used to studying to rock 'n' roll music and that it did not distract them. Subsequent sessions proved this to be true; although the stimulative music did produce some reaction, it proved to be sedative because it produced a more comfortable social situation for the group.

Case 5—Group Experience with Drama. After discussing the techniques of role playing with several clinicians, the music therapist used it in some of her drama classes with ninth and tenth graders. Eight boys were in the first class. Because they were receiving academic credit for the course, fundamentals of acting were taught first (characterization, stage jargon, make-up, stage projects, and so on). During this time, the class worked mostly on small, short-term individual projects that dealt with various types of characterization sketches. The students would present these sketches in creative ways without a script, attempting to incorporate instructional devices. They had a large margin of freedom in the presentation of characters, and a great deal of acting out occurred during these sessions.

After about two months of this type of activity, limitations were imposed on the group. The students could no longer react to the character roles in terms of their own personalities; they were given direction on how to play the roles. In addition, they sometimes were given sketches (created by the teacher) that approximated some of their own problem areas in real life. This brought forth many interesting and enlightening episodes. It produced a wealth of material on how these children interpret other people, how they feel in contrast to the average child in given situations. This aspect of drama was welcomed by the psychiatric staff; it provided information useful in therapy sessions and an acceptable channel through which children could drain off more aggressive feelings. Many times, the sketches and plays were quite horrifying in character—murders, rapes, stabbings, and court trials were common. However, when the therapist gradually began to help the students with the interpretation of their own behavior, they did accept criticism and retained enthusiasm for the group. They managed to write a few plays that were acceptable and proceeded to learn a one-act play in spite of memorization difficulties. The group formed the central core of a Christmas pageant, and the members were able to shoulder the more difficult parts.

Drama, as well as music, can be an explosive activity. It can lead to the very core of the child's problems and can easily become an impossible activity to control. Role playing should be considered carefully before it is introduced. It is extremely important that the teacher be assured of a secure relationship with her students prior to the use of this technique. If it is approached before this relationship is adequately established, the students might find it entirely too threatening to tolerate. The teacher had worked with most of the students in the group just described for six months to a year prior to this activity. They not only trusted the teacher; they were aware of limits and what could and could not happen in such a setting. As it was, the students expressed anxiety frequently—"Don't tell my doctor"; "Please don't write this up in my progress notes"; "What do you think of me now?" They needed constant reassurance that behavior in the group would not be used against them.

The examples presented demonstrate well the nonverbal level of musical expression (Gaston, 1958, p. 297) with students in the experimental school. Note that most of the classes exhibited negative expression through music until considerable progress had been made. As the classes became more accepting of controls, they began to utilize music in more positive forms of expression (cases 1 and 3). An important point to consider here is seen in case 1: The instructor consistently encouraged positive responses, rather than placing emphasis on ego demands that had resulted in unacceptable behavior patterns. This was, in effect, an effort to channel the expression of inappropriate emotional thought. This was a demonstration, beyond question, of promoting emotional growth rather than inhibiting expression. Much of the success of such a program depends on the instructor's skill in establishing rapport and using degrees of emphasis with the children when they are ready to tolerate them.

The effort toward becoming task-centered and producing behavioral change was considered the second step in accomplishing nonverbal expression through music in these groups. The *change* concept was also indicated when working with individual students and was always much easier to accomplish on a one-to-one basis because of the closer, less threatening relationship between the student and teacher.

Each case presented demonstrates the wide adaptability of music. Cases 4 and 5 indicate particular areas of interest in this adaptability. The positive attitude referred to by Gaston (1958, p. 298) is an ideal that is seldom seen while working with disturbed children. If it occurs at all, it is usually when the children begin to show signs of general personality improvement, as demonstrated in case 2; but it is the exception, not the rule. However, this concept is not to be discarded; music contributes a great deal toward the positive attitude, but there are musical factors involved in this contribution that block overt signs of positive attitude.

Music helps to free from aloneness for even stronger reasons than those set down in the preceding paragraphs. For the most part, moods elicited by music are derived from the tender emotions. The tender emotions are those having to do with, primarily, race preservation. They include love, love-making, family, love of parents, religion (the extension of love of parents), patriotism, loyalty, and similar relationships held in great esteem by our culture.

It is evident, then, that not only does music dissipate aloneness by providing freedom but it dissolves aloneness in a much stronger way by speaking of one's good feeling for another. . . . The positive feelings engendered by music will be of great value in the establishment of the most important function of the music therapist, that of building a strong and adequate relationship with the patient. The most important achievement of the music therapist will be the establishment of the proper relationship with the handicapped child (Gaston, 1958, p. 299).

The attitude of students toward the music program was somewhat puzzling from the very beginning of the school, particularly in comparison to their attitude and behavior in other classes. Because the music teacher also taught English, she could not dismiss the problem as one of teacher-pupil relationship. There was a great deal of acting-out behavior in music classes; students presented their most destructive and negative behavior, it seemed. Hostility existed in the music classes that did not appear so evident in the English classes. Because the teacher was the same, the assumption was made that the hostility was more possible because of the music. Students would often state that they hated music, yet when given the opportunity to quit or leave, they would not do so. It was determined, after examining this problem constantly, that the situation was due to several factors:

1. The children needed an activity that could absorb a certain amount of hostile expression, yet retain organization—a suitable channel for hostility. Some days the survival of the drums was questionable; they were played in a loud, distorted manner, although this seldom occurred during individual lessons.
2. Inappropriate behavior during the music class was directly related to *fear*. As has been said, music generally expresses some positive feelings. Because the core of the problems of most of the students centered around the expression of these tender emotions, the children continued their rejection of them musically and became hostile to the music classes.

With this concept in mind, a great deal of hostility from children in any musical activity would be expected. Classes often presented an explosive picture in which tolerance was short-lived because the children were threatened by the activity. The music teacher was dealing with exceptionally negative behavior, even for disturbed children, and this behavior was in opposition to the expectations a therapist usually holds in regard to the therapeutic benefits of group music. Of great importance is the consideration here that teaching the child to be more positive and accepting in the music class may help to reduce some of this rejection of emotion in other activity areas. *Proving that music can be a nonthreatening experience may be the greatest single contribution of the teacher in this situation.*

Case 2 demonstrates a group of disturbed children who were able to survive the threatening aspects of music and who made the big step toward a more mature sharing process on their own. The groundwork for this step had been established through the contact of the instructor with each of the students in private lessons. This one-to-one relationship on a limited basis enabled the teacher to achieve closeness to a greater degree with each student individually, blocking out some of the fearful aspects of group music participation. By the time these students decided to organize themselves, there was very little hesitation in displaying positive and even sentimental attitudes toward music. There was a great improvement in skills—students began to practice more and to utilize practice time more effectively. In addition, behavior patterns improved in other school areas; the children were able to express themselves much more adequately in problem situations without resorting to extreme aggression. They did not hesitate to discuss problems with the music teacher, as well as with other staff members.

When a disturbed child is able to form one positive relationship, it usually paves the way for him to accept other relationships. He may rely on this closeness with one person for some time, and this may even approach a temporary state of dependency. As he continues with this relationship, he will begin to accept closeness with others. For this reason, it is felt that isolated contact with disturbed children in an activity can be extremely important but only if it is directed toward acceptance of group activity. This is one advantage of the music instructor; he can include some time in his program to provide students with private lessons, inviting this aspect of closeness. He cannot build his program around individual activity; however, a careful choice of candidates (especially group leaders) can prove to be quite beneficial. Gaston (1958) states that "sharing is a sign of maturity" (p. 300), and the problem of teaching the child to share and broaden this delicate relationship is a function of the teacher.

Each example presented here illustrates gratification in musical performance (Gaston, 1958, p. 301). The fact that the child may not overtly appear to enjoy musical activity does not necessarily mean that music is not providing gratification.

Note that many of these examples demonstrated the use of performing plays and programs before an audience as a tool in motivation. As seen in case 5, drama can also become an extremely successful tool and is easily combined with music for performance purposes. The therapist chose to present a Christmas pageant as an experimental form of performance gratification. A detailed examination of the pageant and how it was produced will illustrate the purpose and intent of the author in using the pageant as a therapeutic tool.

The advisability of using public performance with disturbed children is controversial. It was tried for two reasons: (1) The staff felt that one large-scale school project that would involve the total participation of the entire staff and student body might be beneficial in creating enthusiasm, cooperation, teamwork, and respect for the school. Diagnostic material obtained through the observation of anxiety patterns and the testing of the children's reactions to authority in a stressful, yet meaningful, activity might also be of value. (2) The students, as well as the staff, needed to find ways to prove that the school, as a new concept in special education, was beneficial and successful. A simple performance, fairly well done, might serve to raise the status of the school in the eyes of parents, staff, and hospital and school personnel.

It was expected that anxiety would become evident in many forms of acting out; therefore, details of staging were carefully planned prior to rehearsals. *The Littlest Angel* was adapted for the school performance for two major reasons. First, it was a story understood and liked by adults as well as children; hence, both elementary and secondary students could enjoy being in it. The plot itself seemed to be particularly meaningful to our students; it involved a "bad" boy who was loved by God in spite of his faults. The theme was a starting point for discussions of problems with several children who identified strongly with the central character. Second, the production could be done effectively without elaborate stage scenery. In fact, the children were able to help in building and completing projects for the stage. Costuming was done simply; some of the home economics students were able to help with the sewing.

In the process of production, one problem was outstanding: Many students refused to participate from the beginning or dropped out at some point as a result of anger and anxiety. Because of the awareness of serious problems that might produce psychiatric criticism, the parts were carefully chosen. Principal parts went to the drama class—children who were more aggressive and needed an acceptable way to channel exhibitionistic impulses. Many of the parts were cast from volunteers. Students who were withdrawn and extremely fearful of stage appearance were often given off-stage duties, such as making programs, doing behind-the-scenes work, and ushering. Musical ability or talent did not take precedence over emotional problems; tolerance limits and anxiety had to be considered first. The staff worked very hard to motivate students who were using refusal to participate as a hostility mechanism. In a few isolated cases, students were told they *had* to participate, although this was done only after careful consideration of their needs and the consequences of such demands. The first attempt to handle the children was by keeping them out of a rehearsal. Often isolation from others and the subsequent group pressure produced cooperation.

The pageant was extremely successful for these children. It was unusually moving in effect because of a polished simplicity. The music was familiar, sung in unison, and sung well, and the students in the chorus were able to memorize all the music; this had not been anticipated. A professional volunteer who helped with lighting enhanced the effectiveness of the pageant. The impact on the audience (primarily hospital and school personnel and parents) of emotionally disturbed children coming out of themselves, so to speak, was notable. Of greatest importance was the pride of the students in such an accomplishment. Only one student out of the whole school refused to participate during the actual performance.

Anxiety level during rehearsals and performance was high among both staff and students. However, the staff, for the most part, felt that the good aspects of the performance outweighed the bad. The combination of all activities in performance went a long way toward producing positive group experiences. This points to an obvious need on the part of the music teacher—ability to create and adjust material so that it can be adapted to the individual needs of a school. It is certain that undertaking such a project opens one to many forms of criticism. The price of its success must be considered.

Gaston (1958, pp. 302–303) speaks of the resentment of handicapped children toward logical approaches to behavior control, suggesting that music offers qualities of persuasion that are nonthreatening and nonpunitive. As noted in case 1, the characteristics of patriotic and religious music occasionally reduced some hostility in the children and they became more accepting of group expectations. However, most of the time, even though they probably got the message, they responded negatively to this nonverbal demand for conformity. The youngest group of children (aged seven to nine) responded most positively to music as a behavior control, probably because defenses were not quite so rigid. These children are, generally speaking, too hostile to accept even the subtle persuasion of music. The very fact that music exists at all is sometimes extremely threatening to them. Because the majority of disturbed children are hyperactive, aggressive, and demanding, sedative music can often produce some changes in behavior. As seen in case 4, when music does produce responses in the adolescent, they are not always the same kind of responses that would be seen in the adult.

In spite of the fact that acting out is sometimes excessive during the music activity, the teacher is able to produce an extremely warm relationship with the music class. Children in the experimental school sometimes expressed a desire to be in music just to work with the therapist and often indicated that some sort of special closeness existed in this relationship. On the other hand, what often seemed to be a sincere expression of interest was actually just a skillful manipulation by students in order to get out of regularly scheduled classes.

When the defenses involved are as complex as those seen in most disturbed children, one cannot operate in as permissive or positive a philosophy as music therapy dynamics usually indicate. When this is attempted, the destructive aspects of groups and individuals will prevail and the music education, as well as the therapy, fails. The following items represent the primary uses of music in a school for disturbed children. The goals of the music classes must point toward integration of three specific areas—psychiatric treatment, educational training, and control rehabilitation. An examination of these items reveals the following techniques as primary effective uses of music:

1. An activity geared toward socialization and teamwork
2. A reward technique
3. Performance gratification
4. Promotion of the tender emotions
5. Learning in a group situation
6. Promotion of close relationships with authority figures

References

BARUCH, DOROTHY. *New ways in discipline.* New York: McGraw-Hill, 1949.
BORELLI, G. Guidelines for evaluation. Unpublished manuscript, Glenwood School, Columbus, Ohio, 1965. Pp. 1–4.
COHEN, S. The educational setting. Paper read at Special Study Institute for Seriously Emotionally Disturbed Children, Ohio State Univer., June 12–17, 1966.
GASTON, E. T. Functional music. In N. Henry (Ed.), *Basic concepts in music education.* Chicago: The University of Chicago Press, 1958. Pp. 292–309.

25

MUSIC FOR DEAF
AND HARD-OF-HEARING CHILDREN
IN PUBLIC SCHOOLS

HARROLD W. SPICKNALL

A music program for deaf and hard-of-hearing children in a public school system has been established on an experimental basis for the past several years. Students included in this program are enrolled in special education classes with trained teachers. A music therapist directly supervises music activities for the children, who range in age from four to thirteen years. A music therapist is also available for consultation concerning students at the junior and senior high school levels.

The program has been directed toward the following goals: (1) to help improve self-image, (2) to increase oral vocabulary, (3) to stimulate lipreading, (4) to promote more rhythmic speech, (5) to supplement the teacher's knowledge of the nature of the individual's hearing loss, and (6) to help the children become aware of the variety of sounds and vibrations in their environment.

Goals 1 to 4 are served by similar activities, based mainly on song material but having variations of emphasis. Songs involving actions are used to promote the self-concept of specific body parts and their bilateral, unilateral, and cross-lateral movements. Songs relating to posture, locomotion, and direction are used to teach concepts such as "up and down," "right and left," "stand and sit," "walk and run," and "slow and fast." Songs having new ideas and new words that supplement the standard reading fare are used to increase oral vocabulary. The meanings of new words are illustrated both with pictures and actions. After a song sequence has been learned, the children perform the actions while watching the teacher sing the song. This serves as a motivating factor in lipreading. As the children progress in their responses, they are encouraged to use the words they can speak along with the teacher or therapist. Most of the children are able to "sing" the words by the time they are admitted to the fifth or sixth grade.

Whenever speech is added to the actions, attention is given to the rhythmic impulse in each word or phrase. Preschool and kindergarten children gather around a large bass drum laid on its side. Each child places his fingers on the head of the drum and watches the teacher's face as she speaks the word or phrase while she simultaneously taps the rhythm on the drum head. Older children may receive the vibrations of the rhythm through the floor or air, or may tap or clap it themselves.

Goals 5 and 6 are achieved through participation in activities that involve the use of musical instruments such as drums, bells, wood blocks, and wind and string instruments. Often a child's response to these sounds indicates the extent and nature of his hearing loss more clearly than does the audiogram. In game fashion, he is asked to respond to auditory stimuli, first by counting the tones, and later by making discriminations between sounds. Because visual clues are eliminated, the child is given opportunities to perceive the tones by three different means of vibrational transmission—direct, semidirect, and air.

For direct transmission, the child holds or touches the instrument while it is being played. Semidirect transmission occurs when the instrument is placed against a table or on a wooden floor that the child touches. Reception solely on the basis of air transmission is effected by elimination of direct and semidirect transmission. Semidirect transmission is eliminated to some degree by having both the child and the instrument on a carpeted area. Where this is not possible, the instrument is cushioned well to prevent continuing vibration through solid resonant material.

Application of this procedure to many different sounds enables the teachers to gain insight into the functional hearing losses of their students. At the same time, the children gain experience with a wide variety of environmental sound stimuli that, in turn, serves to increase their awareness of the world about them. The counting of tones also promotes the development of number concepts. Whether this should be listed as a goal or a by-product is a matter of emphasis.

Recent investigation has been directed toward the use of frequency discrimination to help some deaf and hard-of-hearing children bring their voices into normal pitch range. The objective is to determine whether the child who has learned to discriminate between high- and low-frequency vibrations can learn to perceive the relationship of these vibrations to his own voice production.

The music program for the deaf and the hard-of-hearing in the public schools has contributed toward the improvement of self-image and the development of language in these children. In addition, some music activities have proved to be of diagnostic and stimulative value. Finally, the positive results of the program have enlisted interest in further investigation; for example, in the possible values that pitch discrimination in music might have for the control of voice inflection in speech.

The therapist, or the music consultant for special education, functions as a resource person for the special teachers and for the speech therapist. He visits the classrooms on a regularly scheduled basis and is available at other times when a special need arises. The philosophy underlying the overall program of the school is to help each child to become a citizen— self-sufficient and independent. Music in the special education curriculum functions as one means in a complete program directed toward appropriate life adjustment.

26

THE MUSIC LESSON

PETER F. OSTWALD

The music lesson exemplifies one of mankind's oldest and most honorable traditions: to influence constructively the sound-making behavior of the young. Yet, if the history of music teaching is traced back to its origins in antiquity, it will be evident how often this form of education is applied rather selectively only to certain social groups (Oberborbeck, 1961). In ancient Egypt (2500 B.C.), for example, music lessons were reserved for ladies of the court. Spartan Greece trained only free youths in music. During the early Christian era musical training was split up to provide the *musicus*, who had an all-around liberal arts training, and the *cantor*, or practical musician. Modern musical training also may show a certain dichotomy, with some teachers focusing on performance, others on the appreciation of music. Music therapy is a form of education that combines both approaches in an effort to provide for the musical needs of a special group of persons. Students of the music therapist, often a music teacher, belong to that, in many ways disadvantaged, group known as the mentally and emotionally ill. The following ideas about music lessons and music teaching are intended to focus on some psychological principles that make the lesson a unique tool for influencing members of this group. The four brief episodes that follow illustrate successful and unsuccessful applications of music teaching.

From Music to Mastery. A powerful, 6-foot, 200-pound teen-ager has worn out a succession of schools and private tutors with his rebellious and aggressive behavior. He is the despair of his parents, who are highly educated people and expect at least adequate school performance from their only son. But Martin's single interest is to play the drums. He refuses to open his school books until a music teacher is found who recognizes and develops the boy's latent intellectual talents. Sensitive to the schizoid pattern of Martin's fantasy life, the music teacher builds a bridge between the rhythmicity of drumming and the orderliness of nature. Martin now finds that mathematics is nothing to be afraid of—there are numbers in

[317]

music and in science, too. The teacher leads him to appreciate extra-musical knowledge, and the resulting pleasure pulverizes the patient's school phobia.

Music Is Not Enough. Pampered, coddled, spoiled, and inadequately prepared for life, P at twenty-five decides to make music his career. To the teacher he brings a hypertrophied speaking knowledge of music but a performance capacity only sufficient to justify applause for an eight-year-old. The music teacher tries scales and basic theory. The student does poorly. The teacher tries to encourage performance, with the result that the student seeks night club jobs. Failure follows failure. Only after P enters psychotherapy does he realize that his submission to the teacher is based on a longing for affection and a secret craving for recognition. In hidden fantasies and dreams he sees the music teacher as parent, rival, and boxing partner. As soon as real gratification comes about through work, love, and lasting interpersonal relationships, the patient abandons music and the music teacher.

The Tide Is Turned. L has two major interests in life—eating and practicing the piano. Except for her parents, whose punitive attitudes control her behavior, there are no significant people in her life. A new music teacher is at first only accepted as an inanimate object—part of the piano —a solid, indestructible creature who cannot hit back. But he very gently detaches himself from the instrument and talks with L about her life away from the keyboard. This produces a panic of such proportions that hospitalization has to be considered. A psychiatrist is consulted. After a few discussions, teacher and student can continue their work. It takes years for L to develop comfort in her relationship with the music teacher who, in turn, learns to limit his attention to the patient's keyboard exercises.

Who Won? On a fellowship for students from a nation once at war with the United States, Kay finds life here a strange but wonderful experience. She runs into trouble when a certain pushiness of personality antagonizes her roommates. Kay's music teacher wisely channels her aggression into a competition, in the hope that she may win a performing contract. Every ounce of energy is spent preparing works of a dazzling, virtuoso nature. Yet Kay only gets to the semifinals. Another foreign student wins the contest. Seething with rage, Kay makes a nuisance of herself, and the teacher quickly modifies his approach to her talents. Competence in performing and joy in playing will be enough. He convinces the student that she should accept music for music's sake and persuades her to abandon the fantasy of using it as a vehicle for conquering the world.

What elements of personality does the teacher bring to bear on the music lesson? How does he apply the psychological leverage needed to help emotionally turbulent students master this most abstract of all arts? Let us look at the music teacher as listener, as guide, as coach, and as healer.

The Teacher as Listener

In music we sense most directly the inner flow which sustains the psyche or the soul.—Michael Tippett

How the teacher listens—with what degree of undivided attention and empathy—often spells the difference between success and failure in the music lesson. In his relationship with the student, the music teacher performs a function that in certain ways resembles a mother quietly contemplating her child. He observes the breathing, the emotional expressions, and the waxings and wanings of inner tension. He focuses his sensory organs—especially his ears—on the student and clears his mind of all thoughts except those pertaining to the music. He places the student on a mental stage elevated above commonplace problems, listening exclusively to him.

Being listened to is one of the most rewarding experiences a human being can have. Communication with sounds, which starts in the earliest relationship between the newborn and its mother, is basic for emotional empathy. Before words ever come into play, each personality experiences the give and take of communication with tones, rhythms, and melody fragments. This is how our needs for comfort, food, warmth, protection, and security are first expressed. The mother who correctly perceives these signals rewards the child with pleasurable, joyful feelings. Frustrated, the child becomes angry, sad, or frightened (Spitz, 1965).

Many of these positive and negative emotions may be reexperienced in the context of the music lesson, which is a kind of immunizing experience for a student preparing himself to go out into the world and perform there. The students and patients of the music therapist-teacher have often been cruelly hurt and disappointed in their life performance. One is reminded of the anxious child who cannot overcome his fear of strangers and starts to frown or cry when a person who has not been identified as safe and loving approaches him; he reserves genuine smiles of friendly joy for only the most intimate relationships. Unhappy, lethargic, withdrawn babies, who have not been favored by the growth-impelling powers of maternal love, continue to show an anxious, unsmiling approach to people for years, sometimes all their lives, hardly ever breaking **through** their shells of social isolation with genuinely warm smiles and laughter. Notice the mechanical rhythms, the harsh humming, and other pseudomusical activities of psychotic children. There is no communication of pleasure. The child is rocking himself, trying to obtain what his mother should have provided. The patient's stiff movements are attempts to find out where legs or arms are located in space—not expressive activities that invite other children to play. His "singing" is rote imitation, the same fragment of melody repeated over and over again like a frantic search for time stability. These vocalizations cannot induce others to join in games or choruses.

The Teacher as Guide

The most beautiful melodies will always indifferently affect the ear which is not accustomed to them. Here is a language that requires the dictionary.— Jean Jacques Rousseau

The music teacher must be concerned with what to listen for. Music organizes time and space by way of acoustic structures. Musical experience based on closely organized rhythm, tone, and volume gradation has been marvelously conceptualized in traditional Western counterpoint and harmony. Eastern music, serial composition, and *musique concrète* call on a more expanded model for the analysis of auditory experience. The following may give a schematic image of what music is able to synthesize.

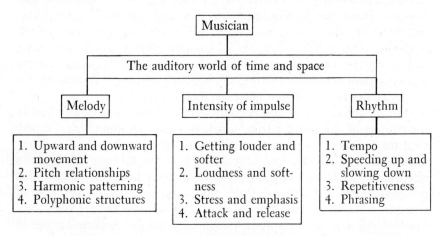

Guides use maps. The music teacher's map was invented by Guido of Arezzo, the genius of the Middle Ages who devised musical notation. Before this time, all music had to be memorized; then a visual aid became available. Notes of the scale were placed on lines and spaces. The

Guidonic hand represented the tone system on the fingers of the left hand, a four-lined staff. The right index finger pointed to the notes. This established a visual-motor image in the mind much like an alphabet and its representation in writing movements. Multipart singing in choruses became possible, permitting the symbolic differentiation of age and sex through the different voices—soprano, alto, tenor, and bass.

In guiding a student's understanding, music teachers face the dilemma of too global versus too particular an approach to sounds, movements, and expressive behavior. Globalism reduces intellectual control and may delete from conscious perception the architectural elements that make musical listening such a uniquely satisfying experience. Excess particularization can anesthetize the student's sensuous perception of musical forms. For instance, one of the most exhilarating moments in listening to classical music is the feeling of recognizing themes that, having been exhaustively varied and modulated through the development section, return in their original version. Too particular an analysis of this can deaden the student's esthetic appreciation. If he already senses the closure of a pattern, it should not be necessary to explain every detail of the composer's craftsmanship, the stylistic habits of the period from which the music is derived, or the interpretive capacities of the performer. Beware of turning musical analysis into a dissection. The guiding teacher trusts his students' innate sensibilities for rejecting what is ugly and false in art. Criticism coming out of the analysis of music should be constructive, showing respect for the enormous self-discipline that musicianship requires.

The Teacher as Coach

I have no use for a school teacher who cannot sing.—Martin Luther

A music teacher communicates the technical skills of his art. Some do this nonrationally—for example, the famous performers who can convey this information simply through demonstration. Others may know a great deal about how to play an instrument—and this can be communicated—without being master players themselves. A teacher lacking skill or knowledge of technique, however, runs a serious risk. Nothing is so tragic as a student whose interest in music has been squelched by inadequate or incorrect coaching. Technical skill starts with a reverence for equipment. Music is a sport as well as an art, and the entire body enters into musical behavior. The teacher must know how the body breathes, how the bones and joints articulate, and where the important nerves and muscles are located. For singers and wind players, knowledge of breath control, phonetics, and facial expression is essential. Pianists and violinists have to learn the pulley system of finger-wrist-elbow and the fascinating many-levered shoulder joint. A good teacher shows the student how to tense and relax his body. As coach, he should teach principles that students can readily apply, but should avoid imposing a set of patterns on the young musician. Each student develops a personal style of expression, integrating the particular strengths and weaknesses of his own body and temperament, the necessities of his musical instrument, and the traditional practices learned from his music teacher. Whether to hold the violin at an angle, whether to sit with elbows above or below the keyboard, how to balance head with chest register—these are technical matters with which the coach concerns himself and for which he encourages each student to find his own solutions.

How to keep musical equipment shipshape should also be taught by the teacher. Our instruments have taken a long time to evolve their present shape, and each has an interesting history. The flutist should know the physics of his flute and its forerunners in earlier pipe instruments. Violinists can be especially proud of their instrument's carpentry tradition, which includes craftsmen whose products are older than the Declaration of Independence and just as durable. Organists are privileged to operate musical machines intimately related to the march of religious history. And the electronic composer of today is part of a technological achievement that goes back to Pythagoras and ancient Greece.

Even the anatomy and physiology of the ear have a place in music teaching. This tiny, delicate mechanism has enormous efficiency. It should be treated with care and respect because of its vulnerability to fluid collections, inflammations, and injury. What an incredible sensing device; the ear is capable of responding to air vibrations smaller than the diameter of a hydrogen atom.

The Teacher as Healer

> Music exalts each joy, allays each grief,
> Expels diseases, softens every pain,
> Subdues the rage of passion and the plague.—John Armstrong

Healing is not synonymous with therapy. Therapy demands an active approach, a willingness for the strong to help the weak. To do his job effectively, a therapist may have to inflict temporary discomfort when cleansing away the debris of a wound that fails to heal spontaneously. Only after this is done can healing processes take place. Healing relies on the organism's innate capacity to repair itself, and the healer has to wait patiently for this to occur. He maintains optimism while trusting health to overcome disease. Relying on nature and the patient, a healer modestly and humbly mutes his own role in the conquest of a malady. The posture of fighting disease has little place in healing.

Music heals the breach between the direct and the symbolic expressions of emotional impulses. Direct expression of emotion leads to movements and actions—running away in fear, lashing out in rage, submitting to hedonism, or giving up in despair. Man's ability for symbolization makes abstract substitutes for direct action possible—words replace deeds, pictures symbolize fantasies, icons indicate actions. Often we are trapped between conflicting goals in direct versus symbolic expression. Music may provide a bridge to cross this conflict because it is both action *and* symbol. The musical experience allows us simultaneously to have very strong emotions and to safely contain these emotions in nondisruptive ways. Music's dual capacity for stimulating and soothing the emotions enables the music teacher to play such a vital healing function in civilization.

Music consists of sounds and silences—both have healing properties. One can even think of music in terms of its ability to organize silence. One important responsibility of the teacher and music therapist may be to prevent choking the patient's environment with music to the point that it becomes intolerable noise. There may be times when he must know how to restrain making music. A closely related healing function is correctly advising the overzealous parents of children who are deficient in talent. Although overtly wishing to foster their child's musical development, the parents' covert purposes may be to exploit the youngster for prestige or financial profit. Exploitation does not necessarily produce bad effects musically speaking, as witness such exploited prodigies as Wolfgang Mozart or Ruth Slencinska. It is the injurious effect on personality we want to avoid. Exploitation gives the child a distorted sense of his own worth; he feels that he exists basically to gratify the needs of others and sees himself as an appendage to their lives rather than an integral entity. Sensing fierce exploitative or competitive motives behind a parent's request for his child's music lessons, teachers should discuss realistically with all concerned the disadvantages as well as the benefits of a musical career.

A cautious, healing attitude also helps in the management of sick children and their families. The wise teacher refers the emotionally disturbed to professional psychiatrists, physicians, and psychologists trained to treat the sick. A knowledge of past experiences with music in the home and family tells the teacher when to encourage further training and when to use other resources for help. He may ask the parents about their own personal experiences with music lessons; whether records are played at home, concerts attended, singing and dancing encouraged. The nursery school or kindergarten child has already been exposed to teaching influences outside the home that may provide useful clues as to whether more or less individual instruction is needed. One should beware of forcing music on a student who does not want to learn; encouragement can turn into discouragement and a fragile glimmer of the potential enjoyment of music may be extinguished forever. "I would have learned to like music had my piano teacher not insisted on scales" is the kind of complaint one hears from some of those whose teachers could not let them go.

To increase our tolerance for new and unexpected sounds may be another of the healing functions of music. All people tend to develop certain acoustical preferences, and some may become conditioned to avoid sounds they do not like. Our basic attitudes toward acoustical patterns probably develop early in life when any sudden and intense stimulus is likely to produce a major reflex response, often a startled reaction. Loud noises can also make an infant uncomfortable and cause him to cry. This cry perhaps adds an unconscious memory trace to the baby's backlog of behavioral experiences with sounds, hearkening back to the ambiguous communication when nobody was quite sure whether the signal was for food, warmth, diaper change, or holding. When vocalizing becomes speech, another layer of values is superimposed on the basic attitude to sounds. Positively, speech is associated with intelligence—"My, isn't Johnny a smart boy to learn so many words." Negatively, speech may be equated with unwanted aggression—"I wish that damn brat would keep his mouth shut." Not only vocal sounds are ambivalently valued in these ways. Rhythmic banging of toys, the cacophony of feet and elbows on the floor or furniture, the crashing of dishes and implements—these and other acoustical elements in a child's behavior elicit both positive and negative reactions from grown-ups. Because a child will identify with his grown-up models, part of his mind can embrace or incorporate such valuations. Inner conflicts may develop between impulses that promote noisy release and those that carry social disapproval. The healer's difficult task is to enter into the child's subjective world of sound valuations in order to reduce, whenever possible, the pressure of such conflicts. If the student can learn to appreciate beautiful (that is, musical) sounds, this may help build up his tolerance for noise (that is, unwanted sounds).

Finale

I have tried, in this brief essay, to compare the work of the music teacher with that of the listener, the guide, the coach, and the healer. Each of these functions may be involved in music therapy, which is the teaching of music to the emotionally and mentally disadvantaged. The music lesson is an ancient and honorable human institution, a mark of civilization. It carries forward the tradition of musical expression, which mediates between the direct expression of emotion and the symbolic sublimation of emotion (Ostwald, 1963).

References

OBERBORBECK, F. Musikerziehung. In F. Blume (Ed.), *Die musik in geschichte und gegenwart*. Bärenreiter, Kassel, 1961. Vol. 9.

OSTWALD, P. F. *Soundmaking—the acoustic communication of emotion.* Springfield, Ill.: Charles C Thomas, 1963.

SPITZ, R. A. *The first year of life*. New York: International Universities Press, Inc., 1965.

Part VIII

DANCE THERAPY

Mary Ryder Toombs

*A*lthough most music therapists have not had sufficient training to use dance therapy in the manner described by Mary Toombs, all music therapists do make use of the dance for therapeutic purposes. Most music in the world is dance music. Only rarely is the dance carried on unaccompanied by music. In nearly all cultures except our own dance is a part of religious activity. Many times the dance is far more complex than its accompanying music. The use of the dance adds a dimension to music therapy that can be achieved in no other way. Dance has its esthetic rewards just as does music. It has many functional advantages also. Its great therapeutic potential has not been fully realized in music therapy. The dance and the therapist persuade behavior change just as surely as does music.

27

DANCE THERAPY

MARY RYDER TOOMBS

Since the time of early man, the dance has played an important role in man's life. Primitive man expressed through dance movements many things that could not be expressed adequately in words—religion, fear, awe of the unknown. Throughout much of our literature, whether it be on esthetics, religion, or social science, there is evidence that primitive man attributed magical powers to the dance. In historical and anthropological reports, small doubt exists concerning its broad function, its power, and its influence, particularly in times that were critical for the individual, a tribe, or many tribes.

A frenzy equal to the Greek Dionysian dance recurred repeatedly in the aborigines of North America. In the Ghost Dance of the 1870s, the Indians danced monotonously in a circle formation until, one by one, all dropped rigid and prostrate on the ground. It was believed by Benedict (1934, p. 92) that during their seizures these dancers had visions of deliverance from the whites. Other examples of faith in the magical powers of the dance include that of the primitive dancers of northern Mexico and that shown in the shaman's dances of California. Both of these dances required some component of cataleptic seizure.

In contrast to those influenced by the cult of Dionysius whose dancing brought on ecstatic experiences, the Pueblo Indians believed the dance was their means of swinging the forces of nature to their purposes. Their dance was a "monotonous compulsion of natural forces by reiteration" (Benedict, 1934, p. 92). To the Pueblos, the cumulative forces of the rhythm of a large group of dancers moving as one man made the dance effective. They believed their dances forced rain from the clouds, coerced the corn to sprout, and brought forth game animals. The occurrence of the "danced-for" effects was evidence of the efficacy of the dance to move the supernatural favorably (Benedict, 1934, p. 93). In Chapter 1 of this book, Gaston has described the phenomenon of the ancient dances of Central America.

At one time both music and the dance evolved from the aura of what is now called mysticism but which to the dancers was often religion. It was the therapeutic value of both media that earned the place of music and dance in the mystical (religious) rites of man. Although it is no less true today that music and dance bring catharsis and creative inspiration to the frustrated and anxious, this is no longer accepted as justification for the label of other-worldliness and only occasionally is the trance induced. Rosen (1957) expresses the potential of dance therapy for the mentally disturbed very clearly in the following statement:

> Because dance uses physical movement of the human body as a means of communication, because of its psychodynamic quality, its social character and its cultural meaning in our society, dance can be utilized in the rehabilitation of the mentally disturbed as an additional means of reaching the patient and helping him achieve his goal of resocialization (p. 4).

Dance therapy is the specific use of dance movements as a means of nonverbal communication, emotional release of both hostile and tender feelings, physical relaxation, and increased self-awareness. Therapeutically, the beauty of perfection of the dance movements is not to be given primary consideration. Instead, the dance therapist interprets the patient's movements as a communication of his individual emotions, mood of the moment, and degree of security. The development of the ability to dance well, gracefully, and with good coordination and skill is subordinate to the needs of the patient.

Because disruption in communication is the important problem for the psychiatric patient, dance therapy provides the individual with a means of reestablishing communication with his personal and social environment when he is otherwise cut off by the patterns of his illness (Chace, 1953).

Dance Therapy with Adults

Chace (1953) considers dance therapy a primary method for initial contact that subsequently provides crucial support for the psychiatric patient. Through the warming-up of the dance, the patient becomes aware of himself as an entity functioning with other entities in comparative safety. Most patients, especially those who are very withdrawn, will unwittingly reveal emotions they could not otherwise express. Along the same line, the more sensitive patients can use dance as an effective vehicle to gain insight into their personalities.

In dance therapy, creative modern dance is the most commonly used type. It is the most adaptable form of dance for mental patients and the handicapped because its form is flexible and its technique is based on natural functional movements of the body. Furthermore, *the movements of modern dance permit the individual to express psychic states that are more primitive than language* (Chace, 1953; Bender and Boas, 1941; Rosen, 1954; Toombs, 1958; Bartenieff, 1958; Espenak, 1963).

Although there are many variations in the application of dance therapy, most therapists employ similar techniques. Much emphasis is placed on the encouragement of spontaneous and individualized expression. Furthermore, the group approach to dance utilizes natural, functional movements, which are preferred and emphasized, rather than stylized forms. The dance leader or therapist assumes an accepting, supporting role when catalyzing dance movements or action in the group.

The patient in the dance therapy group is permitted to relate directly to the therapist through singularly meaningful, albeit bizarre, movements. The patient loses his feeling of isolation and fear of lack of understanding, and through his interaction with the therapist, he becomes acceptable to other members in the dance group. In addition, he learns to accept others and their individualized movements. Gradually he becomes comfortable enough to function satisfactorily as a member of the dance group. This reintegration of the individual into the group is one of the ultimate aims not only of dance therapy but of nearly all therapy. As needed, the therapist works individually with a given patient. Usually the therapist returns the patient to the group as soon as possible so that he can relate as a member of the group to the therapist.

Marian Chace (1953), dance therapist at St. Elizabeth's Hospital in Washington, D. C., has written more about dance therapy and has done more to further its acceptance in hospitals than any other clinician. Because she has had the longest (since 1942) and most continuous role in the clinical use of dance therapy, her techniques, observations, and evaluations have special significance.

In organizing a dance therapy program, Chace did not restrict her groups to any type of patient. Most of her classes were held in a room designated for dance therapy. Initially, she made contact with newly admitted patients on admission wards. In her sessions, patients were free to join in or leave the dancing. She used a circle formation much of the time, and as the patients came and went, the size and shape of the formation changed. The function of the circle, however, was maintained. In describing the movements used to establish initial contact with a patient, Chace stated,

The movements used in establishing initial contact with a patient may be qualitatively similar to those of the patient (not mimicking since this is often construed by the patient as mocking) or they may be as expressive of an entirely different emotion with which the therapist has responded to the patient's gestures. Intense alertness is essential in judging which approach should be used so that the dance therapist may immediately establish herself as a "safe" person (p. 221).

Chace has stressed that the dance movements initially must have a reaching-out quality toward the patient that expresses the therapist's friendliness and acceptance. Making initial contacts on a one-to-one basis with a group of patients can be accomplished by moving quickly from one patient to another. This procedure seemed to make these contacts almost simultaneous, thus providing multiple individual lines of communication that were gradually developed into a group activity with the therapist as the catalyst.

Chace had an interesting viewpoint about touch in dance therapy. The initiative for making actual physical contact was left to the patient, whose freedom to withdraw was never restricted in any way. However, the therapist always indicated through her movements her willingness, availability, or readiness to enter into physical contact. She believed that the circle formation was the most satisfactory means of involving the whole group. It made it easier for a succession of patients to assume the role of leader in movement, by spontaneously improvising movements the other patients could follow. The mood of the patients was a major consideration in determining the type of music used (isomoodic). Eventually, these improvisations could be used in performances of original dances. Through participation in simple movements and expanding to the complex movements of improvisation, the patients gained more confidence in their own body action, which then helped them relate to each other and perhaps even rehabilitated them enough so they could relate to other people. Chace (1954a) emphasized the fact that

Each dance leader will use, from his own technical background, those skills he has developed as tools in helping others to have confidence in their own emotional expressions, rather than in building adept dancers in a particular school of movements (p. 65).

For dance therapy to provide sufficient freedom for the patient to dance by himself with support by group action, there must be a lack of rigidity, the leader must participate as a group member, and there needs to be an accent on free expression rather than absolute conformity to predetermined structure. In another article describing her dance therapy sessions, Chace (1954b) encourages the dance therapist to give the patients complete freedom of expression so they can form a group that will compose dances together, accepting discipline from one another rather than from a leader.

A somewhat different approach to dance therapy is espoused by Rosen (1957), who considers the use of aides or assistants essential to the therapeutic process of the dance. For Rosen, an assistant dance leader is essential in meeting the needs of the individual patients. Even though she agrees with Chace's concept of the role of the dance therapist, Rosen feels that to provide a supporter to the individual and a catalyst to the group requires two therapists, because there are simultaneous demands for the two roles. To meet the contingencies, Rosen had three graduate students with professional training in modern dance who assisted her in the three different patient groups with which she worked.

The degree to which the dance therapist is comfortable in shifting her focus of attention from the individual to the group determines somewhat the need for an assistant dance leader. The size of the group, the severity and complexity of the patients' illnesses, and the existing amount of group feeling would also be factors in evaluating the need for an assistant. In reporting on her study, Rosen also discussed the kind of music and accompaniment preferred, the costuming used, and the methods of recording data.

In contrast to Chace, Rosen stresses the use of a competent pianist over any other type of accompaniment. The accompanist assisting Rosen improvised readily to provide the flexibility and variety of rhythms and melody needed for dancing. Notwithstanding, there were times when she used recorded music, the patients' voices, handclaps, and/or footsteps. It may have been that she chose accompaniments according to the situation and the type and number of patients.

Rosen recorded her data by means of three types of records and accounts: (1) Personal record forms were completed, giving the reactions of each individual; (2) descriptive accounts of each dance session were made; and (3) periodic recordings were collected that noted the growth and development of the individual in terms of his feeling and behavior toward the group. Rosen had psychiatric guidance and interpretation during the study to illuminate the individual responses of the patients.

In her discussion and summary, Rosen pointed out an obvious limitation of her study—the subjective nature of the observations. She stated that the narrative-style progress notes tend to be influenced by the personal enthusiasm and interest of the observer and that, because dance is a momentary creation, its forms cannot be held in time for examination or review except by the camera. At that time, Rosen (1957) felt that neither the camera nor any other objective approach could catch "the dancer's intent, his emotional investment and the spontaneous quality of his response" (p. 140). However, because of the development of technology in video taping, this is no longer true.

The quality of the kind of music accompaniment available is a reality factor to be considered. If there is no competent live pianist or no good piano available for the dance sessions, obviously other types of accompaniment must be used. Similarly, if the only phonograph available is inadequate or the selection of recordings is very poor, a live pianist would be the preferred choice to provide needed accompaniments. A combination of many types of accompaniment would assure the maximum in variety and flexibility.

As an example of techniques, the behavior of the therapist is modified to fit the behavior of the patient. With a very passive, fearful schizophrenic patient, seemingly rooted to one spot in the room, the therapist offers both palms upward and moves forward and backward. This movement gradually and gently develops into a mild clapping of hands with the patient, and as the patient feels release, he can become quite actively aggressive. In contrast, an assaultive patient, moving toward the therapist with threatening gestures, should be met with a dance movement expressive of submission; if the patient's aggressive movement continues, the therapist responds with steadfastness, displayed by erectness of torso and wide, firmly planted feet. Often the therapist may try "putting hands on each other's shoulders and pushing back and forth, setting up a swinging motion across the dance floor. This action is in essence a substitution or sublimation of the assaultive action . . ." (Chace, 1953, p. 222).

Dance therapy must be adapted to fit the severity of the patients' illnesses, the age range of the group, and the physical layout of the day hall or special room used by the dance groups. Dance therapy procedures may have to be further modified when the patient is taking medication. It is often necessary to have shorter dance sessions with less vigorous action to avoid such physical reactions as profuse perspiration, dizziness, nausea, and loss of balance. Patients receiving electroshock therapy often are confused and slow in their reactions. With these patients, the pace of the dance sessions often needs to be much slower to give them sufficient time to comprehend and react appropriately.

Providing both music and dance therapy on admission, active-treatment, continued-treatment, and rehabilitation wards in a unified program of music therapy and dance therapy has been found quite effective (Toombs, 1958). Although dance sessions on the wards usually are alternated with group sings and rhythm bands, they are similar to dance sessions with very regressed men of long-term hospitalizations.

Backgrounds of patients must also be considered in choosing music and the type of dance. The technique of allowing a patient to assume leadership in the circle formation in order to elicit creativity was used with female patients in a Veterans Administration hospital. The reactions of these women tended to be noticeably different from those of women in state hospital settings. Female patients at the VA hospital were former servicewomen, and they preferred exercises more closely resembling calisthenics to the softer, more sustained ballet-like movements preferred by the other group. Most of the VA hospital patients preferred to verbalize their feelings, often negative ones, rather than express them nonverbally through dance movements, the preferred medium of the patients in the state hospitals.

In a recent publication, Chace (1963) describes changes she made in structuring her dance sessions for the varying needs of patients. She explains that such changes were necessary because of the new attitudes and new help extended to the patients from many directions: The increased use of drugs to assist patients in functioning; the interchange between the hospital and the community; and the need to get more patients out of the hospital more quickly made it necessary to change the approaches used by the treatment team. Another modification in the structure of the dance session may be necessary with psychotic patients who communicate verbally but with difficulty. With such patients, the session may be structured as a dramatic scene, because "one of the difficulties of the person functioning in the world is a lack of spontaneity in response to stimuli which call for unstudied speech as well as unstudied movement" (Chace, 1963, p. 68).

Chace states that hospital dance sessions need to be conducted more as classes, with emphasis on the similarities rather than the dissimilarities to outside (community) dance sessions. With the emphasis on day centers and keeping patients on an out-patient basis when possible, dancing must be presented as an outlet the patients could enjoy in the community. Deprivation of painting, music, or dancing may contribute to the difficulties of patients seeking help in the day centers. Participation in the arts can help to sustain some of these patients in a functioning capacity. As a result, many day-care centers include art, music, and dance activities in their programs.

Uses of creative or interpretative movements with psychotic patients were reported by Goldstein, Lingas, and Sheafor (1965). Creative or interpretative movement was used as a sublimation tool for a music therapy group of four rigid, hostile women who had difficulty expressing emotions appropriately and related poorly in a group situation. After several months of a highly structured approach in which the music therapist played the piano and dictated the movements of group members, the therapist suggested to the group that if drawing and movement could be combined, emotional as well as intellectual insight might result. The patients were receptive to this idea, and one of them, who had done many drawings in occupational therapy, agreed to do a series of drawings representing her illness and her stay in the hospital. In using the seven pictures she drew as the basis for an interpretative dance, she and the other three patients volunteered for the roles they were to play. The patients selected their music from a record album according to the mood they felt it expressed. The resulting movements based on the drawings and the music chosen were a nonverbal counterpart of psychodrama, portrayed in creative, interpretative movements.

The dance therapist should always be interested in and concerned with the reactions or responses of the patients to dance therapy and suitable methods of recording these patient reactions. Bender and Boas (1941) and Bartenieff (1958) all have stressed the importance posture plays in expressing mood and emotion. Espenak (1963), a more recent exponent of dance therapy, referred to characteristic postures expressing certain moods or attitudes. Examples of these postures are the following:

1. The dejected attitude: Slumped shoulders, fallen chest, head on chest, fumbling steps.

2. The retiring attitude: Shy, inward-drawn, regressive, shoulders turned in, head between shoulders.

3. The heightened tension (with restricted and ineffectual movement in states of anxiety): Shoulders lifted up to ears, head in the neck, elbows tense, hands nervous.

4. The aggressive attitude: Strutting chest, swagger of shoulders, accent on heels (pp. 3–4).

The observed posture or the adoption of different postures appropriate to specific moods indicates the mood or emotion of the patient and the emotional changes of the patient during the dance therapy session.

Espenak (1963) created a battery of six movement-diagnosis tests in an effort to classify the patient and select the specific exercises that would awaken and strengthen the lacking awareness. The general groupings of her diagnosis tests were (1) confidence, balance, and self-assurance; (2) (emotional) reactions to various moods; (3) kinesthetic awareness—dynamics; (4) coordination; (5) attention span; and (6) anxiety and physical fear (pp. 6–7). The tests had seven gradations: excellent, very good, good, fair, poor, very poor, and yes or no. Periodically, she repeated these tests to check progress of the patient. Espenak felt the greatest value of dance as a specialized therapy is the "conscious build-up of the missing kinesthetic awareness with its work-back on the corresponding emotions" (p. 8). Also, the weekly creative dance class, with an opportunity of outlet, has a stabilizing effect on all participants whether neurotic or not. Espenak refers to this as an emotional thermostat (p. 5).

Characteristic patterns of patient responses to dance were demonstrated in an earlier article by Rosen (1954), and her dissertation research at Manhattan State Hospital corroborated her earlier findings at Hillside Hospital. Rosen (1954, 1957) found that withdrawn patients participated best when the dance form was very structured and set to repetitive, simple, rhythmic patterns. The defensive patient typically showed a reluctance to participate; his emotional response was carefully controlled. The patient rejected the dance just as he would reject any other medium of free expression.

Rosen further described the different values that the dance has for different classes of patients. Aggressive, acting-out patients were more responsive to content, finding a release in expressive interpretation. Often unconscious hostility was released in dance form and then was recognized by the patient. He could talk about it and perhaps utilize it in his treatment. Exhibitionistic patients who were grandiose in manner used dancing for their personal gratification. These patients needed greater permissiveness and more individual attention. They participated only when they were watched and admired for their attractiveness and skill. Patients who used intellectualism as an escape found dance a possible way of stimulating emotional expression. Aware of a lack of feeling responses, they searched for an expressive medium and found it in dance therapy. The fourth and last type of patient response was labeled *voyeuristic identification*. These patients observed the dancing instead of participating actively, and they responded to the movement kinesthetically. They observed very closely, feeling the movement in their own muscles, and at times became so involved as spectators that they would suddenly get up and join the dancing for a moment or two. Rosen (1957) has given long, detailed narrative descriptions of patients' reactions and responses to dance therapy in three different clinical situations.

Dance Therapy with Children

To explain the effects that modern dance and music have on the individual, Bender and Boas (1941) have invoked neuroanatomical mechanisms, specifically those structures involved with audition and space localization. The psychokinetic method of dance therapy (Bunzel, 1948) can be grouped under the same rubric. Bunzel reasoned that the therapeutic effect was achieved in her group of children as they were led through physical exercises and dance, the goal being creative self-expression for each individual. The therapeutic effects of music and dance therapy are generally the same as those of any other effective therapy—relief of tensions and improved human relations, personal appearance, and self-regard (Bunzel, 1948; Chace, 1963).

Of special interest to those concerned with the physically handicapped child is the work of Bartenieff (1958), a physical therapist and a teacher of dance. She stressed that the dance therapist who works with the physically handicapped must base her selection of dance techniques for each patient on the physician's medical evaluation of the patient and the disability in terms of physical therapy. Then the dance techniques must result from a total creative dance expression based on the theories of Rudolf Laban of England.

Dance Therapy with the Mentally Retarded

With the current national interest in helping mentally retarded children and adults, it is important to consider the different approaches to dance therapy for the mentally retarded. Dance therapy with mentally retarded individuals is an educational experience compared to the rehabilitative experience the psychiatric, but nonretarded, patient needs. Because many retarded children have not passed through the period of transition from nonverbal to verbal communication, they are more spontaneous and comfortable when using their bodies in direct action to respond to emotion than are adult patients. A dance therapy session for retarded children should bring them new awareness of body coordination, sensitivity to musical tones and rhythms, and alertness to ways of using their bodies in dance movements. With better coordination, improved posture, and rhythm in his movements, the retarded child develops a feeling of greater confidence in himself and security in his environment. Although an authoritarian method of teaching often has distinct disadvantages, mental patients and children need structured classes with well-defined limits of expected behavior and organized instruction in the use of the body. Limits must be very clearly defined, no matter how much independence of action and initiative are encouraged. Then, as each child develops and is encouraged to assume more responsibility for his actions, the leader broadens the limits set and gives him greater freedom.

THE ROBINSES' EDUCATIONAL RHYTHMICS

One of the most promising newer forms of dance is *educational rhythmics,* a significant therapy technique created by Ferris and Jennet Robins of Switzerland for mentally handicapped children. The Robinses' technique is definitely more meaningful for the severely retarded than for the patient with behavior disorders.

The Robinses created their system of ballet-rhythmic and syncopated coordination to music after years of practical experience with mentally and physically handicapped children in the United States. Their exercises follow a middle road between ballet, gymnastics, syncopation, and esthetic expression. The educational goal is to help children master everyday actions. The techniques of educational rhythmics provide a wide range of opportunities for the handicapped to "experience synchronization at their own individual levels of motor and cognitive ability" (Arje and Berryman, 1966, p. 15). The selection of an exercise to be used depends on the current level of motoric and cognitive ability of the participating members of a given group. Also, the exercise can be modified according to cultural, ethnic, and national origins. The flexibility of educational rhythmics allows persons of all ages and abilities to have some or all of three types of learning experiences:

1. Motoric
   a. Muscle stretching, relaxing, balance
   b. Coordination of body movements
   c. Counter movement and springing

2. Cognitive
   a. Development of ability to concentrate
   b. Recognition of letters, numbers, colors
   c. Counting, telling time, spelling
   d. Self-care abilities

3. Affective
   a. Enjoyment of learning and doing
   b. Growth in creativity, self-esteem, imagination, and poise
   c. Satisfaction of cooperating with others
   d. Appreciation of good manners

The Robinses have developed workshops for training personnel in the use of their technique. In demonstrating some of their exercises and dances, they used nine groups of moderately and severely retarded institutionalized boys and girls. There were approximately ten in each group. The reactions of these children, as observed, were indeed impressive.

The Robinses (1965) have written a book explaining how to teach their educational rhythmics. Included in this book are detailed explanations of each exercise or dance with drawings that show the position of the dancer for each step. A list of the recordings used for the entire method is in the back of the book. The music to be used with the exercise is also given. It should be emphasized that the dances often fit the mood of the music rather than the meter and length of the recording recommended. This is especially true with the sustained dances requiring control and concentration from the children. Even though the mood of the recordings certainly is descriptive of the poems and the dance movements, the extra music is needed only during the learning process. Once the children learn such dances as "The Tree" or "The Seagull," the therapist must adapt the music to the dance, using only as much music as fits the poem and the dance movements.

Two and one-half years of experience with the trainable and educable mentally retarded convince one of the value of expanding dance therapy to include square dancing, educational rhythmics, and folk dancing in addition to creative modern dancing. The mildly and moderately retarded females will certainly benefit from creative modern dancing. However, even girls at this level in an institution for the mentally retarded need considerable help or training in dance movements before they can demonstrate much creative ability. It is this lack of creativity or inability to try to create that seems to be so prevalent among most of the mentally retarded. One reason for this inability may be either a lack of stimulation in the home environment or cultural deprivation. Another explanation might be that some retardates have an inability to assimilate as many stimuli as persons of normal intelligence.

In the creative modern-dance classes conducted at a state hospital and training center for the mentally retarded, modern-dance movements are combined with ballet and some dances from educational rhythmics. The girls in these classes demonstrate poor self-control, low frustration level, limited verbal skills, and, hence, a tendency to act out their feelings. Although these girls do not understand the meaning of creative modern dancing (modern dancing often is interpreted by teen-agers as the current popular forms of social dancing), many of them have heard of ballet or have seen it on television or in movies. Therefore, the girls are quite receptive, and it is most helpful to begin each session with several ballet exercises at the dance *barre* and to end the session with a few minutes of *port de bras* (arm exercises) in the center of the floor. These very specific exercises seem to give the girls the self-control they need to be ready for the dance class and finally to end the dance session in a quiet and relaxed mood.

Even with the more advanced dance class, it took many more sessions of dance therapy for the retardates to feel comfortable and self-confident enough to attempt to improvise dance steps to music than for the hospitalized psychiatric patients. Once the mildly retarded girls have started to create steps for a dance, with much reassurance and encouragement, they can usually create enough different, yet appropriate, steps to complete a dance for the entire piece of music. The mildly retarded, however, are not as spontaneously creative as are many psychiatric patients. With much practice of their dance, the moderately retarded girls master it and remember the sequence of steps quite well. However, it is a slow process to broaden their repertoire of movements.

Retarded girls are very responsive to learning the dances of the Robinses, which are simple dance movements accompanied by poetry set to well-known selections of classical music. Because the girls can learn these dances rather quickly, they gain much gratification and, at the same time, broaden their repertoire of dance movements. The Robinses' dances require the girls to fit their dance movements not only to musical phrases but also to the phrases of the poetry. For many of the retardates, rhythm and coordination are special problem areas. Often the mentally retarded become quite frustrated because they cannot get their dance movements to fit the music. Several of the Robinses' dances are most helpful in teaching rhythmic response and coordination to such girls.

In a dance class of preadolescent girls, learning some of the dances from the Robinses' method has provided new outlets for using dance movements. These girls are most enthusiastic about dance, but they are inhibited and self-conscious about suggesting new movements for a dance or even trying new movements demonstrated for them. Most of them are very awkward and rigid or stiff in many positions of the body. It is helpful to give them simple, structured models to imitate. Good examples of such models can be found in the dances "The Lovely Tree" or "The Clock." The combination of poetry and music seems rewarding to the moderately retarded girls and presents a challenge for them to match their dance movements to the music as they recite the words. For all people, imitation is necessary for learning, but it is vitally important for the mentally retarded. In dance there must be considerable imitative behavior before patients can be expressive enough to dance creatively.

In most institutions for the mentally retarded, many of the patients have marked emotional disturbances in addition to their retardation. It frequently is difficult for such patients to relate to others, either in a group or individually. Also, the more severely retarded patient has so few social responses that his attempts to relate to his peers are often inappropriate. Square dancing or simple folk dancing for the lower-functioning patient is directly helpful in providing the patients with both an appropriate social response and an opportunity to socialize with the opposite sex. The structure of square dancing not only forces the patients to concentrate while dancing, but also requires some degree of coordination, as well as development of discrimination between right and left feet and right and left hands. The changing of partners and the cooperative effort in performing the squares are conducive to developing marked group feeling.

Eichenbaum and Bednarek (1964) found that square dancing was a useful means of alleviating problems of extremely hostile, aggressive behavior in two special classes of mentally retarded children in a regular school. They reported that square dancing was valuable in developing recreational, motor, social, and emotional attitudes and skills. Included in their article are procedures that would be helpful in giving guidance, direction, and confidence to a teacher new to square dancing.

It is common observation that during square dancing the mentally retarded lose their fear of physical contact with the opposite sex. It appears that they find security in the structure of the dance. In part, fear reduction and increased security are enhanced in square dancing and folk dancing because they are group dances. There is not the threat of a one-to-one relationship that frequently is experienced in ballroom dancing. Although square-dance and folk-dance forms require a minimal degree of coordination, patients are not required to have the agility, grace, and balance that is necessary for creative modern dance.

A very important factor that should not be overlooked in dance therapy today is that *patients are going to return to the outside community more quickly than in the past.* Therefore, they need a mode of dance that they can find in the community. Even though a folk-dance group might not be available in some communities, square-dance groups are found all over the United States. If the patients derive satisfaction from square dancing and have achieved some proficiency in it, then square dancing will be quite beneficial in helping the retardate to adjust to the community outside the hospital setting.

In our culture, creative modern dancing is resisted strongly by most males. Also, in many communities there will be few, if any, opportunities for the female retardate to continue her creative modern dancing. Although therapeutic for them, few patients would have the music available or allow themselves to dance creatively alone in their homes. For the retardate, dancing is important as a social activity as well as a means of emotional expression. Frequently, the mentally retarded recognize the social value of dancing, but are unaware of its expressive value for them. Therefore, an experience in a class of square dancing would be the preferred form of dance therapy for most hospitalized mixed groups of mentally retarded adolescents.

With the lower-functioning mentally retarded, simple folk dances are beneficial. (See Adaptive Behavior Levels 3 and 4, Table 2, Chapter 3, p. 49.) Initially, moving together to music is a nonthreatening, pleasurable way to become aware of the others in the group. Also, it becomes easier to attempt to move in rhythm to the music when several other retarded males and females at about the same functioning level are taking part. The simple line or circle dances demand little and provide relatively quick success and gratification for the participants. As the retardates learn to walk forward or backward a specified number of steps and to slide, skip, or hop alone or with a partner, they gain self-confidence, improve in posture and coordination, and increase their attention spans. In some cases, for the first time, they become aware of how to move their feet and arms in different ways, how it feels to turn themselves around, and how it feels to move with a partner to rhythmical music. Frequently, as the folk dancing becomes more gratifying to the participants, they will talk more easily and interact spontaneously with one another.

One stumbling block encountered in all three types of dancing—creative modern, square, and folk—is the inability to know right from left. Steele (1966) recently conducted a study to investigate the effects of a time-out period for social reinforcement as a technique for teaching right-left (R-L) discrimination in a musical activity. Social reinforcement and the small-group setting were adopted because of their direct applicability to many clinical music therapy situations. Steele found that the use of a time-out period for social reinforcement in a group musical activity increased significantly the number of correct R-L responses made in the musical situation, but it did not significantly affect the number of correct R-L responses made by an individual in a nonmusical situation. Also, by using a time-out period for social reinforcement, the number of anticipatory responses made decreased significantly during the group musical activity. Steele recommended that a follow-up study be made to determine whether correct R-L responding in a musical activity (square dancing, action songs, and games) is facilitated by a brief preliminary drill of the desired response.

Personality of the Dance Therapist

At this point, mention should be made of the importance of the personality of the dance therapist. For many years, this has been of much concern in music and dance therapy. Undoubtedly, some of the success of the Robinses' method is due to the dynamic personality of Jennet Robins as she leads children in the exercises and dances. Parenthetically, one might mention that the same could be said of Chace and her effectiveness in working with groups.

Because determining the influence of the therapist's personality on the success of each therapy session is difficult, there has been more discussion than research concerned with this problem. Most therapists do agree that certain important qualities are necessary: There must be a keen alertness on the part of the therapist in order to observe as many patients as possible in the group; the therapist should take advantage of cues from the behavior of individual patients if the dance sessions are to be optimally effective; the therapist must display acceptance of the patients, and she must consistently give encouragement to them; and in dance therapy, if creativity is to occur, the therapist must have the ability to transfer leadership of the group to a patient when this is indicated.

References

ARJE, FRANCES B., and BERRYMAN, DORIS. New help for the severely retarded and emotionally disturbed child. *J. Rehabilit.*, 1966, 32, 14–15, 67.

BARTENIEFF, IRMGARD. How is the dancing teacher equipped to do dance therapy? In E. T. Gaston (Ed.), *Music therapy 1957*. Lawrence, Kan.: Allen Press, 1958. Pp. 145–150.

BENDER, LAURETTA, and BOAS, FRANZISKA. Creative dance in therapy. *Amer. J. Orthopsychiat.*, 1941, 11, 235–245.

BENEDICT, RUTH. *Patterns of culture*. Cambridge, Mass.: Harvard, 1934.

BUNZEL, GERTRUDE. Psychokinetics and dance therapy. *J. Hlth Phys. Educ.*, 1948, 19, 180–181.

CHACE, MARIAN. Dance as an adjunctive therapy with hospitalized mental patients. *Bull. Menninger Clin.*, 1953, 17, 219–225.

CHACE, MARIAN. Techniques for the use of dance as a group therapy. In Mariana Bing (Ed.), *Music therapy 1953*. Lawrence, Kan.: Allen Press, 1954(a). Pp. 62–67.

CHACE, MARIAN. Dancing helps patients make initial contacts. *Ment. Hosp.*, 1954(b), 5, 6–8.

CHACE, MARIAN. The structuring of dance sessions for varying needs of patients. In E. H. Schneider (Ed.), *Music therapy 1962*. Lawrence, Kan.: Allen Press, 1963. Pp. 63–68.

EICHENBAUM, BERTHA, and BEDNAREK, N. Square dancing and social adjustment. *Ment. Retard.*, 1964, 2, 106–109.

ESPENAK, LILJAN. The contribution of creative dance as adjunctive therapy. Paper read at a Staff Conf., New York Medical Coll., Mental Retardation Clin., January, 1963.

GOLDSTEIN, CAROLE, LINGAS, CATHERINE, and SHEAFOR, D. Interpretative or creative movement as a sublimation tool in music therapy. *J. Mus. Ther.*, 1965, 2, 11–15.

ROBINS, F., and ROBINS, JENNET. *Educational rhythmics for mentally handicapped children*. New York: Horizon Press, 1965.

ROSEN, ELIZABETH. Dance as therapy for the mentally ill. *Teachers Coll. Rec.*, Columbia, 1954, 55, 215–222.

ROSEN, ELIZABETH. *Dance in psychotherapy*. New York: Columbia, 1957.

STEELE, LOUISE. The effects of a time-out period for reinforcement on the frequency of correct right-left responses. Unpublished manuscript, Univer. of Kansas, 1966.

TOOMBS, MARY RYDER. Dance therapy in the ward music program. In E. T. Gaston (Ed.), *Music therapy 1957*. Lawrence, Kan.: Allen Press, 1958. Pp. 95–103.

Part IX

DEVELOPMENT OF MUSIC THERAPY IN THE COMMUNITY

Charles E. Braswell

One of the most significant changes in the mental health movement is the establishment of community health centers. As nearly as it is possible to foretell, the community health center movement has so many advantages that it will grow rapidly, displacing, in most cases, the very large psychiatric hospitals. It is far better to effect the rehabilitation of a patient without removing him from family and community than it is to isolate him from both. In the latter case, he must make major adjustments to the isolating institution, and then a second adjustment on his return to family and community. The community health center will not only make new demands on the music therapist, it will necessitate changing emphases on some of his continuing practices. Undoubtedly, community health center practices will compel changes in the academic and clinical training of music therapists. All of this indicates the necessity of a full understanding as soon as possible of the community health center and the function in it of the music therapist.

28

OVERVIEW

CHARLES E. BRASWELL

The music therapist is a competent musician who has received training in the biological and behavioral sciences. The concluding phase of his undergradauate education involves a period of supervised clinical experience in a psychiatric hospital. This broad training allows him to assume increasingly varied roles within the psychiatric institution, and in other areas as well. The need for versatility among music therapists is demonstrated in the reports that follow, wherein each writer describes activities that may be important not only now but in the future of music therapy. The clinical settings are different in each section, but there is a common pattern: The programs described represent a movement toward the community and away from institutional isolation.

The community mental health movement is not a new phenomenon. In 1946, Congress passed the National Mental Health Act, which recognized the inadequate conditions of the state hospital system. The Federal government offered help in research, manpower training, and the development of community facilities for psychiatric treatment. Official recognition of the mental health problem stimulated criticism of the state hospital system (Wilmer, 1948). In 1955, Congress, realizing the limitations of the National Mental Health Act, called for a comprehensive evaluation of mental health problems in the United States. An official organization, the Joint Commission on Mental Illness and Health, was formed to undertake an extensive five-year study. Thirty-six professional organizations engaged in caring for the mentally ill were invited to participate (Albee, 1959). The results of this study were published in a report entitled *Action for Mental Health* (1961).

After receiving the commission's report, President Kennedy made the following statement in his health message to Congress in 1962:

I want to take this opportunity to express my approval, and offer Federal cooperation, for the action of the Governors of the 50 states at a special National Governors' Conference called last November. In accepting the challenge of the report of the Joint Commission on Mental Illness and Health, they pledged a greater state effort—both to transfer treatment of the majority of mental patients from isolated institutions to modern psychiatric facilities in the heart of the community, and to provide more intensive treatment for hospitalized patients in state institutions (*Congressional Record,* 1962, p. 3144).

Congress appropriated 4.2 million dollars to be given to the states to initiate plans for the construction of comprehensive mental health centers. In 1963, Public Law 88164 provided funds for the construction of many of these centers (Bell, 1964). This sequence of events is unparalleled in the history of American psychiatry. Never before has such broad legislation been enacted on behalf of the mentally ill. Congressional involvement has supplied the goal, the means for its implementation, and a tentative timetable for completion. The community movement, in effect, is social progress decreed by legislation (Hewitt, 1960; Knoff, 1960; Smith, 1960).

Although each community mental health center will reflect the needs of the community in which it exists, there will be some common patterns of services. Each treatment complex will offer evaluation and diagnosis, therapy, rehabilitation, and aftercare (Barton, 1964, pp. xiii–xvi). It is likely that both inpatient and outpatient facilities will be provided. These community centers probably will be called mental health centers rather than psychiatric centers, and the treatment offered, in a majority of cases, will be described as counseling rather than psychotherapy. This change in nomenclature may help remove some of the stigma attached to treatment. The convenience of community centers and the reduction of stigma may motivate patients to seek treatment. Barton (1964) suggests that individual psychotherapy is not practicable.

"There are many indications that most of the centers consider individual psychotherapy as the treatment of choice, or, as one director put it, 'the backbone of our therapeutic program.'" This may be interpreted to mean that individual psychotherapy is the ideal toward which the psychiatrist wishes to move. This idea, if it is one, should be recognized as a fantasy, for the numbers of persons requiring help are such as to make prolonged psychotherapy (and even individual psychotherapy by the physicians as the principal form of therapy) impractical in the majority of cases (pp. xv–xvi).

It is likely that group psychotherapy and an extensive activity program will be adopted.

The following chapter is a shortened version of an official report to the Clinical Practices Committee of the National Association for Music Therapy. Many changes that are taking place in the organization and practice of therapy are documented. Because these changes are likely to alter the practice of music therapy, they are of serious concern. Although some of the factors described are not directly pertinent, they are included so that a more complete view may be obtained.

In Chapter 30, it is suggested that music therapists working in community settings should be aware of the relationship between basic social and interactional skills and adjustment. A different aspect of the use of music therapy with exceptional children is reported in Chapter 31 by Crocker. Her work covers purposes ranging from eliciting biographical data during musical improvisations (with the resultant music often used as a projective technique) to initiating and reinforcing positive behavior patterns. Crocker's approach allows professional cooperation with psychiatrists and clinical psychologists.

Another community music therapy service is reported by Tyson in Chapter 33; she discusses the history, goals, and organization of a creative arts rehabilitation center in a large Eastern city. Her program aims for comprehensive coverage by the use of a number of music therapists, each a specialist. The report by Alvin in Chapter 34 is concerned with England's community psychiatry movement. The development of community treatment services was begun in England earlier than in the United States. Music therapists in England have had more time to adjust to changing concepts and patterns of patient care. In Chapter 35 Clemetson and Chen report the use of music therapy in a day-treatment program. Changes from traditional music therapy practices are described.

References

Action for mental health. Final report of the Joint Commission on Mental Illness and Health. New York: Basic Books, Inc., Publishers, 1961.

ALBEE, G. W. *Mental health manpower trends.* New York: Basic Books, Inc., Publishers, 1959.

BARTON, W. E. Introduction. In R. M. Glasscote, D. S. Sanders, H. M. Forstenzer, and A. R. Foley (Eds.), *The community mental health center.* Washington, D.C.: Joint Information Service, American Psychiatric Association and National Association for Mental Health, 1964. Pp. xiii–xvi.

BELL, J. National trends in mental health program planning. *Bull.,* Division of Mental Health, No. 8–2. Washington, D.C.: Department of Institutions, March, April, 1964. Pp. 27–33.

Congressional Record, February 26, 1962, to March 15, 1962, *108* (3), 3144.

HEWITT, R. Trends in the care of the mentally ill. *Publ. Hlth Rep.,* 1960, 75, 15–19.

KNOFF, W. F. Modern treatment of the insane. *New York State J. Med.,* 1960, 60, 2236–2243.

SMITH, LAUREN H. New horizons in psychiatric hospitalization. *J. Amer. Med. Assoc.,* 1960, 174, 1382–1385.

WILMER, H. A. *Social psychiatry in action.* Springfield, Ill.: Charles C Thomas, 1948.

29

THE DEVELOPING SITUATION

GENEVA SCHEIHING FOLSOM

Barton (1962) has predicted some occurrences that will affect planning in mental hospitals.

1. First admissions will increase 17 percent in the next 10 years.
2. First admissions will increase 37 percent by 1980.
3. There will be little change in the number of children under six.
4. The number of children under 18 will increase 20 percent.
5. The number of admissions to mental hospitals will increase 40 percent for the age group 15 to 44, 40 percent for males over 65, and 60 percent for females over 65 (p. 260).

The increase in first admissions will probably mean added work on admissions wards. Because of staff shortages, active treatment usually is concentrated in these wards. With the increase in the number of children between the ages of six and eighteen, there will be more emphasis on music therapy for children and adolescents. The music therapist must be able to provide music for these age groups. A greater number of admissions between the ages of fifteen and forty-four implies that many current practices will continue to be useful, because most music therapy activities have been geared to this age range. The increase in the number of hospitalized patients in the age group of sixty-five and over emphasizes the importance of techniques in music therapy for geriatric patients.

With the increase in hospital admissions, several important changes in the pattern of treatment of mental illness will occur. The duration of hospitalization for many patients will be reduced. Many persons will be treated in the community without initial hospitalization. Three of every four persons newly admitted for inpatient treatment will be returned to the community in thirty days. Perhaps half of the cases admitted will be able to leave the hospital after fifteen days, although they usually will continue therapy in the community setting (Barton, 1962, p. 623). Among the factors responsible for these shortened hospitalizations will be the following: (1) availability of acceptable services in the community; (2) knowledge of where to turn for help at any hour; (3) individualized therapy promptly applied; (4) early return home after obtaining relief of symptoms; (5) more families participating in therapy; (6) preparation for return beginning at admission; and (7) availability of day hospitals and aftercare treatment centers.

Perhaps the most important change for music therapists will be the short stay of many patients. If music therapists have only fifteen to thirty days in which to work with a patient, some adjustments in present practices and initiation of short-term goals will be necessary. There will continue to be a need to treat some long-term patients, but it seems that much emphasis will be on short-term treatment programs. Many present techniques will be used, but new skills will have to be developed for giving more immediate musically satisfying experiences. Patients will need to be taught skills in thirty days that they can take home with them and continue. This means that patients should be placed in the correct musical situations as soon as possible because of the short time they will be in the hospital.

Students in training for music therapy probably will learn those instruments that provide immediate satisfaction, such as the guitar and ukulele. Patients will be taught to play by ear rather than by sight, because one month is too short a time in which to develop an adequate sight-reading skill. Group work will have to be geared to a more adaptable repertoire because there will be a constant turnover in membership in the music groups. More families will be participating in therapy.

It appears that about half of the hospital-destined patients can be treated in the community without inpatient admission. Many patients with emotional and psychological illnesses will be admitted for initial care to general hospitals or to community mental health centers. Others will be served by home treatment, outpatient clinics, or other agencies (Barton, 1962, p. 622). Because numbers of patients will be released from hospitals for continued treatment in community settings and others will be treated entirely in the community, the work of music therapists will not be confined exclusively to mental hospitals but will be included in community treatment programs also.

Changes in treatment patterns for mental illnesses will help hospitals meet the predicted increase in admissions.

Early recognition and treatment of mental illness through the use of home visiting, outpatient clinic, day hospital, and general hospital beds can greatly reduce admission pressure on the public mental hospital. If these trends are encouraged, and the evidence indicates they will be, no additional mental hospital beds will be required to meet population increases except for the age group over sixty-five (Barton, 1962, p. 621).

The shift to community treatment settings will cause mental hospitals to concentrate their efforts on two major aspects of psychiatric care. These are the rehabilitation of the chronically ill mental patient and the care of the aged. State hospitals also may be used for the care and treatment of all chronic medical diseases (Barton, 1962, pp. 625–626). The value and function of music therapy in the mental hospital will remain much the same.

There are problems in current hospital practices that may or may not be present in the community health center. In the new setting, it may be necessary for the music therapist to make the following adjustments:

1. The expansion of the patient's relationships with a few persons into the demand that he form relationships with many different people.
2. The use of most of the time of workers in staff conferences and meetings rather than in patient treatment.
3. The use of a costly escort system to bring patients to offices and off-the-ward activities instead of making the ward the central focus of therapy.
4. The limiting of medical services to the period of 9 A.M. to 5 P.M. Monday through Friday (Barton, 1962, p. 629).

Therapy on an individual basis to develop an extensive interpersonal relationship with a patient will become less practical, and music therapy will need to channel its development in the direction of group activities. Part of the therapeutic process will take place in the interrelationships of group members and will be much less limited to an individual relationship between the patient and therapist.

Another trend is summarized in *Action for Mental Health* (1961):

A . . . more recent trend combining sociology and psychology with psychiatry has been the systemization of "normal treatment" or social treatment, based on interactions of groups living, working, and playing in a "therapeutic milieu," or beneficial environment. [This has] the advantage of better adaptation to mass application (p. 244).

It is in this trend that music therapists will find their most useful function. There are many opportunities to promote interactions in groups playing and working together in a therapeutic milieu. What has been done with music in therapeutic situations will remain applicable. Probably the greatest change will be in the reduction of available time. Musical groups will have to be developed quickly while making sure that the group process is therapeutic and musically satisfying.

Recommendations for Better Use of Present Knowledge

In 1961, the Joint Commission on Mental Illness and Health made some recommendations for the better use of present knowledge and experience.

In the absence of more specific and definitive scientific evidence of the causes of mental illness, psychiatry and the allied mental health professions should adopt and practice a broad, liberal philosophy of what constitutes and who can do treatment within the framework of their hospitals and other professional service agencies, particularly in relation to persons with psychoses or severe personality or character disorders that incapacitate them for work, family life, and everyday activity. And, all mental health professions should recognize:

A. That certain kinds of medical, psychiatric, and neurological examinations and treatments must be carried out by or under the immediate direction of psychiatrists, neurologists, or other physicians specially trained for these procedures.

B. That psychoanalysis and allied forms of deeply searching and probing "depth psychotherapy" must be practiced only by those with special training, experience, and competence in handling these techniques without harm to the patient—namely, by physicians trained in psychoanalysis or intensive psychotherapy plus those psychologists or other professional persons who lack a medical education but have an aptitude for, training in, and demonstrable competence in such techniques of psychotherapy.

C. That nonmedical mental health workers with aptitude, sound training, practical experience, and demonstrable competence should be permitted to do general, short-term psychotherapy—namely, treating persons by objective, permissive, nondirective techniques of listening to their troubles and helping them resolve these troubles in an individually insightful and socially useful way. Such therapy, combining some elements of psychiatric treatment, client counseling, "someone to tell one's troubles to," and love for one's fellow man obviously can be carried out in a variety of settings by institutions, groups, and individuals, but in all cases should be undertaken under the auspices of recognized mental health agencies (*Action for Mental Health*, 1961, p. 244).

Obviously, music therapists are not qualified under A and B, but they do fit the qualifications under C. It would seem a waste of training, however, to do general, short-term psychotherapy as described when much can be accomplished by using the knowledge and skills of music therapists. Perhaps this was implied under C in the statement that "such therapy . . . can be carried out in a variety of settings." The setting for music therapy is the unique milieu provided by participation in musical activities. We find this recommendation:

Persons who are emotionally disturbed—that is to say, under psychological stress that they cannot tolerate—should have skilled attention and helpful counseling available to them in their community if the development of more serious mental breakdowns is to be prevented. . . . In the absence of fully trained psychiatrists, clinical psychologists, psychiatric social workers, and psychiatric nurses, such counseling should be done by persons with some psychological orientation and mental health training and access to expert consultation as needed (*Action for Mental Health*, 1961, p. 256).

Mental health consultants, such as psychologists, social workers, nurses, family physicians, pediatricians, and psychiatrists, should be available for systematic consultation with the mental health counselors. The consultants would render three basic services.

1. Provide counselors with mental health training at the helping professional level—briefly, on-the-job training.
2. Provide general professional supervision of subprofessional activities.
3. Provide the moral support and reassurance that has been found essential for most persons working with the emotionally disturbed or mentally ill, whether medically trained or not—a support most important for persons in training (*Action for Mental Health*, 1961, p. 258).

Music therapists qualify for the classification of mental health counselor and could be members of the mental health professional team. Many music therapists have held such positions already in their clinical practice. Although not mentioned in the list of qualified mental health consultants, music therapists have had as much training as psychiatric nurses. Some have directed the clinical training of music therapy students, thereby gaining experience that could be of use in the training of mental health counselors. Trained music therapists are able to provide general professional supervision of subprofessional activities in music.

We should recommend pilot studies in the development of centers for the re-education of emotionally disturbed children, using different types of personnel than are customary. . . . It is desirable to find alternative patterns of care for large groups of emotionally disturbed children both of normal and retarded intelligence. It is suggested that a system of schools and training programs for re-education of emotionally disturbed children be established on a research basis.
The schools would be operated by carefully selected teachers working with consultants from the mental health disciplines. They would not take the place of facilities for seriously disturbed children, nor of special classes in the public schools, but would relieve pressure on hospitals, mental health centers, and public schools (*Action for Mental Health*, 1961, p. 259).

Music therapists who have specialized in working with emotionally disturbed and/or mentally retarded children should be valuable in a program like this. They can work specifically with music and at the same time act as consultants for the teachers.

There is a need for expanding treatment of the acutely ill mental patient in all directions, via community mental health clinics, general hospitals, and mental hospitals, as rapidly as psychiatrists, clinical psychologists, psychiatric nurses, psychiatric social workers, and occupational, physical, and other non-medical therapists become available in the community. . . .
Community mental health clinics serving both children and adults, operated

as outpatient departments of general or mental hospitals, as part of state or regional systems for mental patient care, or as independent agencies, should be regarded as a main line of defense in reducing the need of many persons with major mental illnesses for prolonged or repeated hospitalization. Therefore, a national mental health program should set as an objective one fully staffed, full-time mental health clinic available to each 50,000 of population . . . (*Action for Mental Health*, 1961, pp. 262–263).

Music therapists should be prepared and ready when these community health clinics are formed, and they should be cognizant of their possible roles.

Intensive psychiatric treatment centers are also of concern.

Smaller state hospitals, of 1000 beds or less and suitably located for regional service, should be converted as rapidly as possible into intensive treatment centers for those patients with major mental illness in the acute stages or, in the case of a more prolonged illness, those with a good prospect for improvement or recovery. All new state hospital construction should be devoted to these smaller intensive treatment centers (*Action for Mental Health*, 1961, p. 266).

Because music therapists have worked with patients on active-treatment wards, they will be able to serve in an intensive psychiatric treatment center.

Chronic Mental Patients

The recommendation for the care of chronic mental patients is as follows:

No further state hospitals of more than 1000 beds should be built, and not one patient should be added to an existing mental hospital already housing 1000 or more patients. It is further recommended that all existing state hospitals of more than 1000 beds be gradually and progressively converted into centers for the long-term and confined care of chronic diseases, including mental illness. This conversion should be undertaken in the next ten years.

Special techniques are available for the care of the chronically ill and these techniques of socialization, relearning, group living, and gradual rehabilitation or social improvement should be expanded and extended to more people, including the aged who are sick and in need of care, through conversion of state mental hospitals into combined chronic disease centers (*Action for Mental Health*, 1961, p. 268).

It is suggested that these centers have fewer psychiatrists and a larger number of nurses, occupational therapists, and—it is hoped—music therapists.

Geriatrics

Music therapy could serve well in the clubs and community programs of old people. Many of these persons have used music as a hobby at one time or another in their lives. A number have sung in church choirs, and some may have been involved in community bands or orchestras. If these interests have been dropped because of age, they should be reactivated. Moreover, it is possible for these persons to develop new interests.

A section in *Action for Mental Health* (1961) deals with convalescent nursing homes for the aged.

Convalescent nursing homes have long been a facility for caring for the elderly infirm. Only recently has the idea become prominent that nursing homes can be a better solution than the mental hospital for the care and treatment of the aged and aging mentally ill. . . .

At present there is a general absence of nursing homes willing to take elderly disturbed patients. Moreover, those that do accept such patients rarely use rehabilitation or the prevention of further deterioration as their major goals. Generally little attention is given to the psychological and social needs of these patients. Often, too, both psychiatrists and social workers take a dim view of the rehabilitation and treatment potential of these patients. This pessimism is generally hedged by the statement that it is more expedient to use scarce personnel in service to those whose life is ahead of them (pp. 184–185).

Although at the present time it seems unlikely there will be a call for the services of music therapists in convalescent nursing homes, it is hoped that the attitudes concerning these homes will change and that they will be considered as rehabilitation areas rather than as places to wait for the inevitable. It is possible for a ward of elderly people to have an optimistic and forceful program. The psychological and social needs of such patients often outweigh any physical needs they may have.

The general advantages of activity therapy for the aged are reviewed in *The Encyclopedia of Mental Health* by Stern (1963).

Activity therapy geared to aged patients' capacities aims at stimulating minds and bodies and encouraging social activity. Among its many forms are recreational therapy, music therapy, and occupational therapy. Even passive recreation like entertainment may be therapeutic by sparking imagination or arousing dulled interests. Some hospitals feature mixed social dancing in their geriatric service. Many older patients flatly refuse to embark on crafts new to them, but skilled occupational therapists help others to achieve a mentally healthful sense of accomplishment and renewed self-confidence (p. 178).

One way to arouse these patients' attention is through musical entertainment. If the music therapist is enthusiastic and a good leader and if the staff participates, it should be difficult for a patient to remain completely passive during group musical activity. Sometimes the attention of these patients can be gained by singing or playing the piano.

Rehabilitation

There is a new active, valuable, and somewhat all-inclusive branch of medicine attracting attention at the present time because, through its efforts, people who otherwise might be condemned to life-long invalidism are being returned to health and usefulness which restores their self-respect. Known as "rehabilitation," the discipline treats those who suffer permanent limitations because of chronic illness or crippling injury. Since in these areas the emotional outlook of the patient is of prime importance, for both good and ill, the contribution psychiatry makes is weighty and specific, and therefore the subject should be mentioned here (Braceland and Stock, 1963, p. 217).

Broadening of the range of interests through the wide variety of occupational thereapeutic activities available in well-equipped hospitals has resulted, for many patients, in the discovery of totally new areas of curiosity, competence, or striving (Ewalt and Farnsworth, 1963, p. 362).

In rehabilitation the teaching of worthwhile leisure-time activities can be as important as vocational experiences, if not more so. In some instances, the music therapist may help in the vocational rehabilitation of a patient who has been a professional musician. In most cases, however, the greatest need is to provide leisure-time pursuits that will help integrate the person into his community and provide him with emotional satisfaction.

The principles of remotivation formulated by Vaught, Mering, and Kind and reported by Ewalt and Farnsworth (1963) are fundamental to all phases of rehabilitation.

1. Aides must be made part of the treatment and should share in the responsibility for patient care and improvement.
2. The role of members of the ancillary services should be broadened so as to make them consultants to individual ward programs, resource persons who possess special skills and information that can contribute to a more effective treatment program.
3. To decrease staff-patient "distance" all members of the staff should participate in the patient society by portraying socially acceptable and "normal" standards of behavior on the ward.
4. A change in one aspect of the patient's social life is followed by changes within himself and in other aspects of his social life.
5. Remotivational programs should utilize the idea that the sick can help the sicker and that within patient groups themselves there are potential sources of help toward more mature social action.
6. Specific media in remotivation are not so important as the purpose behind

the techniques and the interpersonal closeness of staff and patient in shared activities.
7. Every attempt should be made to introduce activities on the ward that are as normal as possible and oriented toward future life outside the hospital (pp. 364–365).

Other Treatment Centers

Organizations for Former Mental Patients

The treatment centers in this category have several different names, but all of them work around the need for organizations for former mental patients. The first of these is the therapeutic social club. In *Action for Mental Health* (1961, p. 188), a similar organization, called a social rehabilitation center, is described. A few of these have been developed. They differ in orientation from rehabilitation centers for the physically handicapped in that social relationships are the major emphasis.

Community Day Centers

Day centers were developed as a rehabilitation service for former mental hospital patients. They provided a meeting place for clubs composed of released patients. Clubs of former patients, largely self-organized, fill an important need for mutual aid and support preparatory to engaging in the regular social life of the community. Professional staff additions made possible the organization of social and vocational retraining and guidance activities and supportive psychotherapy, mostly in groups but also on an individual basis (Forstenzer, 1963, p. 1114).

Residential Treatment Centers

Residential treatment centers for emotionally disturbed children are beginning to meet another long-standing need.

There are centers that provide 24-hour care in a therapeutic milieu for children with severe emotional problems. The program is an integrated one of education, group living, group therapy, and clinical treatment. A principal advantage of these centers over children's units in state hospitals is their proximity to families and the possibility of extensive family involvement in the treatment program. Return to full community living is facilitated by easily arranged transition to day or night services and the use of regular school facilities as the child improves. There is as yet no consensus as to the range of childhood disorders that can be successfully coped with in these centers, or on the size, staffing, and building plans for the centers (Forstenzer, 1963, p. 1116).

OUTPATIENT PSYCHIATRIC CLINIC

The outpatient psychiatric clinic is the most numerous community mental health service.

It is defined by the United States Public Health Service as a unit that provides outpatient mental health services and has a position for a psychiatrist who has regularly scheduled hours in the clinic and who assumes medical responsibility for all patients. A full-time clinic is one with the equivalent of four full-time professional people including the equivalent of one full-time psychiatrist, one full-time clinical psychologist, one full-time psychiatric social worker, and one additional full-time psychiatric social worker or other professional person. The latter may be a psychiatric nurse, a public health nurse, a pediatrician, a neurologist, an additional psychiatrist or psychologist, a speech therapist, a play therapist, a remedial reading teacher, or a professional with other training related to mental health (Forstenzer, 1963, p. 1111).

THE FIVE-DAY HOSPITAL

Another recent development is the establishment of the five-day hospital.

This reflects the practice of many institutions to allow and even encourage their patients to go home on all weekends. This is another phase of the growing tendency to keep patients from remaining in hospitals for a long period of time, or if that is undesirable, to have their stay at the hospital broken up by frequent visits to their homes (Blain, 1963, p. 1136).

THE NIGHT HOSPITAL

The night hospital is another innovation of psychiatric service.

The night hospital is the converse of the day hospital. It has been described as a psychiatric unit offering treatment to patients after working hours. Its main function is to make treatment possible for persons who work, without interrupting their employment or interfering with their daytime responsibilities (*Action for Mental Health*, 1961, pp. 181–182).

THE OPEN HOSPITAL

The open hospital is becoming more of a reality than a long-range goal.

The "open door" to the mental hospital ward and the increased freedom that it brings does not diminish the responsibility of the nurse to provide good care. Patients must be helped to manage their new freedom, helped to find some useful work to do and to plan a more constructive use of their leisure time (Barton, 1962, p. 22).

INPATIENT SERVICES IN GENERAL HOSPITALS

One of the trends in modern psychiatry is toward inpatient services in general hospitals. The traditional wide separation of the treatment of the mentally ill from the physically ill is lessening as a result of the steady expansion of general hospital psychiatry.

Changing attitudes and the efficacy of psychotropic drugs are producing a trend toward dispersal of the psychiatric patients throughout the hospital, with provision for a very small number of secure rooms. . . . Psychotherapy, both individual and group, physical treatment, drug therapy, activity therapy, all are used in well-organized psychiatric units of general hospitals (Forstenzer, 1963, p. 1112).

Family Therapy

Family therapy is a significant addition to other types of mental health services available in a community.

A specific therapy for the emotional disorders of the family group, a method of ameliorating the harmful forms of emotional interaction of the individual with his family, fills a critical gap in the pattern of mental health practices. . . . The problems of the family are not the monopoly of any one profession. All interested professional people in the fields of social work, education, psychology, medicine, and psychiatry have a valid claim. Coping with the health problems of the family group is a broad venture in public health. As a matter of sound policy and sheer efficacy, public health services for the family taken as a group call for an integrated health team. . . . Because this method of treatment is relatively new, it is not yet widely available; however, health service of this type is expanding rapidly (Ewalt and Farnsworth, 1963, p. 244).

Foster Family

Another way of treating the patient in aftercare programs is through the foster family.

Foster family care for ex-patients is probably the oldest form of aftercare in this country. Placing a mental hospital patient with a foster family makes it possible to maintain in the community persons who do not need to be in hospitals but who cannot return to their families or live on their own. Many mental hospital patients seem to make further improvement only when living outside the hospital in a normal social setting. Thus, family care is considered as a way of rehabilitating former patients and returning to normal living many who otherwise would remain hospitalized. Family care relieves overcrowding of mental hospitals, it is less expensive than hospitalization, and it often convinces patients' families they should take them back (*Action for Mental Health*, 1961, p. 183).

Music therapists have much to offer in the various therapeutic settings just described. Although general principles may remain the same, there are differences in application and emphasis. It is of importance that new aims and new practices be understood fully. This more complete understanding of new developments will have to begin with educational programs for music therapists. Clinical training undoubtedly will need to be more inclusive. Certainly, music therapists will have to become increasingly aware of the greater integration of community and treatment if they are to be current in their practice. Imagination, improvisation, and continued learning directed toward community-centered institutions will characterize the successful music therapist. Awareness of the rapid developments in the field of mental health will enable the music therapist to demonstrate successfully his usefulness in psychiatric endeavors. This, of course, must be done if he is to take an active therapeutic part in the new settings.

Research and the Future of Music Therapy

If music therapy is to gain status as a profession, one of its greatest needs is the carrying out of significant research. *Action for Mental Health* (1961, pp. 231–240) recommends basic research instead of applied research and long-range as well as short-term projects. Barton (1962, pp. 630–631) suggests that people should be trained for careers in research. A document prepared for private circulation by a working staff of the Social Science Research Council (Hilgarde, Gill, and Shakow, 1963) states the long-term goals of research in mental health to be fourfold: (1) the cure of mental illness; (2) the prevention of mental illness; (3) preventative mental health services in a community; and (4) a positive program for improved mental health. Although most research in music therapy has been concerned with the cure of mental illness, all four of these long-range goals should be kept in mind.

Interdisciplinary research is more productive than the work of a psychiatrist working alone. "Scientific togetherness" is not necessarily more productive than one man's superior ability. Often, however, a psychologist or sociologist, a physiologist or specialists in other areas may add dimensions to the study that enormously increase its value and utility (Barton, 1962, p. 636).

Notwithstanding the suggestion that basic research is of more concern, *Action for Mental Health* (1961) does give some advice on applied research.

In applied, or clinical, research the method, approaches, and concepts used in any one study may be drawn from several different disciplines. The concern is with the prevention and treatment of mental illness and with the development of more effective services for patients.

Primary prevention is an important area for applied research. Many of the specific studies in this area reflect our growing interest in and understanding of the effects of social forces. It must be said that systematic studies are still infrequent but topics such as the following are now among the serious interests of applied researchers: the evaluation of mental health education programs, particularly those directed at parents; the influence of various school curricula, different educational policies, and teaching procedures on the adjustment and mental health of children; the effects of large-scale readjustments and changes in the society such as the introduction of automation in industry, the desegregation of our schools, and the relocation through urban renewal projects of large numbers of persons (pp. 207–208).

One area of applied research, pertinent to the field of music therapy, might be a study of the influence of various schools' music curricula. If ways can be found in which music programs in public schools can aid in preventing emotional problems, such research would have great value.

In summary, if music therapists can remain informed of current and predicted trends in the prevention and treatment of mental illness, their profession should continue to grow. These new developments should be incorporated in training programs for music therapy students, and registered music therapists should constantly promote the work of their profession so that music therapy will be included in these developments. A broad program of research should be a characteristic of the profession. With the current emphasis by the Federal government on the promotion of mental health, grants are available for studies that may make great contributions to the field.

References

Action for mental health. Final report of the Joint Commission on Mental Illness and Health. New York: Basic Books, Inc., Publishers, 1961.

BARTON, W. E. *Administration in psychiatry.* Springfield, Ill.: Charles C Thomas, 1962.

BLAIN, D. Mental hospitals. In A. Deutsch and Helen Fishman (Eds.), *The encyclopedia of mental health.* New York: F. Watts, 1963. Pp. 1122–1145.

BRACELAND, F. J., and STOCK, M. *Modern psychiatry.* Garden City, N.Y.: Doubleday, 1963.

EWALT, J. R., and FARNSWORTH, D. L. *Textbook of psychiatry.* New York: McGraw-Hill, 1963.

FORSTENZER, H. M. Mental health services in the community. In A. Deutsch and Helen Fishman (Eds.), *The encyclopedia of mental health.* New York: F. Watts, 1963. Pp. 1103–1121.

HILGARDE, E. R., GILL, M. M., and SHAKOW, D. Planning proposal for re-

THE DEVELOPING SITUATION [363]

search in emotional growth in mental health. New York: Social Science Research Council, November, 1963.

STERN, EDITH M. The aging and the aged. In A. Deutsch and Helen Fishman (Eds.), *The encyclopedia of mental health.* New York: F. Watts, 1963. Pp. 153–178.

30

SOCIAL FACILITY
AND MENTAL ILLNESS

CHARLES E. BRASWELL

The manner in which music therapy will fit into the psychiatric treatment centers of the future is somewhat uncertain, but no more uncertain than is the place to be taken by other activity therapies. Not all of the techniques that have proved effective in residential settings will be of equal value in community clinics. In the acute-treatment centers of the future, length of treatment will be measured in weeks rather than months and therapeutic procedures must be adjusted, or even changed, accordingly. The problem will be to form the necessary relationships in a short period of time.

Psychotherapeutic methods are sometimes divided into two categories; the first of these is termed *reconstructive* and is derived from medical traditions. This method has as its aim the restructuring of the personality, usually through the investigation of early experiences. The second is termed *supportive;* it is concerned with the social nature of the individual and seeks to help him adapt to his environment (McCary, 1955, p. 2). Sullivan (1934) spoke of supportive psychotherapy when he said:

> Thus we try to proceed along the general lines of getting at some notion of what stands in the way of successful living for the person, quite certain that if we can clear away the obstacles, everything else will take care of itself. So true is that, that in well over twenty-five years . . . I have never found myself called upon to "cure" anybody (pp. 578–580).

Music therapy generally is considered to be supportive as well as educational.

In state, veterans', and private hospitals, a familiar pattern occurs too often. Patients adjust successfully to hospital routine. They perform satisfactorily in music, recreation, and occupational activities. Yet many of these patients leave the hospital, fail to adjust in the community, and are forced to return. Freeman and Simmons (1963) put it this way:

The doors of the hospital are not one-way exits into the community used solely by persons restored to health and able to take up active instrumental roles and assume the full responsibilities of community life. Instead, they are doors used by both the sick and the well—and revolving doors at that. If the goal of the hospital is merely the temporary dismissal of patients, then perhaps the problem of hospital treatment has been fairly well solved, at least for the so-called functional disorders. Even from an administrative point of view, however, it is clear that the revolving door situation is undesirable. Fewer beds may be needed, but the patients keep them warm for each other. While it is true that the temporary goal of decreased use of hospital facilities is being reached, there can be little argument but that it is transitory at best. As an ultimate accomplishment, there is no virtue in transforming mental hospitals into way stations or holding operations.

The problem, then, of the former mental patient and of his tenure in the community is of major concern (p. 2).

This problem has been one of the main reasons for the development of the community-treatment concept, and a major goal of community clinics will be either to help patients adjust in the community or to help them create new environments in which some satisfactory maintenance can be achieved.

Adjustment primarily concerns the patient's relations with his family, his job, and other individuals and his participation in a varied and satisfying complex of group interactions, both formal and informal. Secondary considerations include his mode of dress, his manner of meeting people, his ability to assume varying social roles, and his fund of specific social skills—dancing, singing, card games, or athletic accomplishments—that could enable him to gain entrance to and find acceptance in certain community social organizations. Social skills and techniques contributing to adjustment can be collectively termed *social facility*.

The various components of adjustment are difficult to isolate and to study objectively. Most of the studies reported ignore the components and simply measure the individual's participation in formal and informal associations. Much of the literature deals with the relationship between social participation and adjustment. However, amount or degree of participation also has been correlated with age (Taietz and Larson, 1956), occupational adjustment (Wilensky, 1961), scholarship (Reeder, 1938), socioeconomic status (Nolan, 1956), rural versus urban residence (Hay, 1950), and so on.

There is no contention that social isolation *causes* behavioral disorders. The contention is that *there is more than a chance relationship between social isolation and behavioral disorders*. The evidence to be presented shows that with the majority of subjects studied, the greater the social isolation, the less healthy (in terms of adjustment) were the subjects. No therapist can afford to be unaware of the values of social facility.

Goldhamer (1942) studied the relationship between membership in formal associations and neurotic score, as measured by the Thurstone Neurotic Inventory. It was found that as the degree of neuroticism increased, membership in formal associations decreased.

The inverse relationship between membership frequency and total neurotic score demonstrates that even the segmental and relatively formalized relations involved in associational activity are not immune from the circumscribing effect . . . of deviational personality traits. The socially constrictive influence of such tendencies in the personality may in fact be even more prominent in the case of segmental, secondary relations than in the case of more intimate relations, since in the latter instance a greater possibility of an assortative development of social relationships based on more intimate understanding and compatibility exists (p. 73).

Essentially the same results were reported by Fraser, who found that the "incidence of neurosis steadily increased from the group [of factory workers] with many social contacts to the group with social contacts under average" (Halmos, 1952, p. 90). In comparing background factors of fifty delinquent and fifty nondelinquent boys, Francel found that "in eight out of ten comparisons on categories of participation in some form or other, the nondelinquent group displayed greater participation than did the delinquent group, both as individuals and in family experience" (Chapin, 1939, p. 164). Chapin (1939) used the Rundquist-Sletto Adjustment Scale to measure the relationship between personal adjustment and participation, and found that "the evidence of three experimental studies shows that high degrees of community and personal adjustment are associated with a higher degree of social participation in the groups and institutions of the surrounding community" (p. 165). Tolor and Boitano (1960) measured differences in social attitudes of patient and nonpatient groups. Seven stimulus words were presented to the groups, each word having five socially desirable and five socially undesirable descriptions. It was found that the patient group endorsed significantly fewer socially desirable items than nonpatient groups. Jaco (1954) attempted to test some aspects of the relationship between schizophrenia and social isolation. A Southwestern city was divided into areas having high and low incidence of schizophrenia. These areas were chosen on the basis of patient records obtained from a local state hospital. It was found that samples taken from high-incidence areas exhibited significantly greater social isolation than samples taken from low-incidence areas. Individuals in the high-incidence areas knew the names of fewer neighbors, had fewer friends and acquaintances, and belonged to fewer social organizations. A study reported by Langner and Michael (1963) includes a section on social participation. Each subject was asked to report "the number of his close friends, the number of organizations to which he belonged, and the number of neighbors with whom he was friendly . . ." (p. 284).

The number of the respondent's close friends was very highly associated with mental health risk . . . having no friends . . . involved considerably greater risk than having two to fifteen or more friends. . . .
The number of organizations whose meetings the respondents attended was only moderately related to mental health. . . .
Those friendly with ten or more neighbors ran less than the average [mental health] risk (Langner and Michael, 1963, pp. 285–299).

Leighton (1959, pp. 312–327) has written in some detail of those social conditions that are conducive to the breaking up of human relationships. He found that human relationships break up when both leadership and followership are weak, when channels of communication are deficient, and when the sentiment patterns are confused and, except for hostility, lacking in affective strength. At such a time there is a high frequency of broken homes. There are few clusterings about such activities and interests as religion, work, or recreation. An absence of sports, hobbies, and avocations is noted. In short, there is a weak and fragmented network of communication. A gross simplification of social disintegration in relation to individuals is seen in the following diagram by Leighton (1959, p. 327.)

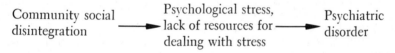

In a study investigating the relationship between social participation, social adjustment, and scholarship, Hill (1944) used two groups matched according to scholastic achievement and degree of social adjustment, each containing 266 college students. Adjustment was measured by the Washburne Social-Adjustment Inventory and a Guilford adjustment scale. Members of the experimental group were encouraged by a university guidance staff to participate in a number of extracurricular activities. At the end of the experimental period, the two groups were again tested. The experimental group showed an increase in both scholarship and personal-adjustment scores. Comparable results were reported by Livingood (1936). Another study dealing with social participation was reported by Rose (1959), who hypothesized that persons whose social participation is limited would exhibit some degree of individual disorganization. This hypothesis was confirmed by reports from 219 respondents. Halmos (1953) investigated the relationship between frequency of social contacts and certain character traits, measured by two personality tests. Anxiety and depressive symptoms were more evident in those subjects having fewer social contacts than for those participating more fully in social activities.

Some partially contradictory evidence has also been reported. A recent extensive study by Freeman and Simmons (1963) deals with posthospital experiences of former mental patients. The authors used the one-year period following hospitalization as the criterion for success or failure. Those patients who were able to remain in the community for one year were termed successful, and those who were admitted again to the hospital before the end of the year were designated as failures. One part of this study dealt with social participation. The four types mentioned were "participation in voluntary associations, social activities with friends, social activities with relatives, and participation in religious activities" (p. 55).

Among both male and female patients, few are members of voluntary associations, and even they rarely participate in them. Both membership and participation are higher among male than female patients, and among successful than unsuccessful patients. Among males, membership and participation predominate in religious, veterans', and fraternal organizations. Among females, both membership and participation are concentrated in church-affiliated groups. Friendship patterns were elicited by a number of questions regarding visits to other persons and to the home, and whether or not the patient was accompanied by other family members. Of most interest is the finding that, among successful patients, approximately 25 percent of the male patients and 20 percent of the female patients lived in virtual isolation from friends, in that they neither visited nor were visited during their twelfth month in the community. Among the failures, the proportion is somewhat higher; about 30 percent of the males and 25 percent of the females neither visited nor were visited in the month preceding their return to the hospital (Freeman and Simmons, 1963, p. 55).

The authors stated that their findings were confirmed in a study by Dinitz, Lefton, Angrist, and Pasamanick (1961).

From these studies, it can be seen that the seemingly nebulous concept of adjustment is related to social participation. Eleven studies confirmed this; two did not. The investigation by Freeman and Simmons (1963) as well as the one by Dinitz et al. (1961), failed to find clear-cut evidence that social participation is related to success or failure on the part of returning patients.

The reason for the discrepancy may be that most of the subjects used in the eleven confirming studies had not been hospitalized, whereas in the studies not confirming the hypothesis the subjects used were, or had been, hospitalized for behavioral disorders. Few returning mental patients, successful or unsuccessful, were found to be engaged in normal social activities. Furthermore, many of the successful patients lived in near social isolation. In other words, in the two nonconfirmatory studies, there was not enough contrast between successful and unsuccessful patients to report a notable difference. It is possible that former patients were often rejected by individuals and organizations in the community. The evidence is conflicting. Public attitude toward the mentally ill may be changing. For example, in a mental health bulletin it is stated that "an ever-increasing number of people are beginning to manifest a heightened degree of interest in and sensitivity toward the needs of the mentally ill. This represents an extraordinary reversal of the predominant public opinion and attitude of only a few years ago" (Community Participation in Mental Health Programs, 1964, p. 2). Ridenour (1961) reports that a recent opinion poll indicates that the public is "more willing to be taxed for the care of the mentally ill than for any other major public service" (p. 137). However, a study by Whatley (1959) reports a number of pessimistic conclusions about public attitudes toward returning mental patients. The study conducted by the Joint Commission on Mental Illness and Health (*Action for Mental Health*, 1961) strongly supports this negative view.

There is probably a more important reason for the lack of social participation by convalescing or former mental patients. Experience indicates that many returning patients possess asocial characteristics that inhibit their acceptance in community groups. In such cases, even those who make initial attempts to join social organizations drop out after a few rebuffs. It would seem that the "participation" evidence is worthy of serious consideration.

Although the merits of social facility suggest some modifications of hospital activity programs, their major usefulness should be to those music therapists who work in community clinics. From the hypothesis relating adjustment to participation, at least one type of program is indicated. The first step would be accomplished by the social worker. The history of each patient should include an accurate picture of his home, immediate community, and social environment. Included in this history should be the church, civic, and neighborhood social groups for which the patient would be eligible at the conclusion of treatment. Second, the music therapist, along with other personnel, should make as complete an assessment as possible of each patient's specific social skills. These skills include anything that might help him to be accepted in available community social organizations. From this profile of skills and available organizations, an individually designed, realistic program of activities could be initiated to correct whatever deficiencies exist, so that the patient, for the first time or once again, might function beneficially in a group.

In planning for the patient's return to the community, the partial failure of some hospital programs for some patients should be noted. We speak of *resocialization,* but the highest level of performance expected in hospital activities seldom approaches levels that would be demanded in comparable community groups. It is, at times, forgotten that patients probably will be expected to conform to community standards of performance. In order to help bring the patient to these standards, interpretation of behavior—within limits—could be another function of the music therapist. If inappropriate dress or unacceptable modes of social interaction are noted, these should be reported in staff meetings or discussed with the patient, depending on the policy of the treatment center. Unacceptable social interaction usually cannot be seen as clearly in formal psychotherapy as in a music therapy setting. Reports of patient-patient, patient-group, and patient-therapist interactions would provide valuable data for the psychotherapist.

The suspicion that such a program might be superficial may well exist. How can a music therapist, who deals with patients for a period of three to six weeks, contribute significantly to patient recovery and bring about meaningful relationships? The answer is that these groups will be continuous; new patients will be entering and old patients leaving. If proper structure is maintained, group feeling can be maintained. Another aspect of the question can be answered by evidence from the Langner and Michael (1963) study. Those authors suspected that "the degree of social contact involved in . . . spare-time activities was . . . related to mental health" (p. 293). Activities were divided into solitary, small-group, and large-group categories. On the basis of activities reported, each subject was put into one of these three categories. Those engaged in large-group activities were better mental health risks than those engaged in small-group activities.

Now that the movement from the traditional institutions has begun, music therapists will want to know how they can best fit into the new treatment settings. To make music therapy useful to psychiatrists, music therapists must thoroughly understand the functions of community centers and related new orientations. Although the basic principles of music therapy still obtain, new techniques and skills will be necessary. Competent clinical practice will be achieved best when research and systematic study on a broad scale have been carefully organized.

References

Action for mental health. Final report of the Joint Commission on Mental Illness and Health. New York: Basic Books, Inc., Publishers, 1961.

CHAPIN, F. S. Social participation and social intelligence. *Amer. Sociol. Rev.,* 1939, *4,* 157–166.

Community participation in mental health programs. *Bull.*, Division of Mental Health, No. 8. Washington, D.C.: Department of Institutions, 1964.

DINITZ, S., LEFTON, M., ANGRIST, SHIRLEY, and PASAMANICK, B. Social and psychological factors in the rehospitalization of female mental patients. *Arch. gen. Psychiat.*, 1961, 4, 363–370.

FREEMAN, H. E., and SIMMONS, O. G. *The mental patient comes home.* New York: Wiley, 1963.

GOLDHAMER, H. Some factors affecting participation in voluntary associations. Unpublished doctoral dissertation, Univer. of Chicago, 1942.

HALMOS, P. *Solitude and privacy: a study of social isolation, its causes and therapy.* London: Routledge, 1953.

HAY, D. G. The social participation of households in selected rural communities of the northeast. *Rural Sociol.*, 1950, 15, 141–148.

HILL R. An experimental study of social adjustment. *Amer. Sociol. Rev.*, 1944, 9, 481–494.

JACO, E. G. The social isolation hypothesis and schizophrenia. *Amer. Sociol. Rev.*, 1954, 19, 567–577.

LANGNER, T. S., and MICHAEL, S. T. *Life stress in mental health.* New York: Free Press, 1963.

LEIGHTON, A. H. *My name is legion.* New York: Basic Books, Inc., Publishers, 1959.

LIVINGOOD, F. G. Directed extra-curricular activities and adjustment. *Ment. Hyg.*, 1936, 20, 614–623.

McCARY, J. L. Introduction. In J. L. McCary and D. E. Sheer (Eds.), *Six approaches to psychotherapy.* New York: The Dryden Press, Inc., 1955. Pp. 1–7.

NOLAN, FRANCENA L. Relationship of "status grouping" to differences in participation. *Rural Sociol.*, 1956, 21, 298–302.

REEDER, W. W. A study of selected factors influencing socialization and leadership on the Utah State Agricultural College campus. Unpublished master's thesis, Utah State Agricultural Coll., 1938.

RIDENOUR, NINA. *Mental health in the United States.* Cambridge, Mass.: Harvard, 1961.

ROSE, A. M. Attitudinal correlates of social participation. *Soc. Forces*, 1959, 37, 202–206.

SULLIVAN, H. S. Psychiatry. In. E. R. A. Seligman (Ed.), *Encyclopedia of the social sciences.* New York: Macmillan, 1934.

TAIETZ, P., and LARSON, O. F. Social participation and old age. *Rural Sociol.*, 1956, 21, 229–238.

TOLOR, A., and BOITANO, J. J. Selection of socially desirable items in patient and non-patient groups. *J. clin. Psychol.*, 1960, 16, 95–98.

WHATLEY, C. D. Social attitudes toward discharged mental patients. *Soc. Prob.*, 1959, 6, 313–320.

WILENSKY, H. L. Orderly careers and social participation: the impact of work history on social integration in the middle mass. *Amer. Sociol. Rev.*, 1961, 26, 521–539.

31

MUSIC THERAPY
IN A PRIVATE MUSIC STUDIO

DOROTHY BRIN CROCKER

Referrals of patients for music therapy generally are made to music therapists in hospitals, special schools, or outpatient settings, where the emphasis is on rehabilitation. The private music therapist is involved in a like manner, but he also emphasizes prevention of mental illness. This liaison with preventive psychiatry is seldom found elsewhere in music therapy and merits consideration, especially with children. Even though such functions of the music therapist can be classified as health services, they are rehabilitative or preventive and benefit the individual as well as the community.

The music therapist follows treatment goals set by the person making the referral. Music sessions are structured to promote the establishment of a good relationship between the music therapist and the patient. Thus, music sessions become therapeutic experiences. The therapist is interested primarily, at times, in indications of trouble and poor behavior and secondarily in musical growth. However, when a modification of faulty attitudes or behavior has been achieved, there is usually progress in music. There may be instances when an emphasis on musical progress can lead to better mental health. The music therapist decides, in most cases, what the structure of each patient's program will be and the nature of that program. Often he will find flexibility a necessity in order to develop music activities into constructive sessions.

Referrals have been made for various reasons. One clinical psychologist explains hers as follows:

Except in cases where a psychotherapist can see a child patient almost daily or in cases where child psychoanalysis is possible, it seems highly practical to extend the therapeutic experience into other areas of life where the actualization of the therapeutic relationship can become more meaningful to the child. Adjunctive therapies may be in speech, reading, or other academic areas, music, dancing, or similar appropriate activities for the child. More important than the type of activity or the subject matter is the personality of the individual conducting the adjunctive therapy.

A decision which must be made on the basis of the individual patient has to do with whether highly structured adjunctive therapy is advisable or loosely structured and permissive adjunctive therapy. Music therapy offers the possibility of modification of some of its dimensions according to the need of the individual patient. For this reason, a music therapist may offer a reinforcement of the gains which can be derived in individual psychotherapy. . . .

A second important reason for making use of music therapy with young children lies in the possibility of their seeing their fantasy, their private world, their creativity accepted as having validity and as being worthy of expression. . . .

A third reason for advising music therapy for a young child, particularly when the cooperative therapist is warm and somewhat maternal in attitude, is in the opportunity of extending the child's experience with an accepting, flexible, and perceptive mother surrogate. . . .

A fourth reason for utilizing the services of a musical therapist with disturbed children is derived from the connection that the experience makes between the child and the broader cultural environment. . . .

In short, the extension of a positive, growth-producing experience beyond the hour or two a week scheduled for individual psychotherapy can be made possible specifically through the adjunctive efforts in music therapy through which the child's adjustment to external controls, his gradual incorporation of control patterns, his satisfaction of dependency needs, the enhancement of his own sense of worth, and the sense of identification with the broad world beyond himself stimulate and promote the integration or the healing process which can make possible the restoration of healthy growth patterns (Brown, 1964, pp. 1–2).

The psychologist quoted has referred children to music therapy with the following problems and disabilities: inability to trust anyone, inability to gain acceptance from peers, lack of control over impulses, low frustration tolerance, difficulties in completing a task, hyperactivity, and brain damage. She indicated that the children needed clearly defined, consistent limits set for their performance and for their behavior during music periods. When a child defied or tested these limits, the music therapist rejected his unacceptable behavior, yet continued to accept the child and helped him conform to expectations.

Reasons given by psychiatrists for referring children to music therapy are similar: Playing a musical instrument enables the performer to express feelings that might result in neurotic symptoms were an acceptable outlet not provided; children of some adult patients profit from music therapy; improvisation should be taught so that children can vent pent-up feelings of tension, frustration, and confusion created by a disturbed parent-child relationship. Techniques employed in teaching the children to improvise include harmonizations played in solid chords, arpeggios, Alberti bass accompaniment, chords played on the offbeats, Latin-American rhythms, and so on. Notably, musical improvisation results in feelings of gratification for accomplishment as well as providing an outlet for emotional expression.

A pediatrician recommended several nervous, overly conscientious schoolchildren for piano instruction with a music therapy approach. His previous discussions with the parents helped them gain an understanding of their unrealistic ambitions for their children. By making the children compete, they were trying to develop them into outstanding achievers. The music therapist helped these children learn to work one step at a time rather than be overwhelmed by the enormity of how much there was to be learned. Gaston (1958) has stated:

> If one subscribes to the thesis that status in our civilization is secured by success through personal competence, then music fits and is acceptable. It may supply the highly essential self-gratification so necessary to security and the consequent lowering of anxiety, and yet provides it, for the most part, in a noncompetitive fashion. Music participation allows a compromise of psychic drives in an activity which has order and predictability. These benefits are important to all children (p. 292).

An orthopedic surgeon sent a six-year-old cerebral palsied girl for music therapy. She had motor involvement of both legs necessitating braces and a wheelchair, right-arm involvement, and a moderately severe speech problem. To give variety and to relieve some of the monotony of repetitious exercises, songs were composed with a text containing directions for the exercises. Songs also were used to supplement her speech therapy. She derived much pleasure from the musical games for her arm exercises, but learning to play short pieces with her left hand was her greatest gratification.

Much can be learned about a child during a music lesson by observing how he responds to music, views himself, accepts criticism or praise, relates to the teacher and children, accepts or resists authority, controls impulsivity, and tolerates frustration. The private music therapist frequently can be of particular help to children who cannot tolerate limits and are anxious and fearful.

Several children were enrolled as beginning piano students and were assigned to a music-appreciation group or a music-readiness group. The sixty-minute readiness-group lessons emphasized rhythmic activities such as clapping, marching, walking, jumping, hopping, galloping, and rhythm band. There was also singing and the dramatization of feelings about attitudes and behavior. The music-appreciation groups played flutophones, Autoharps, drums, and guitars and did creative movement. The music therapist was reassuring and supportive, not only sharing the musical experiences but enjoying the group and its members. Unrestrained expressions of hostility and aggression were not permitted because of the threat to group unity. Praise and encouragement were given in every way possible. In both groups, easily learned songs and music instructions were presented first to establish group unity and the sharing of a common goal. Reaching more advanced goals meant that frustration tolerance was tested and raised, satisfaction was felt over completion of a task, and self-esteem increased as errors were corrected.

In the weekly piano lesson, each of these children was given pieces that were on three levels of difficulty: (1) The easy music developed feelings of confidence and built a repertoire. (2) The pieces of medium difficulty were more challenging and provided a means of analyzing the work habits and weaknesses that arose. Learning pieces neither too simple nor too difficult agrees with Barnard's (1953) statement about playing scales.

This can be an experience in adapting oneself to authority and following prescribed rules for an impulsive anti-social person; it can be a creative experience for the person who has never done anything for the sheer pleasure to be derived; it can be a gratifying experience for the person burdened with an "I can't learn anything" attitude; it can be a task to perfect for the compulsive person; it can be a medium for aggressive pounding and banging where needed; it can be a never-ending task for the guilt-ridden person; it can be a stepping stone to verbal communication for the withdrawn person; and so on with endless variation (p. 47).

(3) The pieces classified as too difficult presented long-range goals and resulted in frustrations and defensive reactions. But when the child was denied the satisfaction of seeing the therapist reacting to his expressions of frustration in a retaliatory manner, his feelings took on a different significance. This is illustrated in the following case history.

Ten-year-old C had normal musical intelligence. She sang well and showed definite interest in learning to play the piano. In group music, she presented no discipline problem but was quiet and withdrawn, followed directions hesitantly, and participated passively. She did not relate to the other children except in a superficial way.

In her private piano lessons, she was sullen, moody, and resentful of corrections and acted rudely. She squirmed and stretched constantly; occasionally during a lesson, she would stop playing and half sprawl to put her head on the back of the keyboard every eight or ten measures. She insisted antagonistically on her own way of fingering, regardless of corrections or explanations as to why certain fingerings were better. The psychiatrist's instructions were not to react to the child's hostility with anger or nagging, to limit the lesson to the length of time she kept her head off the keyboard, and to refrain from arguing.

Pieces with simple fingering were chosen, and C was told that the indicated fingering made the music easier but that there would be no further correction of her fingering. This eliminated some of her need to defy authority and test adult reactions. As C gained insight into her behavior patterns through guidance, she modified her behavior and no longer tried to force adults to become angry and hostile. This apparently had been a way of justifying her own hostility. It lessened her guilt over ambivalent feelings of hate and love for her mother (Crocker, 1957).

In private sessions, conversations following the lessons revolved around the way a child felt about the music, his ability, and his relationship with the music therapist. The discussion about music problems and how to handle them carried over to a discussion of responses to other problem situations. This was reported to the psychiatrist. One child said, "You are the only person who believes I can learn hard things. Everyone else makes me feel like something is the matter with me." Another remarked, "I was afraid to choose my pieces at first, but now I like to make choices." A third child, who was afraid to assume responsibility and make decisions, was encouraged to select the chords he liked for harmonizations and the fingering for his pieces. He was extremely dependent at first and worried over the accuracy of his choices. With much encouragement and lack of criticism, he slowly improved. His parents reported later that he began to select some of his own clothes and occasionally suggested a game to his peers. His psychiatrist said he was less concerned with whether he measured up to expectations. He was able to trust the psychotherapist first, then the music therapist, then parents and siblings, and cautiously, one or two children of his own age.

A child's stories relating to improvised music he requested have been a successful music therapy approach for several years. Many stories are given to the psychiatrist to use as springboards for discussions in psychotherapy. The child is told that his story is an interesting response to music and is asked if he would like to have it told to his doctor.

When eleven-year-old M was asked what kind of music she wanted to hear, her reply was "sad music." An improvisation was played on the piano and, after listening, M verbalized her thoughts as follows:

Once there was a little girl, and her name was Judy. She was a very sad little girl because nobody played with her. She decided she would try to make some friends, but she just couldn't do it. So she kept on trying. She was so determined that one day she asked her mother how would she ever get people to like her? So she tried what her mother told her. She kept on trying until one day everybody decided to like her, and when everybody liked her, they played games with her and talked to her. They never fought with each other again.

The first part of the story expressed accurately her desire for friends, but the latter part was fantasy and wishful thinking. She was not accepted by any of her peers. She was so threatened by closeness that she was unable to relate except in a superficial way to either psychotherapist or music therapist.

N, aged ten, requested a "happy piece." After a gay dance had been played, he told this story:

Well, once there were these people, and they didn't believe in God. They didn't have any religion, and so, anyway, they went outside and they started worshiping. They had a god, and it was called Amonia. They started worshiping him, and a bolt of lightning came down. At the end of the bolt of lightning was a donkey. And the donkey's name was Miranda, and Miranda belonged to Ted. And the donkey picked up his heels and went over and killed the god. And so they worshiped Jesus from then on.

His psychiatrist thought that, in addition to bizarre thinking, N was disturbed over religious teachings.

T, aged twelve, told the following story to mildly stimulating music:

He killed himself because he was unhappy so much. He killed himself. Once upon a time there was a little boy, and he killed his parents, and so he got the gun in the house, and he killed himself because he hated them because they made him go to a school he didn't want to because they thought he had problems. They thought he had emotional problems because he couldn't get along with people. He was always fighting and teasing and having fits—getting mad and screaming; so he killed them. They made him go to this school, and they started to hate him. His parents hated him so he killed them. They sent him away. They just wanted to get rid of him so he went home and found his father's shotgun and some shells with it, and he went upstairs and loaded it and killed them. He blew their heads off. His brothers and sisters probably hated him. They'll probably hate me if I do it.

T's psychotherapist was getting the same kind of verbal aggression and wishful thinking, in addition to much acting out. Yet this boy was able, in time, to gain insight and self-knowledge. He became better integrated and able to function in a healthy manner.

In conclusion, the music therapist can function effectively in a private studio if a therapeutic relationship is established with the referred patient and if treatment aims are given precedence over musical goals. Reports should include observations of the child, his attitudes and behavior, and evaluations of the degree of talent or lack of it. The music therapy sessions can be part of a rehabilitation program or part of a preventive psychiatric program. Although only music therapy with children has been discussed in this chapter, patients of all ages can be accepted as referrals.

References

BARNARD, RUTH. The philosophy and theory of music therapy as an adjuvant therapy. In Esther G. Gilliland (Ed.), *Music therapy 1952*. Lawrence, Kan.: Allen Press, 1953. Pp. 45–49.

BROWN, GLADYS GUY. Rationale for using music therapy as adjunct to individual psychotherapy. Unpublished manuscript, Psychological Center, Dallas, Tex., October 27, 1964.

CROCKER, DOROTHY B. The therapeutic value of music. *Southwestern Musician and Texas Music Educator*, 1957, 25, 23.

GASTON, E. T. Functional music. In N. Henry (Ed.), *Basic concepts in music education*. Chicago: The University of Chicago Press, 1958. Pp. 292–309.

32

MUSIC THERAPY
IN A MENTAL HEALTH INSTITUTE

EMILY A. STEVENS

In a large Southern city, the mental health institute has developed recently as a type of short-term treatment center. The three primary goals of the institute, in order of emphasis, are (1) to train persons in all the mental health disciplines so that the state's treatment facilities can be staffed more effectively; (2) to conduct pure and applied research in a variety of areas associated with mental illness; and (3) to provide the best-known treatment for patients under carefully controlled conditions, while utilizing case material in support of training and research operations.

The physical complex of the institute includes a five-story building for administration, research, and training and eight surrounding patient cottages. Each cottage, complete with its own staff, provides inpatient, outpatient, day, night, and aftercare services. Each cottage accommodates a maximum of thirty inpatients. Five cottages are designated for adults, and one each for children, adolescents, and geriatric patients. Because the music therapy building has not been constructed, several rooms of a vacant cottage are being occupied by the music therapy department.

As a result of the changing treatment patterns developing in the mental health institute, there is a need to adapt traditional music therapy practices and procedures. The belief has existed for many years in some places that the psychiatrist was the sole influence in a patient's treatment. In the institute setting, this idea has been abandoned in favor of an interdisciplinary treatment approach. For music therapy, this means that referrals can come not only from physicians but also from other members of the psychiatric team, including the music therapist. This method gives continued opportunity to the music therapist to educate uninformed staff about music as a therapeutic medium.

Once a patient is referred to music therapy, he is interviewed by the therapist and programed in relation to his background, interests, and treatment goals. Programing the patient is very important in this short-term center where the maximum inpatient stay is three months. Depending on the goals and nature of the case, the patient is seen individually, in a group, or in both ways. Working on the principle that benefits from music listening and performance contribute toward better mental health, music therapy in an institute setting must adapt its methods accordingly. Many instruments are being used and taught that do not require note reading—for example, fretted and rhythm instruments, drums, and many play-by-color/number/letter instruments such as Autoharp, chord organ, handbells, and melodica. Of course, a study of the theoretical and historical aspects of music to provide structure and meet other goals is needed for many patients, and these needs can be met through music appreciation and theory groups. Because of the lack of supplies and personnel in the new music therapy department, choral group work has not yet begun. At present, however, there are no anticipated changes in the music therapy approach that would vary from those discussed. The frequency of discharges and weekend home visits by patients will present some stability problems in the chorus, but these will not be insurmountable.

Another phase of music therapy traditionally discussed is that of written progress notes. As a result of frequent cottage staff meetings, verbal communication about the behavior of patients is transmitted steadily. By this method, the music therapy treatment process can be evaluated periodically and suggestions can be made by team members for a more effective total approach. Written records in the patients' charts remain important, however, as sources of historical, evaluative, and research data.

Although the training programs of most disciplines in the institute are at the graduate level, music therapy will be concerned with a clinical training program for undergraduate students and some inservice training for music therapy aides, volunteers, and other mental health disciplines within the institute. The trends of music therapy in the changing treatment setting will affect the student training program. Specific points for consideration are the (1) rotation of students among several cottage units to offer music therapy experience with different age groups; (2) availability of long-term patients to offer the student experience in maintaining relationships; and (3) adaptation of students to the teaching methods and approaches used in short-term music therapy settings.

None of the practices discussed in this chapter concerning music therapy in a mental health institute have been supported by research data. Because of the great emphasis on research for all institute disciplines, music therapy will of necessity produce in this area. In addition to studies conducted by the music therapy department itself, further investigations using an interdisciplinary approach will be made. Foremost among the changing trends for music therapy in this institute setting will be the inclusion of various research equipment to measure behavioral changes. Data processing will be done for all disciplines through a center located at the institute. Because the consistent plea still exists for scientific research in music therapy, the field for research is very wide. The uniqueness of the institute setting, however, will probably encourage music therapy research in the following areas: (1) treatment procedures for use with inpatients, outpatients, day and night patients; (2) uses of music in community psychiatry and family therapy; and (3) influence of music on animal behavior.

33

THE COMMUNITY
MUSIC THERAPY CENTER

FLORENCE TYSON

The reentry of psychiatry into the community (Branch, 1964) has made it possible to develop music therapy as a community-based rehabilitative modality (Tyson, 1963). The music therapy center is a pioneer program, and a description of the experience accumulated in establishing and evolving a community service may provide constructive guidance and direction for similar efforts.

The music therapist's range of influence and responsibility tends to increase as he moves from the hospital into the community. Music therapy in the hospital usually functions as one of many activity therapies in a total treatment setting. However, when the music therapy program is established on an independent basis, new dimensions are added. Members of the professional community may hesitate to refer their patients to the independent music therapy center. The hesitation often reflects an unwillingness to "pinch off" patients from the central milieu and expose them to an independent so-called ancillary treatment that might interfere with, or operate at cross-purposes to, the ongoing basic therapy.

The patient and the music therapist are more vulnerable and exposed in the community than in the hospital. The outpatient has to contend with complex and sometimes frightening realities involving family relationships, vocational training or job seeking, and social isolation. He is often overwhelmed by recurrent failures and ensuing despair (Tyson, 1959). The music therapist has to work with patients who are frequently more upset, volatile, or threatened than their counterparts in the hospital. There is an increased possibility of savage verbal attacks or of impulsive acting-out behavior, and there may be frantic telephone calls or visits when a patient cannot contact his psychiatrist. The patient may call threatening suicide, and there is sometimes an impulse on the part of the patient to drop psychotherapy and discontinue music therapy. What assurance is there that the music therapist can cope adequately with such possibilities inherent in the community situation? Does an independent music therapy service have a meaningful and useful enough function to justify its existence in the community? Simply transferring to the community the departmental operation as it is known in hospitals will not suffice.

Music therapy acquires different dimensions in community practice. The music therapist seems to become even more aware of the patient as a whole person and of the fact that each interpersonal contact may have immediate and crucial implications for the patient's total life situation. (It is not merely a question of his adjustment on a sheltered hospital ward.) The *constant impinging of the entire community environment on the music therapy contact* creates the necessity for a broad framework within which music therapy can serve the outpatient's needs.

In the hospital music therapy department, one goal is the resocialization of the patient. The community music therapy center has the same goal. The music therapy center provides a milieu for the promotion of social rehabilitation—the agency concept. While the rehabilitation objectives prescribed by the patient's psychiatrist continue to be served in individual weekly sessions, there is also an intention to stimulate and implement interaction among the patients referred for individual work. This interaction occurs among a patient population having a wider range of diagnoses than that of the hospital music group.

Experience in starting a community music therapy center demonstrated that the goal of socialization could not be reached when the music therapy program consisted of a single music therapist having consecutive appointments with individuals. As the number of patients increased, two or three music therapists held concurrent therapy sessions, and social interaction of the patients began in the waiting room. The patients, waiting for their appointments, sat, stood, or paced about without communicating. Several compulsive talkers broke down the reserve and stiffness of some patients but disturbed and irritated others. However, patients became acquainted with one another, and the variety of individuals present was broad enough to allow friendships to develop. This opportunity for friendship expanded during preparations for the center's semiannual musicales. The musicales resulted in strikingly improved social interaction among new combinations of patients.

As the program developed, patients began to feel an identification with the center and looked to it to help gratify expressive and creative needs. A recorder group, vocal group, art group, and dance group were formed at the request of patients. The groups were organized at the level of the patients' capabilities. Although community music therapy may follow a similar programing pattern in other cities, the course of internal developments probably varies according to the needs of the patients in each program.

The music therapy center could not serve the community successfully until its staff was sufficiently extensive and competent to meet a variety of musical and therapeutic needs. Hospitalized patients tend to respond in a more passive way than nonhospitalized patients. The patients in the community, some of whom have had advanced musical training, often challenged the music therapists' qualifications. In such cases, a patient's skepticism and conflicts seemed to be overcome most readily by a demonstration of the therapist's musical performance. *The first concern* was to meet the needs of the patient, who may have verbalized his needs as being musical. (Therapeutic and interpersonal needs often are denied by the patient.) Outpatients seemed willing to spend the necessary time, effort, and money only if they perceived music therapy to be meeting their needs. Therefore, the staff of the music therapy center included therapists capable of teaching instruments, voice, theory, composition, and keyboard harmony—both popular and classical—at beginning, intermediate, and advanced levels. There was a therapist whose clinical specialty was working with exceptional children, and a number of the therapists were skilled in small-group singing, ensemble playing, and music-listening techniques.

The staff included a sufficient number of people of both sexes and of various ages so that patients could be assigned to therapists in accordance with the referring physicians' recommendations and/or the patients' wishes. Unless there was sufficient variety of choice, a patient's negative reactions ("She reminds me too much of my mother") sometimes prevailed over his interest, in which case he may have dropped out of the program. A majority of the staff members of the music therapy center became registered music therapists on the basis of experiential equivalency. Almost all of them had been educated to the master's level, and most had professional careers as instrumentalists, composers, or teachers. This breadth of experience proved to be of value, particularly in that setting. Sometimes the young therapist who has only an undergraduate music therapy degree has difficulty in meeting the musical demands of the musically sophisticated patient.

The second concern was the growth and acceptance of the music therapy center on a community-wide basis. It appeared that the program was accepted more readily by both lay and professional communities when few musical limitations and restrictions were placed on admissions. Acceptance of the music therapy center was won slowly—patient by patient, physician by physician, agency by agency. With each successful individual contact, growth of the service was abetted in a most effective way—by word of mouth.

For maximum therapeutic effectiveness, the music therapy staff should meet regularly with a consulting psychiatrist. In working with patients, therapists encounter many questions that require the clarification and problems that require the guidance of a psychiatrist. The music therapist's consultation needs may revolve about problems of setting limits; personal prejudices or characteristics that consciously or unconsciously interfere with the development of a positive therapeutic relationship; disagreement with the referring psychiatrist's point of view; or an incomplete understanding of the behavioral dynamics involved in a particular case. The music therapist must be careful not to work against the instructions of the referring psychiatrist and thus unwittingly add to the patient's confusion or ambivalence. The therapist must guard against being taken in by the patient's resistance to treatment. These are eventualities that can be clarified, rectified, or avoided if regular consultation is provided.

Some of the questions that face music therapists in the community are the following: How can the music therapist work adequately with a patient if the referring agency has not provided sufficient background information? (To protect confidentiality, sometimes the diagnosis is indicated merely as "mental illness.") What happens when the patient already in the music therapy program suddenly loses his own psychiatrist? Should there be an automatic cut-off date for the term of music therapy treatment? What are the determinants for dropping a patient from the program?

As the number of clients grew, additional professional staff members were needed. Among these were a part-time psychiatric social worker to expedite referrals and liaison with referring agencies, to handle intake, and to write up the periodic progress reports to the referring sources; a consultant in psychiatry for staff advisory needs; a consultant in psychology or sociology for research needs; and activity therapists for group work.

The use of volunteers required care and discretion. Many individuals trained as teachers or performers were attracted by the community music therapy setting and were eager to serve. Traditionally, the use of volunteers has been an important means of maintaining the interest of the public at large. However, it is rare to find a volunteer whose background combines the required therapeutic orientation and practical application. The decision in each case rests on individual merits.

Successful rehabilitation "requires a coordinated effort by many professions, agencies, and community resources" (Black, 1963, p. 2). The community music therapy center maintained communication with all referral sources. Many referrals were initiated by social workers, who inquired frequently as to the appropriateness of the service, the length of waiting time, the fees, and the referral procedure involved for some particular client. The social worker was asked to have a music therapy referral form filled out, including proper medical signature. He was also asked to prepare a letter giving as much of the patient's history as possible. The cooperation of social workers and their endorsement of the music therapy center were important aids in its development. Unlike the private psychiatrist, the institutional or agency psychiatrist was rarely available to contact community resources directly. The social worker usually effected liaison between the music therapy center and the institutional or agency psychiatrist. This is made clear in the following case.

A twenty-year-old female patient was referred by a psychiatrist to the music therapy center after having spent eight years in a state mental hospital. She exhibited withdrawn behavior, confusion, loss of emotional control, and difficulty in concentration. Her initial response to both staff and peers was positive, and she soon confided in her music therapist and in the director. She progressed in individual music therapy work and in the development of social relationships with other members through participation in the center's drama and art groups. Because of her inability to get along at home, she desired to move away from her family. Her psychiatrist and social worker were apparently in agreement because they helped her prepare an application for residency at a halfway house. The center's therapists supported the patient's strivings for social life and independence (these were also among the goals indicated by the psychiatrist on the original referral form). Subsequently, the social worker telephoned to express the clinic's fears that plans for independent living were premature and that the patient might be forging ahead too rapidly at the center for her own good.

The home situation was unhealthy. The mother was continually covering up and feared that the patient would reveal some of the home difficulties. There were indications that the mother would sabotage the patient's moves toward independence (by sending her daughter back to the hospital) unless she were reassured, placated, and made to feel that it was her decision. Therefore, it became necessary to be less directly supportive of the patient's strivings and to take every opportunity to build up her mother's self-esteem. The mother was invited to observe a drama group session and to sit in on one of her daughter's individual music therapy sessions—all in an indirect attempt to reassure her that no one was working against her.

Periodic reports prepared for referring agencies summarized progress toward prescribed rehabilitation goals by reviewing the musical methods used, musical progress, and the general behavior of the patient. Information for such reports was abstracted from individual reports prepared after each therapy session. Repetitive patterns or changing patterns revealed the patient's method of adaptation. The reports described the patient's emotional responses, reactions to others, mannerisms, likes, dislikes, manner of speech and dress, posture, punctuality, and so on, as well as musical responses. These regular progress reports tended to refresh agency contacts.

Occasionally, the music therapy center initiated a referral to another agency. Referral to a vocational rehabilitation agency may have been indicated when a patient appeared to have a persistent employment problem that had not received specialized attention. However, most patients were in psychiatric treatment as well as music therapy, and their referral needs were discussed with the referring agency or doctor and left to the discretion of the agency or doctor for follow-through.

The music therapy center collaborated with other agencies operating at the community level. Meaningful communication was facilitated by a realistic "mutual awareness of the needs and subsidiary goals of other participants on the team" (Clausen, 1956, p. 48). It proved helpful to participate in the programs of closely related professional organizations in order to increase our awareness of their concepts and methods.

The music therapy center provided aid for some persons after they were discharged from hospitals. In these cases, it was found helpful to have the referrals come from each person's psychiatrist or social worker, rather than from the hospital music therapist. In this way, more adequate diagnostic and case history material was provided and channels were established for better supervision and guidance on an outpatient basis. However, the music therapists in the music therapy center and those in the hospitals communicated with and assisted one another as much as possible in planning treatment for the patients.

References

BLACK, B. J. (Ed.) *Guides to psychiatric rehabilitation.* New York: Altro Health and Rehabilitation Services, 1963.

BRANCH, C. H. Psychiatry re-enters the community. *Ment. Hyg.*, 1964, 48, 343–350.

CLAUSEN, J. A. *Sociology and the field of mental health.* New York: Russell Sage, 1956.

TYSON, FLORENCE. The development of an out-patient music therapy referral service. In E. T. Gaston (Ed.), *Music therapy 1958*. Lawrence, Kan.: Allen Press, 1959. Pp. 129–134.

TYSON, FLORENCE. Therapeutic elements in outpatient music therapy. In E. H. Schneider (Ed.), *Music therapy 1962*. Lawrence, Kan.: Allen Press, 1963. Pp. 81–93.

34

CHANGING PATTERNS IN MUSIC THERAPY
—THE MENTAL PATIENT AND
COMMUNITY CARE IN ENGLAND

J U L I E T T E   A L V I N

Because of the use of new drugs, there has been in the last twenty years a dramatic change in the treatment of behavior disorders. These drugs also help shorten the hospital stay of a number of patients; they sometimes enable the sick person to receive psychiatric treatment as an outpatient. During this period of years, a new philosophy emerged. Mental health, in the words of the British National Association for Mental Health, is "everybody's business," and the mental patient, former patient, or prospective patient should be as much as possible under community care. This concept underlies the British Mental Health Act of 1959, the National Mental Health Act passed by the Congress of the United States in 1946, and more recent legislation. Today, the policy of community care is applied in a number of facilities in different countries. The day hospital, the aftercare or halfway house, and the psychiatric social club express this new philosophy under different names. Although some of them do more than rehabilitation work, for the sake of brevity they can be classed under the heading "rehabilitation centers."

These changes in psychiatric treatment and the new attitudes toward mental illness are bound to alter techniques—and perhaps some concepts—of music therapy, because therapy should follow psychiatric advances to be of real service to the mental patient. For many years, especially in the United States, there has been developed a methodical and successful application of music therapy to patients hospitalized for many months or years. For them the music program has to be structured and its timetable integrated with the hospital setting. The music, the music therapist, and the patient function in a sheltered and semipredictable situation that can be planned accordingly. The music program is part of the hospital scheme and applied as such. But now techniques must be found that are applicable to (1) short-term patients in hospitals, (2) patients under treatment but not hospitalized, and (3) former patients in the process of rehabilitation. These three categories of patients demand from the music therapist imagination, insight, and the ability to find varied techniques to cope at once with unusual or unexpected situations. The music therapist should be mature enough to understand the dynamics of the community and family life of which the patient is a member.

The Short-Term Patient in the Hospital

Long-term patients usually need a well-structured program, but the short-term patient often needs an individual, flexible approach. The music therapist should be conversant with the musical history of the patient in order to approach him correctly and answer his immediate and future needs.

Music therapy with short-term patients can have two distinct goals. First, it can relieve the traumatic effect of hospitalization on many patients, help to create a familiar nonthreatening atmosphere, and aid in the fight against boredom. These factors are important from the first month of hospitalization, and they may influence greatly the successful treatment of the short-term patient. If the subject is sensitive to musical experiences, music therapy can also contribute directly and rapidly to psychiatric treatment. It may provoke immediate gratification, relaxation, stimulation, imagery, association, catharsis, abreaction, or sublimation—effects that may be immediately beneficial.

Second, a flexible program of music therapy may give the patient an incentive to continue music activities when he returns to the community, provided the community can offer him the necessary facilities to do so. Music activities and other factors that contribute to his social rehabilitation and stability may prevent him from being hospitalized again. The short-term patient rarely has enough time or strength during his brief hospitalization to learn or increase musical skills. But the music therapist should try to make him conscious of the pleasure of listening to or making music—experiences he may try to repeat on his return to normal life. This consists of an orientation toward the future when he may avail himself of musical opportunities found in his community.

In Britain, special efforts are made to impress on various local bodies the value of music to mental health and to persuade them that it should be part of community-care services as a therapeutic or preventive agent.

Emphasis is placed on the need for rehabilitation centers in which music activities can be organized. In these centers, mentally ill people can feel needed and accepted by the community through their participation in a music group. In order to be of real value, the music group should be in the hands of a music therapist.

The Outpatient

Social rehabilitation is a gradual process that can begin in the sheltered situation of a hospital music group. The second step may take place in a rehabilitation center in which the atmosphere is different from the usual organized and planned life of the hospital. In these rehabilitation centers, the environment is permissive and not as demanding as in communal or family life. The prevalent theory in most of them is that the patient should try to work out his own therapy. Even when he is encouraged to play, sing, or listen to music, the patient enjoys the experience and gains from it only when he makes some effort, however small, toward self-control. Music can allow a great deal of freedom on a permissive basis but also involves discipline and initiative. The patient should be helped to gain self-confidence and to develop a sense of responsibility and purpose within the group. The music therapist should allow him as much freedom as possible, sometimes even staying in the background and letting him organize or decide on musical matters. Nevertheless, the therapist should always provide the guidance necessary to bring any plan to a satisfactory outcome.

The outpatient or former patient may not be able to hold a job. Even if he meets people at his place of work, he is in danger of feeling lonely. Human contacts of value to mental health are rarely those made through work; they are not always found in the family circle either. They are made mostly through sharing common interests in which people can express themselves and communicate. Music is one of these interests.

The Music Therapist

Music therapy is applied on the same therapeutic principles with patients in or out of the hospital, or with former patients. But the music therapist working in a rehabilitation center in England is not a member of a hospital medical staff; he does not work under specific regulations. He has duties to perform on a much larger scale and is usually left to his own initiative and discretion. He should not be regarded as a medical aid by patients but as a musician, teacher, or friend. Music, too, should gradually lose its therapeutic connection and become associated with community life. Music then is regarded by the patient as a means of self-expression, enjoyment, and recreation. Nevertheless, he may continue to appreciate the therapeutic values of musical experiences.

All rehabilitation centers have a similar goal. They help the patient return gradually to community life. Some centers are really small-scale communities. The music group is a small unit that belongs to all members, even to those who do not participate in music activities, because it is part of the whole rehabilitation program. From the small, sheltered music group of the center, the patient can step into the larger unit of the entire center, and from there, when he has acquired the necessary strength and stability, he can move into the community at large. This gradual process applies to music when the patient progresses from an informal singsong among the members, for instance, to a fuller and more integrated singing group in the center and finally joins a local church choir in his community. He still is sheltered by the group but meets people enjoying music for its own sake and with a purpose.

Music therapy in a rehabilitation center is an arduous task. Attendance is voluntary, and the irregular presence of members often is disturbing or even disruptive. It may happen also that outpatients under treatment are not in the proper mental or physical condition to participate, another disruptive fact that has to be accepted. The music therapist should provide the motivation that can attract the members toward formation of a group, aiming chiefly at enjoyment and emotional release, provided the behavior of those participating is socially acceptable. In some centers, the groups achieve fine musical results of lasting value and use. In such a setting, the relationship between the music therapist and the patient is on an individual basis. The music therapist has to make use of any flicker of good will and interest that may arise but should not feel frustrated if members do not come or if some of them are callous.

The therapist's musical and technical equipment should enable him to answer most requests made by patients. The music therapist may have to transpose or read by sight some difficult piano part, arrange or write suitable parts for an ensemble, organize a dance band among the members, give information about a good music teacher available in the community, organize parties of members to go to concerts, arrange informal visits to the center by performing amateurs or professionals, and encourage the members to give musical performances. Above all, there should be *live* music to create personal communication, for recorded music, except for special purposes, is likely to fail.

The music therapist working in a rehabilitation center has another responsibility. He should be interested not only in musical goals, but in other aspects of social rehabilitation. He has to relate his work to the medical and social services in the community, those likely to give his patient an opportunity to join and integrate with a musical group. He must see the patient not as a sick person, but as a citizen who can share in community life and has something to contribute, perhaps in music.

35

MUSIC THERAPY
IN A DAY-TREATMENT PROGRAM

BETTY C. CLEMETSON
RONALD CHEN

The day-treatment service at a Middle Western state hospital is an integral part of a comprehensive mental health program (Chen and Bay, 1965). It combines individual, family, group, medical, and activity therapies according to the needs and psychopathology of each case. The basic goal of treatment is the rapid resolution of symptoms that are disruptive to the individual's personal, social, and vocational adjustment. Emphasis is placed on the patient's healthy functioning with an attempt to hold regression to a minimum. Experience through the years in treating and studying psychiatric patients has led to understanding further the important factors influencing human behavior in healthy and unhealthy directions. Although acutely disturbed and destructive individuals are poor candidates for our day-service facilities, there are many who can benefit from a daytime-treatment program instead of hospitalization, particularly if the illness is secondary to intrafamilial and environmental distresses. The day-treatment program is described first, and the application and function of the music therapy program within the service is described later in the chapter.

The Day Service

The term *day service* is preferred over *day center* or *day hospital* because it represents a variety of functions and services beyond the physical setting of a day center and is more consistent with one of the primary efforts of the day program—the involvement of the community, the family, and other agencies as component parts of a total service. Even though the physical setting is adequate for about one hundred patients, there is some doubt as to whether the census will go beyond sixty because of the population (125,000) and the abundance of other psychiatric facilities available in this community. Our present staff pattern is geared to serve about sixty clients. The psychiatrist-director works closely with directors and chiefs of other services in the state hospital and attends to administrative matters, programing, and clinical problems, as well as the supervision of all staff personnel. In the long-range planning, a second physician will assume responsibility in clinical areas. Other staff members include a psychologist; two social workers; two psychiatric nurses; a senior activity therapist (in our case a music therapist) to coordinate the activity programs; a music therapist; a recreational therapist; an occupational therapist; three activity therapy aides for music, recreation, and occupational therapies; an activity therapist in charge of the work program; and two secretaries.

To be admitted for treatment in the day service, a prospective patient must (1) need more than psychotherapy alone, (2) be able to live out (family support), (3) want help (voluntary admission), (4) have potential to improve, and (5) either come to day service on his own or be brought in by his family. Psychotic disorganization does not necessarily prevent a person from being a candidate for day treatment. Persons with long-standing personality problems and character disorders may be admitted if they experience a need to change. Certain patients may need a structured program following hospitalization to prevent relapses. Individuals who see no need for treatment and do not want help, who are self-destructive or have an overaggressive behavior problem, or whose behavior is too disruptive to the treatment of others, ordinarily will not be admitted to the day service.

Day patients live at home to maintain personal ties and preserve social responsibilities. By doing this, they have more incentive to deal with problems they must face each day at home and in the community than if they were taken out of these situations. It also may minimize the adverse effect of separation from the family and the adjustment required after returning home.

Formal individual and group psychotherapy are readily available as part of the day program. What might be called patient-staff meetings also take place three times a week. Eight to ten patients meet with two members of the staff to focus on problems and areas of concern. These areas may range from difficulties involved in daily living through interpersonal relationships to internal pathological problems that influence their behavior. A staff member uses various approaches, depending on the type of patients in his group. He may serve as a catalyst, promoting discussion. If the discussion remains superficial for too long, he may direct the conversation to more meaningful issues; he may open up areas for discussion in the case of a regressed group; or he may point out resistances, such as when patients want the staff to do their work for them. Whatever approach is used, the staff member refrains from providing answers and emphasizes the clarification and understanding of problems.

Family and life situations are assessed carefully in every case. Participation of members of the family is mandatory, as they must deal actively with the patient after his hours at the day service. They are encouraged to attend a two-hour session one evening a week. They discuss with a social worker their own feelings and reactions to the patient's illness, and learn about the treatment program as well by talking with an activity therapist. Additional work with families, such as individual and conjoint casework, is required upon clinical indications. In some instances, the spouse may be brought into the day program to facilitate better understanding of the patient-spouse relationship. The day service is also open from 5 P.M. to 8 P.M. on Mondays. These hours are used by patients who have full-time jobs or daytime obligations and by follow-up patients. The director is available for consultation during the evening hours. Patients generally are encouraged to use daytime hours, 8:30 A.M. to 3 P.M., if at all possible.

Once a week, all the patients meet together in the presence of a staff member to plan community projects. They extend their activities into the community and broaden their resources. Tours of factories, museums, and other places of interest are arranged, with minimum supervision from staff.

The preemployment meeting is a preparation for patients who are anticipating employment. One of the staff members and a counselor from the vocational rehabilitation service conduct a course of ten or more meetings in which patients discuss their feelings, attitudes, apprehensions, and concerns about employment. For example, a patient may need to clarify for himself why he has not been able to keep a job. Role-playing techniques are often used, and the patient may take part in a simulated job interview. The preemployment meeting is a part of a total work program that consists of a transitional workshop, a patient employment bureau, and industrial assignments. The transitional workshop provides contract work for which patients are paid in accordance with their performance. Emphasis is placed on work adjustment. In conjunction with the work program, state and local rehabilitation facilities are actively utilized.

Individuals from the community who have particular skills such as sewing, bridge, or dancing and who have the desire and ability to work with people may serve as volunteer staff. Each volunteer works under the supervision of a full-time staff member and reports to him any significant interactions with, or observations of, the patients. Other volunteers may aid the staff as technical consultants in areas such as woodworking, ceramics, or art. Some patients from other settings serve as volunteers in the day center. This seems to enhance their confidence and self-esteem, and promotes their recovery. Day patients may do volunteer work in community agencies; this work is found to be most desirable for those who need a community contact and a broadening of their interests. For others, volunteer work serves as a preparation for employment. The two-way volunteer program (patient to community and vice versa) provides opportunities for the community to learn about mentally ill patients and the treatment facilities available for them.

The Music Therapy Program

Like the other activity therapies, the music therapy program schedules a variety of events each day to provide therapeutically indicated activities. Dance groups include folk and square dancing, mixers, modern dancing, and social dancing. Folk dances are useful because they are lively, not too difficult to learn, and promote interaction; yet neither the social interaction nor the physical contact is so close as to be extremely threatening. Patients are kept in contact with reality; there is little opportunity for fantasy. The same advantages are found in square dancing. There is pressure from the group to participate and to do well. When a dance is done correctly there is a feeling of group, as well as individual, accomplishment. However, there are certain limitations to group dances. Good records and instructions are hard to find. The small and changing population often makes it hard to maintain the right ratio of men to women. When a patient is discharged or changed to a part-time basis, there is not always another patient who needs this particular activity. It can be a problem to adapt dances to a given group. Mixers are used in all the dance groups. These are usually spontaneous and help to vary the routine. They are very useful when the size of the group changes, and they also relieve tension and make for spontaneity.

Modern dance helps patients feel free to express themselves and to learn control. In learning to control their bodies, they must also exercise mental discipline. The way a patient stands and walks reflects his attitude toward himself as a person. Improvement can come either way— the therapist may help the patient gain self-esteem and thus induce better posture, or he may encourage more acceptable demeanor and behavior and in so doing change the attitude toward self.

A variety of social dances—bossa nova, cha-cha, tango, conga, jitterbug, fox trot, waltz, rhumba, twist—is taught. As patients learn the dances, they begin to lose some of their inhibitions. Many of them are passive, and this is shown in several ways in the dance groups. They often sit down as soon as the music stops, even though they know the activity is not over. They do the steps with as little body movement as possible. When they cannot learn steps quickly, they become angry, refuse to speak, and sit down. This pattern of giving up, of continually defeating themselves, is characteristic of many of the day patients. As these things are pointed out to them in all their activities and discussed in group meetings each day, they begin to see themselves as others see them, sense disapproval, and become uncomfortable enough to change their behavior.

G is a good example of some of the effects of a social dancing group. When first admitted, she could not tolerate close contact with men. She reportedly had not slept with her husband for some time. At first she would not dance with a partner. When she did, she stood back with her arms straight and her fingertips barely touching his shoulder. She was impatient in learning the steps and easily frustrated. She had low expectations of herself and felt she would never be able to dance. This attitude carried over into many other areas. Now she dances quite naturally with her partner; she is still a little hesitant in some dances but keeps trying and works very patiently and deliberately in helping one of the slower patients learn the dances.

There are probably many reasons why G, at first, could not tolerate closeness and why and how she was able to change. She is now beginning to discuss some feelings she has about impulsively going out and drinking with other men. She is afraid she may act on these impulses and in order to guard against them, has built a wall between herself and all men. As she watched other couples in the group (and perhaps identified with the therapist), she was able to involve herself in the dances while letting go of her fantasies.

Patients in the instrumental ensemble generally play melodicas and Autoharps because acceptable music can be produced almost immediately. Many patients struggle with feelings of inadequacy, and being able to produce a melody in a short time helps to build confidence as well as supply gratification. As they continue, they learn that it takes patience and hard work to produce anything lasting and worthwhile. They also develop tolerance for the mistakes of others and learn to play as a group. When self-centered patients first come into a group, they pay no attention to others and act as though they were alone in the room. In time, they develop an awareness of others and an interest in the group.

Because of the short-term affiliation of most patients in the day program (three to six months), few are taught band or orchestral instruments. If they have played before, they may continue individual or group lessons. An exception is noted in the following case.

B, a shy, withdrawn, seventeen-year-old boy who was deprived of the usual positive experiences in childhood, had many angry, hostile feelings and did not trust people. He required special attention and, at the same time, needed to be part of a group. He started individual trumpet lessons and was assigned a daily practice time. Then, after learning to play simple tunes, he joined one of the groups. Now when he practices, he stops to work out his mistakes; when he plays with the group, he learns to go on after making mistakes and keeps up with the others. No time is spent in this group helping him learn songs; he is expected to arrive prepared to play them. With help, he has selected his own material for study and will soon be able to transpose and copy melodies for his trumpet. Because he was the only one studying an instrument of this kind, other patients looked up to him and admired his diligence. He began lessons with a private teacher in town and hopes to play with a dance band in the future.

Although it is not our goal to develop patients as musicians, it has happened in several cases. Some patients, after participation in guitar classes, bought their own guitars to play at home. A few even play in groups out of the treatment setting, which helps build self-esteem and confidence. Individuals in groups that meet only once or twice a week generally are given private lessons.

One of the music-appreciation groups is composed of older patients, many with problems in adjusting to advancing age and retirement. Many types of music, including records about the lives of great composers with examples of their music, classical music, operas, and musicals, are well accepted in this group. Old favorites and other songs are also enjoyed. Usually, part of the hour is left to the patients' choice. Some music is played for the effects of the music itself. Other music is intended to stimulate conversation among group members. Sometimes conversation is related directly to their problems; at other times, they just have a chance to enjoy one another and socialize. This group is more relaxed than many other groups, and one of the goals is to learn to relax and enjoy oneself and others. Patients are encouraged to share their interests with one another; some bring their own records to play for the group. "Name That Tune" contests between men and women or in teams add competition, motivation, and group spirit to the hour. Familiar songs are mingled with new songs so there is a time to reminisce and a time to enjoy the present. The future is discussed when the topic of conversation is the use of leisure time.

A more active music-appreciation group has younger patients with varied emotional problems. The goals in this group vary according to patients' needs. Generally, they learn to become more appreciative of good music, to be a part of a group, to share their likes and dislikes, and to express feelings through music that they are unable to verbalize. They are encouraged to give their interpretations of the music and to do expressive movements to it. Competition in this group can be healthy and stimulating.

A rhythm group plays guiros, claves, tambourines, bongos, conga drums, castanets, maracas, wood blocks, sand blocks, and drums. Usually, the drummer sets the tempo and the other instruments are added one by one, building up to a cymbal crash at the end. Sometimes patients play along with rhythmic records or with the piano. Occasionally, they write out their own parts to accompany Mancini songs. Clapping ensembles can become very lively and require concentration and collaboration. Patients contribute actively to such a group function and, in the process of rhythm making, considerable energy is expended.

One group performs on a set of drums consisting of a bass drum, snare drum, small and medium tom-toms, high-hat, low-hat, foot cymbals, bongos, and conga drums. Drum pads are used for practice. Some basic strokes are taught and applied to marches, and spontaneity and control are developed. The learning of rudiments permits the development of skill and creativity. Whether the therapist begins with a tight structure and gradually loosens it or vice versa depends mainly on the needs of the patients. The therapist and the activity must be flexible enough to adapt to individual patients within a group, and each patient's individual goals and expectations must be kept in mind at all times. Simple composition is helpful for those who need to build self-esteem by being creative. When they learn to play the melodies they write and to work out chord accompaniments for themselves, there is often a deep sense of accomplishment.

Community singing is scheduled for the last hour of the week and generally is attended by staff. This hour has also been used to prepare Christmas songs for caroling at convalescent homes, hospitals, children's homes, and other places in the community. An activity such as this seems to be a good way to end a week, because even those patients who do not participate actively appear relaxed and pleased with it. And this activity, as well as others that have been described, persuades patients to change poor behavior into better behavior.

References

CHEN, R., and BAY, A. P. The use of a day treatment program in a comprehensive mental health center. *J. Kans. Med. Soc.*, 1965, *66*, 457–459.

36

CLINICAL USES OF MUSIC
IN THE COMMUNITY

Introduction

CHARLES E. BRASWELL

The four reports in this chapter are concerned broadly with the practice of music therapy in the community. There are approximately 5,740 long- and short-term general hospitals in the United States. Of these, about 670, or 11 percent, provide inpatient psychiatric services (Hospital Statistics, 1964, p. 515). Broader insurance policies, which now may include care for patients with mental illness; the development of improved treatment techniques; and convenience of admittance are accelerating admissions rapidly.

Psychiatric wards in general hospitals exist at the apex of a continuum of institutional psychiatric services in this country. The state or Federal residential psychiatric hospital provides the most extensive and elaborate patient care. The halfway house serves as a bridge between residential centers and the community. Community mental health centers provide some features of the residential institution, but their primary mission is to extend psychiatric care without isolation or formal hospitalization. Psychiatric wards in general hospitals usually provide emergency treatment, and nonmedical facilities are kept at a minimum.

The impetus for psychiatry in general hospitals was provided in the 1930s by the development of somatic treatment techniques. The possibility of controlling behavior by drugs (insulin, metrazol) or by electroshock indicated to hospital administrators that psychiatry could be admitted into the general hospital (Boshes, 1961, pp. 27–34). The subsequent development of pharmacologic therapy in the 1950s emphasized this trend.

The music therapist working in a general hospital must cope with a number of problems. Psychiatry currently is engaged in a process of redefinition. Beliefs and practices sanctified by centuries of tradition are being discarded or modified. For example, combative behavior and progressive psychic deterioration were symptoms often ascribed to schizophrenics. Now, indications are that many of these symptoms were due to forceful retention and sensory deprivation (Rafferty, 1966).

Another problem is the almost universal lack of full-time psychiatric staff. Psychiatrists working in general hospitals are often in private practice also, and sometimes their major concern is with their own patients. This results in diminished staff communications and the diminution of integrated treatment programs. A third problem involves the short-term patient. Traditionally, treatment has depended on the development of therapeutic interpersonal relationships, but in short-term treatment settings there is seldom time for relationships, as formerly defined, to develop.

These problems leave the music therapist three discrete techniques, and their combinations, on which to build programs. (1) Programs may utilize the therapeutic effects of music per se without reliance on structured interpersonal relationships for therapeutic effectiveness. (2) The music therapist may attempt a modified team approach by requiring psychiatric prescriptions for patients and supplying progress reports. This approach calls for the education of hospital personnel to the possibilities of a music therapy program. It also involves the difficult task of scheduling enough time with psychiatrists to explain the values of a music therapy program. Private psychiatrists are often unwilling to take time from a busy schedule to enter into this type of relationship. (3) The music therapist may attempt to develop a social psychological program that defines basic social and interactional deficiencies and attempts to modify or correct them.

The program reported by Sister Claire Marie, the first of the four reports in this chapter, combines elements of each of these three approaches. The setting of this music therapy program is in a small general hospital. The remaining descriptions were also written by practicing music therapists. Practices and settings differ from traditional forms of music therapy and may indicate directions in which music therapy will grow in the future. Marsh writes of an insular music therapy program that was transformed into a community activity in a state hospital. The techniques employed are relatively simple and would be applicable in many institutions. The setting described by Glover is experimental, something new, for immediate psychiatric services. It is a state hospital's attempt to serve the community in a less formal manner. Folsom tells of her experiences with an outpatient chorus.

A Music Therapy Program in a General Hospital

SISTER CLAIRE MARIE, O.S.F.

In this report a music therapy program in a church-supported general hospital in the northern United States is described. The program is concentrated on the hospital's psychiatric ward. However, the number and types of activities in nonpsychiatric areas justifies our intention of providing service to the entire hospital. The music program is structured in a manner allowing it to be functionally specialized and custom-built to serve the needs of this hospital.

The first problem in the establishment of the program was to assure its acceptance both in the hospital and in the community. Comments on local radio and television stations were helpful, and local and diocesan newspapers provided information to the general public. Within the hospital, formal and informal conversations with staff paved the way for intelligent cooperation.

As a first step, a choir of Sisters was formed to provide music for religious services and (later) for patients and hospital personnel. Another early activity established for the entire hospital was a "Sunday Dialogue" for patients of all denominations.

The hospital intercommunication system provided the opportunity to broadcast music on tape and records throughout the hospital. Various types of music were tried in all areas, reactions were checked, and the most suitable music for each area was subsequently provided for the greater portion of the day. Special records were selected for mealtime listening and the hour before retiring. Tapes were made for special listening programs including music for Christmas, Easter, St. Patrick's Day, and so on.

Because a successful music therapy program depends on cooperation from staff and personnel, a hospital chorus was formed that included personnel from all shifts. To bring the community into the hospital, weekly entertainments by outside soloists and groups were introduced.

On the psychiatric ward, activities were developed that helped induce a home-type atmosphere. During one specific hour, five days a week, songfests, organ music, singing and dancing sessions, record listening, music games, and discussions were scheduled. Patients from nonpsychiatric areas were welcome. An interview with each patient coming to group or individual music therapy sessions was included to determine interests, social skills, and interactional capabilities. All music activities were medically prescribed, and progress reports in cooperation with the occupational therapy and recreation departments were submitted biweekly.

In conclusion, the program described reflects the philosophy that in a general hospital the music therapy program must be intelligently designed, keeping the individual in mind and yet serving the needs of the entire hospital. Therefore, the most important element is planning. The program must be discussed with professional staff in all areas. In this manner, needs rather than preconceived techniques will determine the program.

A Hospital-Community Music Therapy Program

CAROL W. MARSH

In a state hospital in the South, civic, social, and professional clubs have worked closely with hospital authorities to provide services for patients. Shortly after the music therapy department was organized, a way was sought by which patients assigned to the music department could participate in community activities. It was felt that occasional performances by patient music groups outside the hospital would be helpful, but obvious dangers were involved. Patients might feel that they were being exhibited, and community organizations might invite patient groups merely to have a novel attraction.

In order to solve this problem, all patients participating in music therapy activities were gathered into one organization called the Melody Music Club. In 1955, this group joined the National Federation of Music Clubs. The affiliation immediately changed the atmosphere of the music therapy department. Patients no longer felt isolated, nor did they feel they were being exhibited. They were now members of a functioning unit in a national organization. Since the club's federation, it has performed throughout the state. Several other clubs have set aside time for one program a year by the hospital group. Patients perform for civic clubs, hospitals, nursing homes, and even provide music for style shows sponsored by civic organizations. They also attend events and performances in the community. Considerably more than performance is involved in these activities. Patients feel a sense of identity with the community. In order to maintain community acceptance, they must conform to accepted modes of dress and behavior. Perhaps the most important result of this program is that patients make friends and become accepted in community organizations. When they leave the hospital, these organizations will welcome them as members. In this way, the music therapy department functions not only as a rehabilitative force, but also helps to make the transition from hospital to community less threatening.

Immediate Psychiatric Service

RAY G. GLOVER

In this age of accelerated living, people have asked for and are getting immediate psychiatric service on the "walk-in" unit of a state hospital. This type of service is unique because more treatment resources are available from the hospital staff and facilities than a community clinic might be able to offer. Anyone may seek psychiatric help at any time by walking into the unit. Clients are seen immediately by one of the staff, which consists of a psychiatrist, a psychologist, a social worker, a nurse, and aides. Future plans call for the addition of an activity therapist to the team. This staff member would be responsible for the activity program and should be qualified in several fields including music, recreation, and occupational therapy.

Admission to the fifteen-bed unit does away with much of the red tape connected with admission to the hospital itself. The patient's stay in this unit may last as long as the interview takes or up to three weeks. Frequently, there is a radical change in the patient overnight, with a relinquishing of the symptoms that brought him into the unit. Other patients may improve markedly in a few days. Although this phenomenon is seen frequently in all wards and all psychiatric hospitals, the patients in the walk-in unit can be changed to outpatient status or be dismissed very quickly, compared to the same procedures with regular hospital patients. If further treatment is needed after the three-week period, the client may be admitted to the hospital as a regular patient.

An important part of the treatment goal in this unit is to involve the patients in as many activities as possible during their brief stays. Most activities are in groups; included in these are group therapy and discussion, recreational, and music groups. Other forms of treatment include chemotherapy, individual psychodiagnostic interviews, and special milieu programs.

The activities of the music groups consist of group singing, record listening, and individual performances for the group, in the ward and the music clinic, three times weekly. The goals are motivation, furthering group cohesiveness, socialization, and providing socially acceptable emotional outlets. Observation of the group by the staff is also an important aspect. Much can be learned about the extent of the patient's illness from the degree and type of his participation in activities. In this accelerated setting, the staff must learn as much as possible about the patient in a short time. There is usually a friendly, relaxed atmosphere during the music period, and the response of the patients is generally enthusiastic. The unit director has stated: "I wish we could have more music in the ward because it helps to orient the new patient to the kind of atmosphere we want the ward to have, that is, a cheerful, hopeful, active environment where it is possible to enjoy living for a while. This is but one of the many purposes music serves in this unit."

The Outpatient Chorus

GENEVA SCHEIHING FOLSOM

In working with an outpatient club at a private psychiatric clinic, chorus work, scheduled once a week, was found to be highly effective. It was an open-end musical organization made up of patients coming in after being discharged from the hospital and patients leaving the out-patient club as they left their other treatment. Singing in the group was a nonthreatening experience for most of the participants. Those who had real difficulties in relating to others were not forced to communicate during chorus practice. This gave them some closeness without feeling threatened. After singing, it was easier for them to have a social experience together. In spite of the movement of patients in and out of the group, it was a stable organization, and it was possible to develop the chorus to a point at which the patients were proud of their accomplishments.

This particular organization had professional direction. Those who worked in the club one night a week reported to various social workers and doctors concerning the patients' progress and behavior. Patients were encouraged to direct their own organization, but at the same time, there was always professional direction and supervision.

Probably most important of all, at least as a long-range goal, was that what the patients learned in the chorus enabled and encouraged them to move out into the community chorus and into various church choirs. To assume as nearly as possible one's full function in society, either for the first time or once again, is the chief aim of all therapy.

References

BOSHES, B. The function of the psychiatrist in the general hospital. In. L. Linn (Ed.), *Frontiers in general hospital psychiatry.* New York: International Universities Press, Inc., 1961. Pp. 27–35.

Hospital statistics: a nation's profile. *Hosp.,* 1964, 38, 515.

RAFFERTY, T. The community concept in psychiatry. Paper read at Southeastern-Southwestern Regional Confs., National Assoc. for Music Therapy, New Orleans, March 26, 1966.

Part X

PLANNING
AND UNDERSTANDING RESEARCH

George L. Duerksen
Warren E. George

*T*he closing sentence of the introduction to this book named three necessities for the success of the discipline of music therapy—theory, practice, and research. Without practice and research, theory is impotent and unproven; without theory and research, practice is blind; and without theory and practice, research is inapplicable. To fail to have some understanding of research is to remove one leg of the tripod supporting music therapy. In this last section, the aim is to take each reader as far in scientific attitude, method, and procedure as possible by (1) introducing him to the way a researcher thinks and acts, measures and evaluates and (2) demonstrating thinking, acting, measuring, and evaluating in two research reports. We live in a scientific world—to fail to be scientific in our discipline is to fail in large extent.

37

THE RESEARCH PROCESS

GEORGE L. DUERKSEN

Introduction

The advancement of knowledge and practice in music therapy depends on the quality of the research performed and used by its practitioners. "When practice runs ahead of knowledge, there is the danger that arrogance, dogma, and ritual may replace humility, the search for knowledge, and experimentation" (Levin, 1963, p. 1760). There is need for research that is skillfully and imaginatively planned, carefully executed, and judiciously interpreted and applied. The planning, execution, interpretation, and application of research are interrelated parts of an ongoing process; to do any one of them well requires an understanding of the entire process.

The research studies mentioned in this book can be of use to the music therapist. However, the best use of research information depends on wise evaluation and application, and many of the judgments that need to be made in applying research results depend on the knowledge of research techniques. Such knowledge provides a yardstick for evaluating research.

Research and Scientific Method

Research, as a process of inquiry, is focused on specific problems (Ackoff, 1953, p. 8; Guba, 1965, p. 237; R. Hyman, 1964, p. 9). A problem is encountered, questions are asked, and answers are sought. In seeking answers, man has developed techniques to guide and control his inquiry (Freedman, 1950, p. 15). Control is necessary because it increases his assurance that the answers he obtains are the right ones for the questions he has asked, and it reduces the chance that he will accept incorrect answers as being true. One of the best of these techniques of control is the scientific method. There has been some dispute about whether there is one scientific method or many scientific methods (Bunge, 1959; Caws,

1965, pp. 267–273). This seems to be a dispute about labels, and it depends on whether one is referring to the general scientific approach in investigation and analysis or to specific, specialized procedures for a particular study in a particular science.

In the broader sense, scientific method is a flexible system for studying phenomena. It attempts to be an impartial way of looking at things and makes allowances for those partialities it cannot avoid. It does not aim at persuasion nor at finding ultimate truth; nor does it assume self-evident axioms (Goode and Hatt, 1952, p. 7). This attempt at impartiality means that scientific investigation does not set out to *prove* particular points. To say that the purpose of this study is to show that music is beneficial in the treatment of behavior disorders is not a scientific approach; it is a sales approach. Facts can be selected to support the thesis, and facts that contradict it can be suppressed, ignored, or explained away. Scientific investigation does not set out to prove that music is useful in therapy. Rather, it seeks to ascertain whether music *is* or *is not* beneficial in the treatment of behavior disorders. All the essential and appropriate data are gathered and used to determine what the conclusion will be (Bayles, 1960, p. 87). This reliance on data, rather than on the desires of the investigator, to determine the outcome of a study is one of the prime characteristics of scientific inquiry. Deciding which data are essential and appropriate for a given study is a major problem in research.

There are several characteristics of scientific inquiry that aid the investigator to gather essential and appropriate data. "Scientific research is systematic, controlled, empirical, and critical investigation of hypothetical propositions about the presumed relations among natural phenomena" (Kerlinger, 1964, p. 13). The characteristics of system, control, empiricism, and criticism provide the basis of scientific inquiry. *System* is apparent in the careful planning, organization, and execution of research. Techniques are organized and data are gathered in the hope of answering specific questions or testing specific hypotheses, not in a random fashion with the vague hope of discovery. Scientific research is *controlled*. The investigator analyzes the total situation of inquiry and attempts to control, understand, and allow for every influence that bears on his research problem.

Scientific research is *empirical*. It looks at the world for information (Kaplan, 1964, p. 34), following Aristotle's empiricism rather than Plato's intuition. The procedures of scientific empiricism are public (Berelson and Steiner, 1964, p. 16). Because more than one person can look at the empirical world, scientific studies are available for checking and replication by other investigators. The bias of an individual investigator is not likely to prevail because replication of a study by other investigators will often duplicate the facts but not the bias of an individual. Science is *critical.* It questions its own results and states them in propositional rather than absolute fashion. It develops explanations that it holds until further information appears to provide the basis for more adequate explanations (Simons, 1960, p. 12). Thus, *scientific inquiry never claims to have discovered absolute truth;* its results are always open to refinement and revision. Yet, it seems to be the best way presently known for man to gain verifiable information that allows him to describe and classify, analyze and explain, and predict future events.

Planning the Research Study

Planning research studies calls for skill, imagination, and care. The planning of a study requires looking both forward and backward. The investigator takes into account previous research, the nature of his research problem, possible sources of data, and possible methods of analysis.

Sources of Problems

There is an abundance of problems for research in music therapy. The processes of music therapy described by Sears in Chapter 2 suggest many of them. Problems in need of research continually arise in clinical and educational situations. Some of the studies cited in this book have been described as using no objective techniques of measurement or control. In other words, these studies remain to be validated scientifically; there is no way for the reader to be certain whether the conclusions were based on valid data or on uncontrolled biasing factors. Few of the objective studies reported have been replicated. Many completed studies reveal difficulties in measurement and evaluation and thus provide the basis for development of better methods for use in replications.

Information Bearing on the Problem

Once a problem that requires research has been encountered, the related literature is surveyed. Many times, this essential part of the research process is not used effectively. In planning, it is necessary to consider what is already known. Professional books and journals can help the investigator become well acquainted with knowledge about his problem area. He needs to know possible causes of effects, the experiences of other investigators, what has been investigated, and the difficulties that have been encountered in measurement, control, and analysis. Then he must take all this information into account in planning his own study. If he fails to do this, he may invalidate his study unnecessarily by making errors that could have been avoided had he used information gained in a review of the related literature. *Good research is founded on bibliography.*

Formation of Research Questions or Hypotheses

The problems on which research is based usually begin in general form. For instance, an investigator may wonder whether particular musical procedures can be useful in treating patients with a specific illness. Such a problem, as it stands, is too broad and unspecific to be answered effectively by scientific research. It must be turned into a specific research question or hypothesis, or a series of specific questions or hypotheses. Research questions or hypotheses usually are concerned with topics that are measurable. Measurement involves the assigning of numbers or categories to the events under observation (Stevens, 1951, p. 1). Thus, the investigator may be interested in applying his musical procedures and measuring whether any patients are helped—assignment of categories; what particular patients are helped—assignment of categories; how many patients are helped—assignment of numbers; and how much they are helped—assignment of numbers (Anderson and Smith, 1959, pp. 2–3).

But it is impossible to measure whether patients are helped, how many of them are helped, and how much they are helped unless the investigator knows what the word *help* means. How can help be measured? Definition by synonyms, such as "to aid; assist," does not suffice. Aid and assistance are no easier to measure than is help. Because of these difficulties, an operational definition often is developed (Bachrach, 1962, p. 73). An individual is regarded as having been helped when he exhibits certain specified behaviors. These behaviors can be observed and described objectively. The behaviors may occur a certain number of times, they may simply occur, or they may not occur. In any case, numbers or categories can be assigned and the behavior measured. Different methods of assigning numbers and categories make different statistical tests appropriate for use in analyzing measurements. The proper selection of statistical techniques is discussed in the next chapter, "Measuring and Evaluating Research."

Other aspects of the research problem must be defined. Exactly which patients are to be investigated? There are many types and degrees of severity of most illnesses. Factors including age, educational level, and social development may have some effect on the behaviors of the patient, so they also must be considered. Still further, the specific musical procedures to be tested must be defined. There are many procedures included within the realm of music therapy, and their haphazard application is likely to be less effective than a considered treatment program. If his knowledge of music therapy and the review of related literature have led the investigator to believe that some specific, well-defined procedure is most likely to help (as defined) the patients (as defined), he may present a hypothesis that this procedure will help the patients. The study then will be planned to provide a fair test of whether this hypothesis is true or false. The investigator may not have enough information to enable him to construct a hypothesis. In this case, he can simply pose the research question that asks whether this particular procedure will help these particular patients, and the research study will be planned to provide the best answer to this question.

Design of Studies to Answer Research Questions or Test Research Hypotheses

Once research questions or hypotheses have been posed, ways are planned to answer them. The original problem guides the development of research design. Sources of data, techniques for gathering data, and methods of analysis are interrelated parts of the research plan. The investigator chooses the sources from which he will obtain data, the ways in which he will obtain them, and the ways in which he will organize and analyze them. These choices need to be made conjointly because different methods of organization and analysis are appropriate for different sources and methods of gathering data. To mismatch them could invalidate the results of an otherwise worthwhile study.

The most typical research designs in the behavioral sciences are the case study, the survey, and the experiment (Berelson and Steiner, 1964, p. 18). Underlying these designs is what has been called naturalistic observation and classification of behavior (Butler, Rice, Wagstaff, and Knapp, 1963). Naturalistic research includes activities such as (1) description and categorization of behaviors or events, (2) construction of classifications and taxonomies, and (3) observation of the relationships between the behaviors and events of the various categories. Knowledge obtained through such research is important to the success of case studies, surveys, and experiments.

When the phenomena under consideration are not described well, when relationships at the phenomenal level are not known, the person who insists on starting out with precise experiments lacks the imagination required to observe, to look around and see, at the first level, what seems to be going on. Experiments which precede rather than succeed observation amount to being precise about vagueness . . . (Butler et al., 1963, p. 2).

The classification of the processes of music therapy in Chapter 2 is an example of the sort of naturalistic research that provides a foundation for the advancement of knowledge in music therapy.

The *case study* exhaustively investigates one specified individual or small group. It organizes the resultant data into a description as complete as possible of that individual or group, its characteristics and abilities, and the factors influencing it. This specificity prevents the case study from being practical for studies from which generalizations are to be made. Only if a series of carefully controlled case studies was conducted on a large and representative sample of individuals or groups could valid generalizations be abstracted from the results (Elmer, 1939, pp. 109–129). Much of the case research reported in professional journals and books describes only small or single samples and thus provides little indication of the generality of the factors investigated. The case study finds its primary use in investigations of specific situations in order to describe and understand only those specific situations. However, the results of case studies often provide fruitful hypotheses for testing in surveys and experiments.

The *survey* is a useful research design in the behavioral sciences. There are two general types of surveys (Hyman, 1955, p. 60): One investigates relations between things or events, and the other provides general description. The survey, instead of intensively investigating one individual or small group as does the case study, inquires about a large number of individuals or groups that makes up some population or universe (Kerlinger, 1964, p. 393). If the sampling in a survey is properly done, the results of the study may be generalized to a population or group larger than the sample that is measured. This potential for generalizing results provides a major advantage of the survey: Surveys can provide information about large populations (Kerlinger, 1964, p. 407). In this breadth of coverage, however, there is a decrease in the depth and amount of information that can be gained about any one element in the sample.

Not only can surveys provide descriptive information about large populations, they can also be used to compare samples from different populations. These comparative surveys can reveal correlations and associations, but they are at a disadvantage in the investigation of causal relations. Just because two events or behaviors occur together does not mean that they stand in a cause-and-effect relationship. Both may be results of some underlying cause or their correlation may be coincidental. Furthermore, cause and effect stand in a temporal relationship; cause must precede effect, no matter how short the interval between them. Most surveys are instantaneous studies. They investigate variables concurrently. (The word *variable* is used in research to designate something that can vary or be present in varying amounts.) Thus, it is difficult in survey research to establish the controlled time relationships necessary for the investigation of causation.

The best method for investigating cause and effect is the *experiment*. When properly executed, experimental designs yield results that can be generalized to populations larger than the experimental sample.

By *experiment* is meant any investigation that includes two elements: manipulation or control of some variable by the investigator and systematic observation or measurement of the result. In short, it means active intervention on the phenomena of interest to see what, if any, effects are produced by the intervention (Berelson and Steiner, 1964, p. 19).

Experimental designs not only include manipulation of some variable; they also include a control in which the variable is not manipulated. Both of these situations are then measured (McAshan, 1963, p. 10). Thus, the investigator has a basis for comparison in his study (Campbell and Stanley, 1963, p. 176). All factors in the control and experimental situations are identical, except for the manipulation of the experimental variable. If manipulation of the variable produces some result in the experimental situation and that same result does not occur in the control situation, the investigator can assume that the manipulation of the variable was the cause of the result measured. All experimental designs basically are extensions of this fundamental pattern. Additional experimental and control groups may be added, but the fundamental pattern for comparison remains the same (Kerlinger, 1964, p. 314). Techniques of statistical analysis have made it possible to investigate the effects of several variables at the same time, but they have not eliminated the need for control.

Experimental research begins in the present and extends into the future. This provides the time-sequence relation necessary to establish causality. It also allows more opportunity for the investigator to control or allow for the influences that will affect his results.

The use of experimental method depends upon control, and by control is meant the control of *relevant* conditions or variables. Seldom, if ever, can everything be controlled. Thus, the use of experimental method depends upon previous positive knowledge or upon insight gained in uncontrolled situations (Butler et al., 1963, p. 5).

Three preexperimental designs that are often reported as experiments are described by Campbell and Stanley (1963, pp. 176–183). The one-shot case study is a design in which a single group is studied only once, subsequent to some agent or treatment presumed to cause change. This design has such a total absence of control that it is of almost no value. The one-group pretest-posttest design, in which a group is tested, treated, and tested again, also lacks control. There is no way to know whether any changes found were caused by the treatment or by some other event that occurred between the pretest and posttest. The static-group comparison is identical in procedure with the sample survey, except that the investigator attempts to establish causation. This is not possible through this technique, for "there are . . . no formal means of certifying that the groups would have been equivalent had it not been for the X [variable under consideration]" (Campbell and Stanley, 1963, p. 182).

The ex post facto research design is sometimes classified as an experiment (Chapin, 1955, pp. 32–33). In this design, historical antecedents are sought to explain some situation that already exists; the study starts with the effect and tries to trace back to the cause. This procedure is extremely difficult to control and, therefore, is regarded as being a weak method (Kerlinger, 1964, pp. 292–300).

Sampling in Research

Research designs are spoken of as having external validity and internal validity (Guba, 1965, p. 237). Sampling procedures are important in establishing such validity in research designs. *External validity* refers to the way in which the sample studied in an investigation represents the general population in question. A study with external validity has results that can be generalized to a larger group; the results of a study that does not have external validity cannot be generalized. *Internal validity* refers to the control within the study that prevents the operation of nonrelevant factors that can lead to errors in answering research questions or testing hypotheses.

The general purposes of a research study govern the choice of the research sample. At times, music therapists are interested in comprehensive knowledge about specific cases or therapeutic groups. In such instances, the limited sampling of the case method is most appropriate. However, investigators are often interested in generalizing, in applying research results to groups larger than those from which they can obtain data (Barnes, 1964, p. 35). They may be interested, for example, in geriatric patients in general, but it will be impossible for them to gather data from every geriatric patient. In such a case, data can be gathered only from a sample of the population. Obtaining an adequate sample is a difficult, but most important, task in survey and experimental research.

There are three general problems involved in designing an adequate sampling procedure—definition of the population, size of the sample, and representativeness of the sample (Suchman, 1954, p. 263). In reviewing the problems of research in psychiatric rehabilitation, Kandel and Williams (1959, pp. 117–121) found that many studies lacked any rationale for the selection of their samples. The definition of the population is involved in the development of the research questions; the population should be appropriate for the aims of the study. The population from which the sample is drawn is likely to be the population in which the research problem arose, and it must be the one to which the results are expected to be generalized.

After the population has been specified, the representativeness and size of the sample are considered. The validity of an investigation—the ability of its results to be generalized—depends on how well the individuals who comprise the sample represent the larger population (Riley, 1963, p. 282). There is only one way in which the researcher can safely assume that he has chosen an unbiased representative sample—through the use of random sampling. "Random methods of selection do not allow our own biases or any other systematic selection factors to operate" (Kerlinger, 1964, p. 53). Nonrandom methods may result in a sample in which some members of a population are overrepresented or underrepresented, whereas random sampling allows the researcher to assume that his sample accurately represents the entire population. The techniques of random sampling will be discussed in the next chapter.

The size of the sample is important, particularly for increasing validity. Small samples are usually undesirable and may yield meaningless or misleading results (Smith, 1962, pp. 4–5). Large samples allow the process of random selection to reduce the chance of error or bias in the sample (Kerlinger, 1964, p. 61), and they increase the likelihood that the sample will be truly representative of the population from which it is drawn.

The situations in which music therapists work often prohibit the use of random samples for research. This requires the researcher to attempt to select a sample that seems to be as representative as possible of the population in which he is interested. Such a procedure generally weakens the external validity of the investigation, because it is extremely difficult for the researcher to know the important characteristics of the population that need to be represented and the proportions in which they need to be represented. In experimental situations when the random assignment of subjects or events to control and experimental groups is impossible, an attempt is made to match the control and experimental groups as well as possible on each characteristic that may affect the variable under observation. This matching is best done when it is based on preexperimental testing and is validated statistically.

However, unless the groups are matched on every characteristic that may influence the variable under observation, there is danger that some uncontrolled influence will intrude, reduce internal validity, and increase the chance for false research conclusions. Many factors may result in bias of nonrandom samples. Levitt (1961, p. 109) has described some of the difficulties of using volunteers or forced volunteers such as patient or student populations as research samples. In general, random sampling and random assignment to experimental and control groups provides added strength to research design.

Gathering Research Data

Data for behavioral research can be gathered by a variety of techniques, but in order for the research to be worthwhile, the data-gathering techniques must be valid and reliable (Anastasi, 1961, p. 28). Validity pertains to what the technique measures (Tyler, 1963, p. 28), whereas reliability pertains to how accurately or how consistently the technique measures whatever it does measure (Tyler, 1963, p. 32). Developing and choosing valid techniques for gathering data in music therapy research are difficult tasks. Howery pointed out in Chapter 3 (pp. 47–55) that measured intelligence alone is not a valid measure of mental retardation. This means that the researcher who is interested in studying the effect of some particular musical activity on the improvement of mentally retarded children will not use intelligence tests alone as a valid measure of improvement unless he is interested in improvement in only the sort of activities such tests measure. He must find some technique that will provide a valid measurement of the kind of improvement he wants to effect. A reliable data-gathering device will provide approximately the same result in a series of repeated measures.

In planning his data-gathering procedure, the investigator takes into account his proposed method of analyzing data. Some data-gathering techniques provide information suitable for statistical analysis; others do not. Among the most common data-gathering techniques used in behavioral research are tests and scales, interviews and questionnaires, and personal documents. Numerous data-gathering devices are available in published or unpublished form, but many research studies require the construction of special instruments for gathering information. The researcher is called upon to use his imagination to plan methods that will gather the data he needs.

In music therapy, the focus of research attention is on patients rather than on music. The very fact that data are being gathered may alter the way in which the patients behave. When persons are being observed, their behavior often changes from its normal mode. This change may happen simply because the subjects know that attention is focused on them (Roethlisberger and Dickson, 1939, pp. 15–18). They may change their behavior in order to present themselves in what they consider to be the most favorable light. They may try to please the investigator, or they may purposely attempt to confound the research study. In any case, such changes in behavior make it difficult to have confidence in the research results, for the behavioral changes measured may be caused by factors other than those specified in the study. Field workers in research have developed methods to help minimize these uncontrolled, confounding behavioral changes (Adams and Preiss, 1960). If such techniques are used, they should be described in the *procedure* section of the research report.

Tests and Scales

Psychometric and sociometric tests and scales are useful for gathering research data. Psychometric tests and scales allow the measurement of factors such as intelligence, personality, and attitude, and sociometric tests and scales allow the evaluation of factors such as group interaction, social distance, and socioeconomic status (Chapin, 1955, p. 157). Also of value to the investigator are tests of special aptitudes and abilities, such as tests of musicality, manual dexterity, and coordination (Anastasi, 1961, pp. 365–423). Achievement tests may also prove to be useful measuring devices for research in music therapy. Many of them are standardized and available in published form.

Tests and scales provide data that are in numerical form or are relatively easy to quantify and, thus, are particularly amenable to statistical analysis. The data provided can be useful in statistically matching groups by means of analysis of variance and covariance. Many tests and scales, and their validity and reliability, are described and evaluated in the *Mental Measurements Yearbook* (Buros, 1965).

There are many research questions, however, for which no published tests presently available can provide valid data. In such cases, investigators are compelled to construct their own testing devices. Before such devices can be used confidently, their validity and reliability must be established. There is a variety of methods for testing reliability and validity (Kerlinger, 1964, pp. 429–462). Many research designs in music therapy require the development of rating scales for use by a group of observers who judge the behaviors or performances of subjects. In these cases, validity often is increased by training the judges in the use of the rating scales. Levitt (1961, pp. 190–191) has described a method for estimating the reliability of judgment when more than two judges are used.

Interviews and Questionnaires

The interview is often used for gathering data in behavioral research. The interviewer uses his skill to establish rapport with the subject and motivate him to respond adequately and truthfully (Kahn and Cannell, 1957, pp. 19–21). Often the interviewer uses a schedule that either states exact questions or that has open-ended questions to lead more deeply into the dynamics of the interviewee's situation. A depth interview is most appropriate for case studies, whereas an interview with structured questions is more appropriate for survey or large-group experimental research. Because interviews are liable to a variety of biasing influences, methods have been developed to enable investigators to use the technique in an objective, unbiased manner (Jahoda, Deutsch, and Cook, 1951, pp. 92–117, 152–208; Maccoby and Maccoby, 1954, pp. 472–482; Merton, Fiske, and Kendall, 1956). Large-scale research studies often make use of a questionnaire that can be printed and mailed to persons from whom data are desired. Many of the same errors and biases can arise in the personal interview and the mailed questionnaire (Best, 1959, pp. 143–155; Parten, 1950, pp. 391–402). Sampling errors often arise in studies that use the mailed questionnaire because of the failure of some subjects to answer and return the questionnaire.

Personal Documents

Personal documents (Gottschalk, Kluckhohn, and Angell, 1951) are especially useful in gathering data for case-study research. The data they provide are often difficult to quantify, and thus they are of less use in survey research or studies in which statistical analysis is planned. Some of the most common personal documents available to researchers are biographies and autobiographies, letters, expressive interviews, progress reports (medical and otherwise), and anecdotal descriptions. These papers are often secondary sources of information, and techniques have been developed for determining their validity (Gottschalk et al., 1951, pp. 28–62). Documents created by scientists are regarded as professional documents; they tend to be more reliable than documents written by others.

Analyzing and Interpreting Research Data

Research data, having been collected, cannot answer research questions or test hypotheses unless they are organized and analyzed. The description and analysis of research results can be made nonstatistically or statistically. However, ". . . at its best science is statistical" (Smith, 1962, p. 1). Changes in behavior may be described; but without statistical analysis, the investigator cannot be confident that the changes or differences measured in his research design were true changes rather than chance fluctuations. Statistical techniques help the investigator reduce his chance of accepting incorrect answers to his research questions or incorrectly judging his research hypotheses.

However, statistical analysis gives no indication of the practical value or significance of any research result. To say that a research finding is statistically significant is simply to say that the particular result would not have happened by chance more than a certain number of times out of one hundred (usually five times out of one hundred or one time out of one hundred). In other words, a test of statistical significance gives the researcher a basis for deciding whether the result he observed was caused by the variable he was studying or whether it was a chance occurrence. It provides no indication of any practical significance the result might have.

There might be results that prove to be statistically significant but have little practical significance. Perhaps an exaggerated example will help clarify this. A comparison might be made of the effectiveness of two different music therapy treatment programs. The first of these might be a hospital's typical program; the other a program that requires much additional equipment, an additional music therapist, and eight hours a day of each patient's time for five days of every week. Suppose the progress of the patients were measured by a score computed from a complex battery of measuring procedures designed to estimate personal integration and mental health. A well-designed study might show that patients subjected to the new program for six months scored, on the average, two points higher on the battery of measurements than did patients who were subjected to the regular program for the same six months. The difference in average score might prove to be statistically significant; that is, a difference this size might not have happened by chance more than one out of one hundred times. If the study had been well controlled, the therapist could reasonably attribute this increase in score to the new music therapy program. However, the fact that the difference was statistically significant would not be of any help in deciding whether or not an increase of two points was of enough practical significance to warrant the cost of the additional therapist, the additional equipment, and the amount of patient time required to gain it.

On the other hand, some differences may be statistically insignificant (that is, they might just as easily have occurred by accident as because of the experimental treatment) and still be of practical significance.

Consider, for instance, a study in which patients treated by certain procedures of music therapy did not differ in amount of improvement from patients treated by other procedures such as electroshock, psychodrama, or group therapy. Although no significant difference was found in treatment effects as measured by the amount of improvement, there may be results of practical significance. If each of these treatment procedures results in the same amount of improvement, it may be worthwhile to choose the treatment that has the fewest unfavorable side effects, the greatest positive valence for the patients, the greatest convenience for the therapeutic staff, and the most economy for the hospital. Thus, a statistically insignificant difference may have great practical significance.

Tyler (1934, pp. 67–69) has pointed out that many findings of statistically insignificant differences result from lack of refinement in measurement rather than from actual lack of difference in the subjects or events measured. Many of the measurements made in music therapy research are unrefined; thus, many results that are now statistically insignificant may be significant at some future time as more refined measures are developed and better-controlled studies are planned and executed. It is clear that statistical analysis is a tool. It does not in itself provide answers. It must be used logically and its results interpreted reasonably in light of the purpose, design, and execution of the research study. Statistical significance only indicates how often a given result could have happened by chance.

The interpretation of research results must take into account the entire history of that research study. Care is necessary to determine whether uncontrolled errors in the execution of the study—incomplete sampling, faulty use of measuring devices, or other confounding influences—have invalidated the results. Even if the research design proves to have provided sufficient internal validity, the results cannot be generalized unless the research sample can be assumed to be truly representative of the specified population. The skillful and imaginative planning of a research study has no value unless the plan is carefully executed. The most careful execution, however, cannot remedy the defects of a poorly planned study.

After a carefully designed study has been properly executed and the results meticulously analyzed, the investigator returns to his original research questions or hypotheses and the problem from which they were derived. The research results may help him overcome, or at least understand, the problem. The results, if published or otherwise disseminated, are available for use by others. However, the results of behavioral research should not be expected to be equally applicable in all situations. The human organism is complex, and the research sample that may have been truly representative of a particular population in one year may not truly represent that population in the next. Human beings and their patterns of behavior are constantly undergoing change. Nevertheless, research results provide the best source of validated suggestions available to the clinician for improved practice in music therapy.

It can be seen that the conduct and interpretation of research in music therapy is an involved, highly selective, and rather precarious process. Each situation is slightly different from all others and demands its own adaptation of research techniques. In this, research becomes an art, for its adequacy and success depend on the skill and perspicacity of those who perform and use it.

References

ACKOFF, R. L. *The design of social research*. Chicago: The University of Chicago Press, 1953.

ADAMS, R. N., and PREISS, J. J. *Human organization research: field relations and techniques*. Homewood, Ill.: Dorsey Press, Inc., 1960.

ANASTASI, ANNE. *Psychological testing*. (2d ed.) New York: Macmillan, 1961.

ANDERSON, K. E., and SMITH, H. A. *Topics in statistics for students in education—first course*. Danville, Ill.: Interstate Printers and Publishers, 1959.

BACHRACH, A. J. *Psychological research: an introduction*. New York: Random House, 1962.

BARNES, F. P. *Research for the practitioner in education*. Washington, D.C.: Department of Elementary School Principals, National Education Association, 1964.

BAYLES, E. E. *Democratic educational theory*. New York: Harper & Row, 1960.

BERELSON, B., and STEINER, G. A. *Human behavior: an inventory of scientific findings*. New York: Harcourt, Brace & World, 1964.

BEST, J. W. *Research in education*. Englewood Cliffs, N.J.: Prentice-Hall, 1959.

BUNGE, M. *Metascientific queries*. Springfield, Ill.: Charles C Thomas, 1959.

BUROS, O. K. *The sixth mental measurements yearbook*. Highland Park, N.J.: Gryphon Press, 1965.

BUTLER, J. M., RICE, L. N., WAGSTAFF, A. K., and KNAPP, S. C. *Quantitative naturalistic research*. Englewood Cliffs, N.J.: Prentice-Hall, 1963.

CAMPBELL, D. T., and STANLEY, J. C. Experimental and quasi-experimental designs for research on teaching. In N. L. Gage (Ed.), *Handbook of research on teaching*. Chicago: Rand McNally, 1963. Pp. 171–246.

CAWS, P. *The philosophy of science, a systematic account*. Princeton, N.J.: Van Nostrand, 1965.

CHAPIN, F. S. *Experimental designs in sociological research*. (rev. ed.) New York: Harper & Row, 1955.

ELMER, M. C. *Social research*. New York: Kraus Reprint Corporation, 1939.

FREEDMAN, P. *The principles of scientific research*. New York: Pergamon Press, 1950.

GOODE, W. J., and HATT, P. K. *Methods in social research*. New York: McGraw-Hill, 1952.

GOTTSCHALK, L. R., KLUCKHOHN, C., and ANGELL, R. *The use of personal documents in history, anthropology, and sociology.* New York: Social Science Research Council, 1951.

GUBA, E. G. Experiments, studies, surveys, and investigations. In J. A. Culbertson and S. F. Hencley (Eds.), *Educational research: new perspectives.* Danville, Ill.: Interstate Printers and Publishers, 1965. Pp. 237–248.

HYMAN, H. *Survey design and analysis.* New York: Free Press, 1955.

HYMAN, R. *The nature of psychological inquiry.* Englewood Cliffs, N.J.: Prentice-Hall, 1964.

JAHODA, MARIE, DEUTSCH, M., and COOK, S. W. *Research methods in social relations.* New York: The Dryden Press, Inc., 1951.

KAHN, R. L., and CANNELL, C. F. *The dynamics of interviewing.* New York: Wiley, 1957.

KANDEL, D. B., and WILLIAMS, R. H. *Psychiatric rehabilitation: some problems of research.* Englewood Cliffs, N.J.: Prentice-Hall, 1959.

KAPLAN, A. *The conduct of inquiry: methodology for behavioral science.* San Francisco: Chandler Publications, 1964.

KERLINGER, F. N. *Foundations of behavioral research.* New York: Holt, 1964.

LEVIN, M. M. Research in mental health. In A. Deutsch and Helen Fishman (Eds.), *The encyclopedia of mental health.* Vol. V. New York: F. Watts, 1963. Pp. 1760–1768.

LEVITT, E. E. *Clinical research design and analysis in the behavioral sciences.* Springfield, Ill.: Charles C Thomas, 1961.

MACCOBY, E. E., and MACCOBY, N. The interview: a tool of social science. In G. Lindzey (Ed.), *Handbook of social psychology.* Reading, Mass.: Addison-Wesley, 1954. Pp. 449–487.

McASHAN, H. H. *Elements of educational research.* New York: McGraw-Hill, 1963.

MERTON, R. K., FISKE, MARJORIE, and KENDALL, P. L. *The focused interview.* New York: Free Press, 1956.

PARTEN, M. *Surveys, polls, and samples.* New York: Harper & Row, 1950.

RILEY, M. W. *Sociological research: a case approach.* Vol. I. New York: Harcourt, Brace & World, 1963.

ROETHLISBERGER, F. J., and DICKSON, W. J. *Management and the worker.* Cambridge, Mass.: Harvard, 1939.

SIMONS, J. H. *A structure of science.* New York: Philosophical Library, 1960.

SMITH, G. M. *A simplified guide to statistics.* (3d ed.) New York: Holt, 1962.

STEVENS, S. S. Mathematics, measurement, and psychophysics. In S. S. Stevens (Ed.), *Handbook of experimental psychology.* New York: Wiley, 1951. Pp. 1–49.

SUCHMAN, E. A. The principles of research design. In J. T. Doby (Ed.), *An introduction to social research.* Harrisburg, Pa.: The Stackpole Company, 1954. Pp. 253–269.

TYLER, LEONA E. *Tests and measurements.* Englewood Cliffs, N.J.: Prentice-Hall, 1963.

TYLER, R. W. *Constructing achievement tests.* Columbus, Ohio: Ohio State University Press, 1934.

38

MEASURING AND EVALUATING
RESEARCH *

WARREN E. GEORGE

Introduction

In music therapy, as in disciplines within the behavioral sciences, quality research is of paramount importance. Furthermore, research has to be scientific if it is to have quality. Only in this responsible, scientific manner can research add to the knowledge of a discipline. In the preceding chapter, foundations of the research process were presented. However, this process is not complete without methods for measuring phenomena (observable behaviors) and evaluating the measurement. These methods, which are of prime importance to research, belong to the body of knowledge commonly referred to as *statistics*, a branch of scientific methodology.

A primary aim of scientific research is the description of phenomena in a form so complete and so accurate that it will be useful to the reader. Moreover, it is imperative that the researcher possess some knowledge of the means by which phenomena are described. "Knowledge of statistics is . . . essential to the individual who would perform or even understand research . . ." (Underwood, Duncan, Spence, and Cotton, 1954, p. 4). Whether a person is a researcher or a reader of research, he must have a knowledge of statistics—including the methods for describing and measuring phenomena as well as evaluating the measurement—so there is a basis for communication. Thus, the purpose of this chapter is to present the basic concepts, terminology, and methods of statistics necessary to understand the measurement of phenomena and the evaluation of the measurement. In addition, the most efficient statistical techniques, which are appropriate to various experimental designs and different kinds of data, are presented.

---

* In this chapter, when multiple references to the literature are cited, the best and most explicit source is listed first and the remainder are in decreasing order of excellence and ease of understanding.

Although this chapter was written primarily to assist the readers of research studies, references to literature that explain specific computational procedures and gives examples of statistical techniques are mentioned in the discussion of each topic for those persons who may find them useful in their research. (More references will be found in the annotated bibliography at the end of the chapter.) However, enterprising persons who want to undertake research should not think it is impossible because they cannot do statistics. They can seek the assistance of a statistician or someone schooled in experimental technique to help them plan the entire research study. If this assistance is not available, their research can still be valuable; the most important consideration is to describe the research and any measurement in as orderly and concise a manner as possible.

Measurement

"Measurement encompasses all of the possible procedures by which numbers can be assigned to observable phenomena, in accordance with some orderly, stipulated plan. The numbers are then called scores" (Levitt, 1961, p. 22). Measurement, therefore, involves the assignment of numbers to observable phenomena so that the researcher has some basis for description. It is not always possible in the behavioral sciences, however, to obtain accurate quantitative or numerical data. Often, a number or a score may be only a gross estimate of the behavior in question. In other cases, the investigator may have to judge the performance of a subject on a test by improvement, no improvement, or deterioration. Because of the important function of measurement in research, it is necessary to elaborate further on the three general types of measurement scales employed in the behavioral sciences.

The Nominal or Classificatory Scale

Measurement at its simplest and weakest level is represented by the nominal or classificatory scale, the terms being used interchangeably. It exists "when numbers or other symbols are used simply to classify an object, person, or characteristic" (Siegel, 1956, p 22). For example, when a psychiatrist makes a diagnosis about a patient with regard to a behavioral disorder (that is, schizophrenic reaction, paranoid behavior, and so on), he is using a classificatory scale because he identifies a person with a particular class or set of people by means of a symbol. Similarly, music therapists are a class; males are a class; clinical psychologists are a class. The only relation involved in a nominal scale is *"that observations falling into the same set are thought of as qualitatively the same and those in different classes as qualitatively different in some respect. In general, each observation is placed in one and only one class, making the classes mutually exclusive and exhaustive"* (Hays, 1963, p. 69). Any classification can be broad or specific, depending on the definition of the classes.

A different exa ple of a nominal scale is the use of a plus ($+$) or minus ($-$) sign t ndicate the improvement or deterioration of subjects on one test compa d with another test administered previously. In this situation, there are three classes of people: (1) those who improved, (2) those who did not improve, and (3) those who did worse. There is no measurement of the amount of improvement. The only concern is whether there was improve ent. Nonparametric statistics, which are discussed later, are the appro riate statistical techniques for nominal or classificatory data.

The Ordinal or Ranking Scale

The ordinal or ranking scale of measurement contains the same properties as the nominal scale, except that it goes one step further. As in the nominal scale, the ranking (ordinal) scale requires the objects in each subclass to be equal. In addition, it requires some kind of relationship among the cla es. These relationships are designated by the symbols ($>$) and ($<$) for "g eater than" and "less than," respectively.

One example of ordinal measurement is in the classification of mentally retarded childi n according to one of four adaptive behavior levels. Each level identifie children who are basically equal in their adaptive ability. Furthermore there is a relationship among the various levels. That is, retardates i level 1 adapt to their environment better than ($>$) those in level 2, lev l $2 > 3$, level $1 > 3$, and so forth. Another example of a hierarchy of or ering is the various classifications of socioeconomic status.

One of the most ommon examples of an ordinal or ranking scale in experimental researc is observed when the experimenter is able to establish a rank order mong subjects with regard to their amount or degree of improvement or deterioration on a particular examination. Ordinal measurement is also applicable to the music educator who has to decide a rank order among his clarinet players. It is possible to say that one person is better than ($>$) another and to assign a number to each player, but it is impossible to say how much better. It is especially important to remember that "ordinal numbers indicate rank order and nothing more. The numbers do not indicate absolute quantities, nor do they indicate that the intervals between the numbers are equal" (Kerlinger, 1964, p. 423). Ranking or ordinal data require the use of nonparametric techniques.

The Interval Scale

"*Interval* or *equal-interval* scales possess the characteristics of nominal and ordinal scales, especially the rank-order characteristic. In addition, numerically equal distances on interval scales represent equal distances in the property being measured" (Kerlinger, 1964, p. 424). Thus, real numbers can be assigned to all objects. This is probably the strongest type of measurement that can be achieved in the behavioral sciences. A common example of an interval scale is the standardized achievement test. This scale has the same property as a ranking scale in that persons can be ranked according to their achievement. However, the distances between points on the achievement scale are known. This characteristic makes the interval scale the most powerful of the three types of measurement because it provides for the quantification of characteristics or the association of numbers with the positions of objects on the interval scale.

When measurement is at the interval-scale level, any of the ordinary operations of arithmetic may be applied to the differences between numerical measurements, and the result interpreted as a statement about magnitudes of the underlying property. The important part is this interpretation of a numerical result as a quantitative statement about the property shown by the objects (Hays, 1963, p. 72).

Although some nonparametric methods are appropriate for interval data, efficiency of analysis is increased greatly if parametric techniques are used.

Statistical Methods

After an experimenter has obtained measurements on the persons or variables under investigation, he must have some means to interpret the data. "Statistical methods are the techniques used to facilitate the interpretations of collections of quantitative or numerical data" (Blommers and Lindquist, 1960, p. 3). They provide the researcher with devices for making order out of chaos. "Statistics provides tools which formalize and standardize our procedures for drawing conclusions" (Siegel, 1956, pp. 1–2).

Statistical methods and measurement cannot be separated. Without measurement, statistical methods are useless; and without statistical methods, nothing very valuable and meaningful can be derived from measurement. The advantages of measurement and statistical methods have been summarized by Guilford (1965).

1. They permit the most exact kind of description.
2. They force us to be definite and exact in our procedures and in our thinking.
3. Statistics enable us to summarize our results in meaningful and convenient form.
4. They enable us to draw general conclusions, and the process of extracting conclusions is carried out according to accepted rules.
5. They enable us to make predictions of "how much" of a thing will happen under conditions we know and have measured.
6. They enable us to analyze some of the causal factors out of complex and otherwise bewildering events (pp. 3–4).

It can be concluded that statistical methods have an important and essential role in the research process. Without them, the researcher is handicapped greatly in deriving any meaningful answers from the data that have been collected.

Although there are numerous statistical techniques and many different ways to classify them, it will be helpful in this discussion to consider them according to the following categories: (1) statistics for making descriptions, (2) statistics for studying relationships and making predictions, and (3) statistics for making inferences.

Statistics for Making Descriptions

When a researcher has collected a large amount of data, he needs to have some method for organizing them so that pertinent facts can be described. Descriptive statistics are methods by which it is possible "to organize the data into some orderly form, to make summary statements about the general (average) level of magnitude of the numbers involved, to indicate in some way the extent to which these numbers tend to be alike or different in magnitude, and to show how they are distributed in value . . ." (Blommers and Lindquist, 1960, p. 4).

A *frequency distribution* is generally a good starting point for organizing a large amount of numerical data. The process involves ranking all the possible scores and then counting the number (frequency) of persons or objects having each particular score value. If there are a large number and a wide range of scores, they should be grouped into approximately fifteen equal-sized intervals. After the frequency distribution has been completed, it is a simple task to make some descriptive interpretations of the data. Examples of such descriptions would be (1) where (in what interval or intervals) most of the scores are concentrated and (2) where there is a sparsity of scores.

Although a frequency distribution is usually sufficient to study the distribution of scores, it may be helpful to represent them graphically. Two accepted ways of graphic representation are the *histogram* and the *frequency polygon*. Both involve plotting the score points or midpoints of the score intervals along a horizontal axis and the frequency on a vertical axis. On a histogram, each score value is represented by a bar from the horizontal axis up to the frequency point on the vertical axis. This is commonly known as a *bar graph* and is particularly applicable for comparing the frequencies of individuals in different categories, such as the number of men drafted into the armed services during each month of the year. In a frequency polygon, the frequencies are connected by a line. This is commonly known as a *line graph* and is employed primarily to show trends, such as the changing prices in the stock market. Both these graphic techniques are useful to depict the distribution of a set of scores. However, the frequency polygon is preferred if the scores of two or more groups are being compared on the same graph. Instructions for making frequency distributions, histograms, and frequency polygons are in the following sources: Wallis and Roberts, 1956, pp. 167–182; Garrett, 1962, pp. 12–26; Lindquist, 1942, pp. 11–28, 39–50.

Measures of central tendency are another very useful part of descriptive statistics; they are indices that "reveal the general trend of the obtained scores—whether on the whole they tend to run high, low, or somewhere between" (Adkins, 1964, p. 75). The three in common use are the *mean, median,* and *mode.* The mean $(\overline{X})$, sometimes called the arithmetic mean, "is defined as the sum of all of the values of the observations, divided by the total number of observations" (Edwards, 1958, p. 39). The mean typically is considered the *average* of the scores and is the most common and frequently used of all the measures of central tendency.

The median (Mdn) is used occasionally to describe the "average" of a group. It is the middle of all the scores and is defined as "that point on a scale of measurement above which and below which 50 percent of the observations fall" (Edwards, 1958, p. 43). When calculating the median, the scores are arranged in order of their magnitude, and the median (middle) point is determined by counting. If the scores are grouped into a frequency distribution, a slightly different computational process is involved.

The mode (Mo) is the crudest type of measure of central tendency. It is simply that place in the distribution where there is the heaviest concentration of scores. Because there may be more than one point of concentration, a distribution can have several modes.

If he knows all three measures of central tendency for a particular distribution, the investigator can describe something about the form of the distribution. If the mean, median, and mode are the same, the distribution of scores is symmetrical or bell-shaped. However, this is not always the case, and sometimes one of these measures may be more meaningful than the others.

Because the mean takes into account the magnitude of each score value, it usually is considered the best measure of central tendency. "The arithmetic mean is preferred to the median . . . because it is more stable under sampling—it varies less from one sample to the next" (Dunn, 1964, p. 33). There are, however, some instances in which the median may be more representative of the average. "In general, the median should be used where a few atypical cases of very large or very small value will distort the mean" (Smith, 1962, p. 23). The mode may be an adequate measure when "a very rough estimate of central value will do" or when "we wish to know the most typical case" (Guilford, 1965, p. 63). By reporting all three measures of central tendency, the reader can learn much about the form of the distribution. Most elementary statistics books discuss measures of central tendency together and include computational procedures (Anderson and Smith, 1958, pp. 6–7; Underwood et al., 1954, pp. 44–59; Edwards, 1958, pp. 39–51).

By using only measures of central tendency, a person is rather limited in describing precisely the form of the distribution. It is very helpful to know whether the scores are close together or widely scattered. Descriptive statistics of this type are known as *measures of variability* (Adkins, 1964, pp. 127–161; Anderson and Smith, 1958, pp. 8–15; Guilford, 1965, pp. 68–90).

The coarsest measure of variability is the *range*, which is found by subtracting the lowest score from the highest. The obvious weakness of this measure is that it only considers two scores. The *short range* (the middle 80 percent) and the *semiinterquartile range* (one-half of the middle 50 percent) are somewhat better indices than the range. However, none of these measures considers the exact magnitude of each score. "Ordinarily, range indices are useful only in situations in which a rather crude indication of variability is sufficient for the purpose of the particular analysis" (Blommers and Lindquist, 1960, p. 136).

The measures of variability generally used in research are the *standard deviation* and the *variance*. These are the most stable measures of variability because they take into account the magnitude or size of each score. To facilitate an understanding of these measures, it is best to approach them by way of computational procedure. Computation of the variance involves (1) subtracting each score from the mean (the result of which is called a *deviation*), (2) squaring each deviation, (3) adding the squared deviations, and (4) dividing by the number of scores. "This result means that the variance is a descriptive index of how different each value is from every other value . . ." (Ferguson, 1966, pp. 65–66). After completing the computation of the variance, all that remains to be done to find the standard deviation is to extract the square root of the variance. Because the variance is expressed in squared units, the standard deviation is almost always computed because "it is desirable to use a measure of variation which is not in squared units, but is in units of the original measurements themselves" (Ferguson, 1966, p. 66). Thus, interpretation is easier if the standard deviation is used.

The standard deviation and the variance are also advantageous in that other computations use these values. In addition, many more specific interpretations can be made using these measures of variability. If the mean and standard deviation are computed and the population is normally distributed, it is possible to state exactly what percentage of scores fall between two points. For example, when the mean of an intelligence test is 100 and the standard deviation is 16, 68.26 percent (roughly two-thirds) of the scores fall between + and − one standard deviation from the mean (between 84 and 116). Similarly, approximately 95 percent of the scores fall within two standard deviations either side of the mean (between 68 and 132), and about 99 percent are within three standard deviations (± 3) either side of the mean (between 52 and 148). For practical purposes, all persons of a normally distributed population are within ± 3 standard deviations.

It also is possible to make comparisons among individual scores when the mean and standard deviation have been computed. By subtracting the mean from an individual score and dividing by the standard deviation, the individual score is transformed into a *standard score* (called a *z* score) (Blommers and Lindquist, 1960, pp. 157–176; Smith, 1962, pp. 54–56). In this way, the raw scores can be converted into common units. "Furthermore, a standard score is of such a nature that it expresses a subject's *position in a given distribution both with respect to the mean and with respect to the variability.* It is thus relatively free from ambiguity" (Smith, 1964, p. 55).

The principal advantage of the *z* score, as well as other standard scores, is that the researcher is able to make comparisons among individuals. For example, if two different intelligence tests are administered to two different groups of subjects, it might be concluded that an IQ score of 116 in one group would be equal to an IQ score of 116 in the other. This would be true if both tests had means and standard deviations of 100 and 16, respectively. But if either the means or standard deviations are unequal, persons with these scores cannot be considered to have equal IQs. Suppose that the mean of one test was 100 and the standard deviation was 16, whereas these values were 100 and 15, respectively, for the other test. By transforming the two scores into z scores, it is found that an IQ of 116 on the first test has a z score of 1.00, but an IQ of 116 on the other test shows a z of 1.07. Thus, a person making a score of 116 on the second test has a higher IQ than a person with the same score on the first test. In order to state that a subject in the first group has equal intelligence to a subject in the second group, the first one must have a score of 116 and the second one a score of 115 because these scores both yield z scores of 1.00.

By the use of a table (Blommers and Lindquist, 1960, pp. 502–509; Edwards, 1960, pp. 350–359; Downie and Heath, 1959, pp. 257–264), a z score can be converted to a *percentile rank* (if the population is normally distributed), which may be more meaningful to some people. This technique enables ranking each individual according to his score and the scores of all individuals in the group or population. A percentile rank of 84.13 is equal to a z score of 1.00 and means that 84.13 percent of the persons are below that particular score value. Similarly, a z score of 1.07 is equal to a percentile rank of 85.77. Thus, it can be seen that in the example above, whether one uses a z score or transforms it to a percentile rank, a person scoring 116 on the second test is somewhat more intelligent than a person making the identical score on the first test.

Statistics for Studying Relationships and Making Predictions

In many instances, the researcher may want to study the relationships between two sets of scores from the same group of subjects. In other words, he may want to determine the correlation between two sets of scores or variables. The two most popular statistical methods for assessing correlation are the *rank difference* (a nonparametric technique) and the *product moment* (a parametric technique). If the correlation is a high one, it is possible, by knowing a person's score on only one of the variables, to predict within reasonable limits what his score would be on the other variable. Thus, statistical techniques of this kind may be quite useful for prediction purposes as well as for studying relationships.

The degree of relationship or correspondence between two or more variables is expressed as a *correlation coefficient* (the symbol of which is indicated by r). Theoretically, this coefficient may be any value ranging from +1.00 to −1.00. An obtained value of +1.00 indicates a perfect positive relationship—that is, the person who made the highest score on one test also made the highest score on the other test; the person ranking second on one test was also second on the other; and so on. A value of zero indicates no relationship, whereas a value of −1.00 is a perfect but inverse relationship. In the latter case, the person scoring highest on one test scored lowest on the other.

One word of caution must be stated for the interpretation of r: A coefficient of correlation is *not* a percentage and must not be interpreted as such. It does not imply causation, nor is an r of .80 twice as good as an r of .40. The interpretation must be in terms of a relationship. Just what is a significant correlation poses a difficult question to answer because it depends primarily on the purposes for which r was calculated. If the coefficient was calculated for use in prediction, an r of $\pm$.90 (plus or minus .90) might be considered necessary. However, for purposes of establishing relationships, a value much less than $\pm$.90 may be accepted as being significant. As a general guide, Guilford (1942, p. 219) has proposed the following rules:

Less than .20	Slight; almost negligible relationship
.20–.40	Low correlation; definite but small relationship
.40–.70	Moderate correlation; substantial relationship
.70–.90	High correlation; marked relationship
.90–1.00	Very high correlation; very dependable relationship

The rank-difference correlation coefficient (sometimes called Spearman's rank-difference correlation coefficient) requires at least ordinal measurement. In this case, the experimenter must be able to rank each subject, in relation to the group, with regard to each test or variable. For computational procedures, see Siegel, 1956, pp. 202–213; Guilford, 1965, p. 305–308; Adkins, 1964, pp. 282–288.

The product-moment correlation coefficient (referred to as Pearson r or Pearson product-moment correlation coefficient) is stronger and more accurate because it requires an interval scale of measurement. In other words, "it takes into account the absolute size of the measures and not merely their rank-order" (Smith, 1962, p. 95). Thus, if a person has achieved interval measurement, Pearson r should be used. For computational procedures, see Underwood et al., 1954, pp. 140–151; Edwards, 1958, pp. 66–84; Dunn, 1964, pp. 139–159.

If, after obtaining a high correlation coefficient ($>$.90), a person wants to use it for prediction purposes, it is necessary to calculate a *regression equation* (Underwood et al., 1954, pp. 151–155; Garrett, 1962, pp. 100–101). This process makes a reasonable prediction about an unknown score possible, provided at least one of the correlated scores is known.

The rank order and the product moment are the two most popular methods for studying relationships, and the computational procedures offer no insurmountable problems. There are other correlation techniques available for studying two variables, as well as a statistical technique for determining the correlation among more than two variables. However, the rank-difference and product-moment techniques are sufficient for practically all purposes.

Statistics for Making Inferences

Statistics for making inferences (one category of statistical methods) is very important in research studies. From the results of the experiments, which are known as *sampling studies* because they are conducted on a small group (sample), the experimenter generally wants to make inferences about the large group (population). The term *population* refers to a well-defined class of people, objects, or events; it may be very large or very small, depending on the definition of the population. For example, geriatric patients could be a population, as could cerebral palsied children, alcoholics, fifth-grade children, and so on. Because it is virtually impossible to conduct a research study with an entire population, it is necessary to use only a portion of the population and generalize the conclusions to the total group. Statistical methods that help the experimenter accomplish this aim are in the category of statistical inference.

Sampling has an important function in statistical methods and refers to the selection of those persons in the population who are to take part in the experiment. It is imperative that the sample be an accurate representation of the population; that is, the sample should be a true model that correctly exemplifies the characteristics of the population. In general, the inferences one can make from a research study are much more valid if a large number of persons is used and if the population is represented accurately by the sample. However, this does not mean that research cannot be done by using small groups.

The accepted way of choosing a sample is by random selection. This does not imply the dictionary definition of random; in their work scientists have to follow a specially designated set of rules. "*Random sampling* is that method of drawing a portion (or sample) of a population . . . so that each member of the population . . . has an equal chance of being selected" (Kerlinger, 1964, p. 52). Suppose an experiment is being performed in a hospital with a population of one hundred geriatric patients. In order to obtain a random sample of thirty patients, the names of the one hundred patients could be written on separate pieces of paper, which would then be placed in a container. The experimenter would select one paper at a time until thirty names had been drawn. However, the scientific way of drawing a random sample is to list each patient, assign him a number, and then make the sample selection using a table of random numbers. Many statistics books contain these tables; the following books explain how to use them: Edwards, 1958, pp. 129–130; Wallis and Roberts, 1956, p. 631; Rand Corporation, 1955, pp. xxii–xxiii.

Statistical techniques for use in inference are many. A discussion of them is presented later because the specific application of these techniques to experimental designs will facilitate understanding. The important thing to remember is that samples must be representative of the population in order to eliminate bias. If the sample is drawn using IQ scores as the criterion, too many persons with high scores or too many persons with low scores will probably distort the outcome; the sample must be an approximate image of the population. Some opinion polls are not accurate because the samples do not indicate the true opinions of the population.

Parametric and Nonparametric Statistics

The whole body of statistical tests usually is considered as belonging to one of two groups—parametric or nonparametric tests. Some insight into the differences between these two can be gleaned from a definition of parameter. "A *parameter* is a property descriptive of the population" (Ferguson, 1966, p. 10). It is a value that is representative of a characteristic of the population. In other words, "if all the scores of a defined population are available and a mean is computed, this mean is a parameter" (Kerlinger, 1964, p. 257). However, it is highly unlikely that the experimenter would know all, if any, of the actual population values. Furthermore, parametric tests do not require that he know any of them. When using a parametric test, any computed sample value (called a statistic) is considered to be an estimate of the corresponding population value. That is, the experimenter assumes that his sample is a fairly accurate representative of the population. Because of this, parametric statistical tests require certain assumptions about the population.

In general, there are three assumptions of parametric tests that must be met.

1. The samples have been drawn from a population which is normally distributed.
2. The variances of all the groups (samples) are homogeneous.
3. The variables to be measured are continuous and achieve interval measurement (Kerlinger, 1964, pp. 258–259).

The third assumption is the most stringent requirement of parametric tests. Besides requiring interval measurement, this assumption refers to the fact that the variable being measured must lie on a continuum. Such things as height, weight, intelligence, and achievement lie on continua —that is, they have infinitesimally small gradations that are immeasurable —even though they have to be measured in discrete quantities such as feet and inches, pounds and ounces, or fractions thereof, as well as integer numbers. Usually, it is safe to assume that any variable under study in behavioral sciences is continuous. Assumptions 1 and 2 also warrant consideration; however, recent research by Norton with regard to these assumptions makes them less strict than assumption 3 (Lindquist, 1953, pp. 78–86). Thus, providing that the third assumption has been met, it is generally agreed among statisticians that *the experimenter should use parametric tests whenever possible unless there are gross departures from the first and second assumptions.* The most common parametric tests are the various *t* tests, analysis of variance, factorial designs (variations of the analysis of variance), analysis of variance and covariance, and Pearson *r*.

Whereas a parametric test requires the meeting of certain assumptions about the population, "a nonparametric statistical test . . . does not specify conditions about the parameters of the population from which the sample was drawn" (Siegel, 1956, p. 31). Thus, nonparametric statistical tests are sometimes called *distribution-free* tests. Although certain assumptions are associated with some nonparametric tests, they are fewer and weaker than the assumptions for parametric tests and need be of little concern. The main advantage of nonparametric tests is that they "do not require measurement so strong as that required for the parametric tests; most nonparametric tests apply to data in an ordinal scale, and some apply also to data in a nominal scale" (Siegel, 1956, p. 31). Other advantages of nonparametric tests are that (1) they are easier to apply; (2) they may be used with small samples; and (3) they are distribution free (Siegel, 1956, pp. 32–33; Barnes, 1964, p. 78). They have the disadvantages of (1) being wasteful of data if interval measurement is obtained and (2) requiring a great amount of labor if the samples are large (Siegel, 1956, p. 33; Barnes, 1964, pp. 76–77). Among the most common nonparametric techniques are chi square, the sign test, the median test, Mann-Whitney *U*, and others that will be discussed later.

It was stated above that parametric tests should be used whenever possible. This is because they are much more powerful than the nonparametric techniques. By "powerful," statisticians mean that one test is better than another because it will yield the same results with a smaller number of subjects (Siegel, 1956, p. 20). If the assumptions underlying parametric techniques cannot be met, there is no other alternative than to use a nonparametric test. *The only safe rule to follow is to use parametric tests when the assumptions are met so that data are not wasted. If parametric tests are impossible, use nonparametric tests.*

Hypotheses, Regions of Rejection, and Significance Levels

Hypotheses, regions of rejection, and significance levels are interrelated considerations of the early part of the research process. The nature of the hypothesis dictates the selection of the region of rejection and also influences the establishment of the significance level. Although the decisions about these three items depend on each other, they are discussed here in the order in which the decisions about them are usually made.

Hypotheses

The basic purpose of research is to find answers to questions. Statistical techniques help provide these answers, but it is impossible to prove anything as being absolute. Statistics only help the researcher disprove all possible answers except one. It then is considered a tenable answer until it has been disproved.

When planning an experiment, the investigator usually makes a conjectural statement regarding a theory about some particular problem. This is known as the *experimental* or *research hypothesis* and is the answer he believes might be tenable. To eliminate personal bias, it is customary in research to state the *null* hypothesis (H_0) first. It is the hypothesis of no difference and "is usually formulated for the express purpose of being rejected" (Siegel, 1956, p. 7). An example of a null hypothesis would be that "the means of an experimental group and of a control group are equal." If the null hypothesis is rejected, then the *alternate*, or research, hypothesis is accepted.

The alternate hypothesis (H_1) may be stated in different ways, depending on the theory or theories of the experimenter. For example, if the research hypothesis states only that the experimental and control groups will differ with respect to means, then H_1 is that $\mu_1 \neq \mu_2$ (hypothesized mean 1 is not equal to hypothesized mean 2). In this case, the experimenter is not interested in which mean is higher but merely in whether there is a difference. If a prediction is made that the mean of the experimental group will be higher than that of the control group, then H_1 is that $\mu_1 > \mu_2$. Regardless of the situation, H_1 must be established before the data gathering begins. Then, the statistical technique tests H_0 against H_1.

Regions of Rejection

Another item that must be established prior to experimentation is the *region of rejection*. When referring to a region or area of rejection, the experimenter is referring to that portion of a distribution in which the test statistic must fall if he is to reject H_0. Theoretically, if an experiment were run an infinite number of times yielding an infinite number of test statistics, a distribution could be made of these test statistics from the various samples. The experimenter is interested in determining whether the sample value supports H_0 when H_0 is true or whether there is reasonable evidence to reject H_0 in favor of H_1. In order to be most certain that the obtained value is false (does not support H_0), the region of rejection is placed at the extreme ends or tails of the distribution. If the statistic falls in this small area, then H_0 is probably false and the experimenter has reason for rejection.

The placement of the region of rejection depends to a large extent on H_1. That is, if H_1 is that $\mu_1 \neq \mu_2$, the region of rejection is called a *two-tailed test*. On the other hand, if H_1 is that $\mu_1 > \mu_2$ or that $\mu_1 < \mu_2$, a *one-tailed test* is used. These two terms refer to the tails of the distribution —the extremely low scores and the extremely high scores.

Significance Levels

After establishing the region of rejection, it is necessary to decide how small the area of this region is to be. The size of the area of rejection is called a *significance level* and is referred to in statistical terminology as alpha (α). This is the probability of saying that H_0 is false when it is really true; it is the *level of confidence* on which the experimenter bases his conclusion. Because the experimenter needs to be reasonably certain that he rejects H_0 when it is really false, α must be set rather small. The two levels that generally are accepted are the 0.05 (5 percent) level and the 0.01 (1 percent) level. In essence, the experimenter is saying that he is willing to be wrong five times out of one hundred or one time out of one hundred or that the value can be obtained this many times by chance. However, any conclusion based on a value that could occur this few times by chance alone can be assumed to be tenable.

Although it is customary to use the 0.05 or 0.01 level of significance, there is nothing sacred about them and experimenters may often require either lower or higher significance levels to reject H_0. It is impossible to establish any constant level of α that will be appropriate for all situations. If the experimenter is interested in adopting a new teaching method that would amount to considerable expense, the significance level would probably be set quite high (< 0.01) in order to avoid the influence of any chance factors. If the concern is about how many mentally retarded children were helped because of a new therapy technique, a much lower level (perhaps 0.20) would be acceptable. If a level as low as 0.20 were selected, the probability would be increased that chance factors could influence the outcome. No matter what the experimenter decides to accept as significant, it is considered good practice to follow this recommendation. "In reporting his findings, the researcher should indicate the actual probability level associated with his findings, so that the reader may use his own judgment in deciding whether or not the null hypothesis should be rejected" (Siegel, 1956, p. 9).

Choosing the Statistical Test

Before conducting an experiment, it is important to choose an appropriate statistical test. As is the case with the alternate hypothesis, the region of rejection, and the significance level, *this decision must be made before the experiment is performed.* The primary reason for this is that the statistical test chosen must be appropriate for the data (nominal, ordinal, or interval measurement) the experimenter is able to gather. In addition, the assumptions of the statistical test dictate some of the procedures that must be followed in planning the experiment. This section describes some statistical techniques that are applicable in specified pre-experimental and experimental conditions. Only a cursory examination of each particular technique is given, and the reader is referred to specific sources for computational procedures. Other sources will be found in the annotated bibliography. A brief explanation about making decisions after the statistic has been computed is included. These descriptions should help the reader judge whether appropriate statistical techniques have been used and proper conclusions drawn.

The Study with One Sample

The study that uses only one sample or one group of subjects has very limited use. It is called a study because it uses only one sample and only one measurement is taken on each of the subjects in the group. The usual question is whether the sample came from a specified population, either theoretical or known. Statistical techniques for testing a hypothesis of this kind are known as the goodness-of-fit type. The typical situations are that (1) the frequencies observed are the same or are different from what one would expect or (2) the mean of the sample is the same or is different from the mean of the population.

The t Test (Edwards, 1958, pp. 126–128; Blommers and Lindquist, 1960, pp. 343–346). In the one-sample situation, a common parametric technique used is the t test. In order for an experimenter to use this test, not only must his population meet all the assumptions of parametric statistics, but he must know the mean of the population (μ). This particular technique is useful for comparing the sample mean ($\overline{X}$) with the population mean (μ). After completing the calculation of the t statistic, it is necessary to refer to a table of t values. If the obtained value is larger than the table value, H_0 is rejected in favor of H_1. It is concluded that $\overline{X}$ is significantly different from μ, and therefore the sample must be from a different population. If H_0 is accepted, the conclusion is that the sample is from the defined population.

Chi Square (Underwood et al., 1954, pp. 204–205; Ferguson, 1966, pp. 191–193). The chi-square (χ^2) one-sample test is a nonparametric test of the goodness-of-fit type and may be used with nominal measurement—the classification of objects into categories. Chi square is a test of the significance of differences—the differences, in this case, being between the observed frequencies and the expected frequencies in the categories. The classic example of this test is a coin tossed one hundred times. It is expected that the result will be fifty heads and fifty tails. After the number of observed heads and tails is obtained, χ^2 is computed by comparing the differences between observed and expected frequencies. The obvious conclusion, if the value is larger than that in a chi-square table, is that the observed frequencies differ significantly from the expected; i.e., there is some factor other than chance that is influencing the coin.

This particular test also can be used to analyze the responses to a question. For example, it can be hypothesized that the responses of all persons to a particular question will be equally divided among all possible answers. The hypothesized equal division, then, is the expected frequency for each possible answer; the observed frequencies are compared with it. If the resultant χ^2 is significant, there is some factor other than chance that influences the responses. The test is also applicable when the same question is submitted to a number of persons before and after a particular treatment. The responses obtained prior to treatment are considered the expected frequencies; those obtained afterward, the observed frequencies. The χ^2 goodness-of-fit test may also be used to test the hypothesis that the scores on a test are normally distributed. Guilford (1965, pp. 243–247) and Adkins (1964, pp. 203–205, 338–339) outline the steps in this process.

Kolmogorov-Smirnov One-Sample Test (Siegel, 1956, pp. 47–52; Guilford, 1965, pp. 260–262). Another test of the goodness-of-fit type is the Kolmogorov-Smirnov one-sample test. It is also a nonparametric test and is used for the same purposes as χ^2. If the sample size is small, the Kolmogorov-Smirnov test is preferred because it is more powerful than χ^2. This is so because (1) χ^2 requires a minimum number (usually five) of responses in each category, whereas the Kolmogorov-Smirnov test does not; and (2) the Kolmogorov-Smirnov test uses ordinal data.

The Experiment with Two Independent Samples

When subjects from a defined population are assigned randomly to a control and an experimental group, these two groups are known in research terminology as independent samples. That is, the persons in each group were randomly assigned to a treatment group after having been selected at random from the defined population. The purpose of the different statistical tests for comparing two independent samples is to answer the question: After treatment, are the two samples from the same population, or are they from two different populations because of the treatment? This experimental situation involves administering a different treatment to each group and then comparing the two groups afterward by means of a statistical test of some kind.

The t Test (Smith, 1962, pp. 72–77; Edwards, 1958, pp. 130–133). The usual parametric test for this situation is the *t* test for independent samples. Like all parametric tests, it requires that certain assumptions be met, especially interval measurement. The null hypothesis is that the mean of group 1 is equal to the mean of group 2 ($H_0: \mu_1 = \mu_2$), and the alternate hypothesis may be $\mu_1 \neq \mu_2$, $\mu_1 > \mu_2$, or $\mu_1 < \mu_2$. If the obtained value of *t* is less than the table value of *t*, H_0 is accepted and it is concluded that there is no statistically significant difference between the two groups. On the other hand, if H_0 is rejected and H_1 accepted, the conclusion is based on the prediction inherent in H_1.

The Median Test (Siegel, 1956, pp. 111–115; Downie and Heath, 1959, pp. 211–212). The median test is like the *t* test for two independent samples with two exceptions: (1) It is a nonparametric test requiring ordinal data, and (2) it compares the medians of two groups rather than the means. Thus, the primary advantage of the median test is that it compares a different measure of central tendency. The hypotheses and the conclusions are identical to those of the *t* test, except that the median is substituted for the mean.

The Mann-Whitney U Test (Downie and Heath, 1959, pp. 212–215; Siegel, 1956, pp. 116–127). The Mann-Whitney *U* test is perhaps the most common nonparametric test for comparing two independent samples. Because it requires at least ordinal measurement, it tests the significance of difference of the ranks of the two groups. In essence, this test involves ranking all individuals in both groups with regard to the variable in question and then adding the ranks of the members of each group. That the average rank of the two groups is the same is H_0. If H_0

is rejected, it may be said that the average rank of one group is significantly higher than the other.

Chi Square (Siegel, 1956, pp. 104–111; Smith, 1962, pp. 127–129). Another useful nonparametric test is the χ^2 test for two independent samples. The main advantage of this technique over the *t* test and the U test is that it requires only classificatory measurement. Like the χ^2 discussed previously, this technique tests the significance of differences between expected and observed frequencies in discrete categories. This χ^2 is appropriate if the purpose of the study (survey) is to determine, for example, whether boys and girls have differing opinions with regard to the most pleasurable physical activities. The hypotheses are either that they do or do not differ.

The Experiment with Two Related Samples

Whenever the experimenter is able to match the subjects in one group with those in a second group according to some criterion, the efficiency of the experimental design is greatly increased if the groups are matched on a criterion related to the experimental variable. Matching relates the two samples. Another way to match is to administer a pretest and a posttest to each subject in one group. In this case, the pretest sample is related to the posttest sample because each subject is his own control. With two matched groups, the usual question is: Do the experimental and control groups differ significantly after treatment? When one group is given a pretest and a posttest, the question is: Do the posttest scores show a significant improvement over the pretest scores? In both situations, the investigation is centered on the differences between the pairs of scores.

The t Test (Edwards, 1958, pp. 136–137; Garrett, 1962, pp. 129–131). Provided the assumptions for parametric statistics are met, there is a *t* test for studying the mean difference $(\overline{D})$ of the two sets of scores. Although this statistical technique is limited to studying only two sets of scores, it is *the most powerful test* that can be used in this type of experimental situation.

The McNemar Test for the Significance of Changes (Siegel, 1956, pp. 63–67). This nonparametric test is particularly useful in the before and after designs in which each subject is used as his own control. It is particularly suitable "when the data are in frequencies which can only be classified by separate categories . . ." (Siegel, 1956, p. 93). With this test, it is possible to see the number of subjects who change their responses from before to after and to determine if the change was statistically significant.

The Sign Test (Ferguson, 1966, pp. 356–357; Siegel, 1956, pp. 68–75). If it is possible to determine that each subject is better than or worse than his matched subject, the sign test is applicable. This is a very easy statistical technique because it involves only plus (+) and minus (−) signs. Because of its simplicity, it is suitable for making a gross estimate of the number of subjects who improved on the posttest. If the data are stronger than + or − signs, a more sophisticated technique can be used. The sign test should be used when the experimenter has to measure his subjects using only + and − signs and when the sample size is quite small (six or less).

The Wilcoxon Matched-pairs Signed-ranks Test (Siegel, 1956, pp. 75–83; Guilford, 1965, pp. 255–256). This statistical test is very similar to the sign test in that it uses + and − signs. In addition, it takes into account the relative magnitude of the differences. That is, the experimenter is able to rank the differences. Thus, it is a more powerful technique than the sign test. In the Wilcoxon test, H_0 is that the sum of the positive ranks is equal to the sum of the negative ranks. If the departure from H_0 is large enough, the conclusion is that there was a significantly positive difference, provided the positive sum > the negative sum. The reverse is also a possibility.

The Experiment with More than Two Independent Samples

Thus far, the discussion of statistical techniques for different situations has been concerned with (1) comparing one sample to a population or a distribution and (2) comparing two samples. In research, it is often desirable to compare simultaneously the performances of more than two groups. The experimental design when there are more than two independent samples is basically similar to that used with two independent samples. There are specific statistical techniques for comparing more than two groups at one time. Typically, H_0 is that all groups are equal with regard to the item in question. If H_0 is accepted, the computation is finished. But if H_0 is rejected and H_1 (that the groups are significantly different) is accepted, it is usually desirable to compare all possible combinations of two groups using the appropriate parametric or nonparametric technique.

Analysis of Variance (Kerlinger, 1964, pp. 187–200; Edwards, 1958, pp. 141–147). The usual parametric test for comparing several independent samples is the analysis of variance, sometimes called the *F* test. If the assumptions of parametric tests can be met, especially interval (quantitative) measurement, this test is the most powerful one available. If a significant value is obtained, it is concluded that the groups are significantly different and t values are computed for all possible combinations to determine which group, or groups, differ significantly from the others.

The Kruskal-Wallis One-way Analysis of Variance by Ranks (Siegel, 1956, pp. 184–193; Ferguson, 1966, pp. 362–363). The most efficient of the nonparametric tests for three or more independent samples is the Kruskal-Wallis test (Siegel, 1956, p. 194). As its title implies, this test employs ranks to make comparisons. A requirement for this technique is that ordinal measurement be achieved. From the ranked data, the statistic H is computed. If a significant H is obtained, then U comparisons are made between the groups.

The χ^2 Test for More than Two Independent Samples (Siegel, 1956, pp. 175–179). The χ^2 technique has been encountered in many different types of experimental designs and is useful when the data are classificatory. It is equally applicable for more than two independent samples and "is a straightforward extension of the chi square for two independent samples. In general, the test is the same for two independent groups and three or more groups" (Barnes, 1964, p. 104).

The Experiment with More than Two Related Samples

As was stated previously, the efficiency of an experiment is increased greatly if the subjects in each group are matched according to some relevant variable. Statistical tests for two related samples limit the experimenter to two possible comparisons: He can compare one set of scores for two matched groups or two sets of scores for one group. These techniques are inadequate when one wishes to study several sets of scores and groups.

Techniques for making multiple comparisons are applicable for studying several groups that are all exposed to several different conditions. In these designs, each subject or group is assigned a row and each treatment condition is assigned a column. By use of the appropriate statistical tools, one is able to compare (1) the main effects of the different treatments on all subjects or groups, (2) the main effects of all treatments on each subject or group, and (3) the simple or interaction effects of each treatment on each subject or group. Statistical tests for these purposes are often called factorial designs or analysis in a double-entry table. It is evident that statistical techniques are more complex for experimental designs of this nature than for the designs discussed above. However, these techniques are quite important in research because they enable the experimenter to study several effects at one time.

The Two-way Analysis of Variance (Kerlinger, 1964, pp. 242–256; Lindquist, 1953, pp. 108–120). The most commonly used parametric test for multiple comparisons is the two-way analysis of variance, which is an extension of the analysis of variance described earlier. The two-way analysis is appropriate when interval measurement has been obtained, and many variations of this test are possible. It is customary to test for interaction or simple effects first. If a significant F value is obtained, t tests must be computed for all possible comparisons. However, if the F value is not significant, the main effects of rows and columns are calculated separately to find significant differences. Again, if either of these last two F tests is significant, t tests must be calculated for all possible comparisons between rows and/or columns.

The Friedman Two-way Analysis of Variance by Ranks (Siegel, 1956, pp. 166–172; Kerlinger, 1964, pp. 264–267). The Friedman test is a nonparametric two-way analysis of variance technique that requires ordinal data. It allows the same comparisons as the parametric two-way analysis of variance, except that it is less powerful.

The Cochran Q Test (Siegel, 1956, pp. 161–166; Hays, 1963, pp. 628–630). The nonparametric test is especially useful with nominal or classificatory measurement. For example, by analyzing data consisting of pass-fail information on several items for a number of individuals, the experimenter could test whether the various items on a test differ in difficulty. This technique could also be used to study attitudes or preferences of individuals. In these kinds of situations, the Q test allows one to determine the significance of the number of favorable responses.

In the two nonparametric tests discussed, the only thing that the experimenter can ascertain is whether there is a significant, overall difference. If there is, it is necessary to compute all the possible comparisons of two groups by a statistical technique appropriate for data from two related samples. This must be done to determine which groups or treatments are significantly different from each other and which are not.

Other Factorial Designs. Parametric statistical literature abounds with various factorial designs. The preceding discussion was concerned with two-way analysis. However, there are also designs for three-way, four-way, and even more complex types of analyses. Although the computations often require an electronic computer, the principles are quite similar and allow the researcher to study several variables and their interactions simultaneously.

Analysis of Variance and Covariance

There is one more statistical technique that warrants discussion because of its uniqueness. It has been stated several times that matched groups make an experiment more efficient. However, matching is not always possible: Administrative problems may prevent the experimenter from assigning subjects to groups in a way that the groups can be matched; and it becomes increasingly difficult to match subjects when more than two groups are involved—it is almost impossible when the matching is attempted using two criteria. Analysis of variance and covariance (Edwards, 1950, pp. 333–358; Ferguson, 1966, pp. 326–340) mathematically matches all the groups (two or more) in the experiment according to one or more criteria on which interval measurement can be achieved. In addition to the usual parametric assumptions, this test requires that the variables held constant (that is, those mathematically matched) be correlated with the experimental variable. The stronger the relationship, the more powerful is the test. In addition, covariance assumes that the amount of correlation is nearly the same for all groups. If all the assumptions can be met, the analysis of variance and covariance mathematically matches the groups according to the criteria and tests the null hypothesis that all the adjusted means of the experimental variable are equal for all groups. If the adjusted means are significantly different, a special t test must be computed on the experimental variable for all possible combinations of groups.

Evaluation

The primary reason that persons engage in research is to make decisions or value judgments about individuals or treatments. This chapter and Chapter 37 have presented many of the processes, techniques, and methods of performing research. Specifically, this chapter has shown that "in order to improve the decision-making process, we need measurement data about individuals" (Adams, 1964, p. 4). In addition, statistical methods assist in the evaluation by providing tools to summarize the data. However, measurement data and statistical methods only provide a basis for making the evaluation.

In general, there are five steps in any evaluative process.

1. Determining what we wish to evaluate.
2. Defining what we wish to evaluate in terms of behavior.
3. Selecting appropriate situations in which to observe performance.
4. Getting a record.
5. Summarizing the evidence (Adams, 1964, pp. 6–7).

Anyone who has had to evaluate patients in a hospital will realize the importance of these five steps; only after completing them is a person able to make a decision. Provided that adequate records have been obtained and definitive constructs for evaluation have been established, fairly accurate value judgments can be made about individuals.

In experimental studies that use statistical methods to make inferences, the evaluation procedure requires other considerations, many of which have already been taken into account by the authors of the standardized tests used to measure individuals. Although it is impossible to determine specific rules to be followed, "there are three questions of paramount concern in evaluating experimental findings: (a) the scientific importance of the data; (b) their reliability; and (c) their generality" (Sidman, 1960, p. 1). These three considerations cannot be separated from each other.

Unfortunately, there is no set of impartial rules to follow to evaluate the scientific importance of experimental data. Experiments are performed for a specific purpose, but value judgments about the data should not be only in terms of that purpose. "Good data are always separable, with respect to their scientific importance, from the purposes for which they were obtained" (Sidman, 1960, p. 3). Thus, a person must have some idea as to what kinds of data are needed by his discipline. "But he should never be so self-centered in his convictions that he ignores methodologically sound data that arise from other points of view" (Sidman, 1960, p. 41).

Although the scientific importance of the data is an important criterion, it is very unwise to evaluate the data by this criterion alone. The reliability and generality of the data are equally important. Reliability answers the following question: Will the experiment, if repeated, yield the same results? In other words, if chance factors were operative, the same results would not be obtained by replication. If data are to be considered reliable, similar results must be obtained from replication to replication.

When making an evaluation with regard to the generality of the data, the concern is: Of what are the data representative? Although it is wise to use a large group of subjects in an experiment, this, in itself, does not necessarily increase the generalizations one can make. First, the sample must be an accurate representation of the population, and it must be representative of the parameters. Second, one can generalize only to the defined population, whether large or small, from which the sample was drawn.

These three items—the scientific importance of the data, their reliability, and their generality—are all important considerations when making an evaluation, and they are dependent on each other. However, there are no specific rules to follow in order to make an evaluation of these three considerations, so their assessment requires mature judgment. In addition, evaluations will change because science, like people, goes through fads and cycles. Thus, evaluation is a never-ending concern, and "it can be separated neither from the data themselves nor from the techniques that made the data possible" (Sidman, 1960, p. vi).

Summary

The purpose of this section, concerning the planning and understanding of research, is to help music therapists understand the research process. Understanding the concepts behind and procedures of research enables therapists to get more meaning from the studies they read. The applicability of studies that use the various statistical techniques presented will be clearer to the readers, and they will become more astute in making evaluations. It is certain that if music therapists understand research, they will become more actively involved in it. For the most part, only by this objective process can knowledge in the behavioral discipline known as music therapy be increased.

Annotated Bibliography and References

Although there are a large number of books available for studying statistical methods, the references listed below have been found most useful and are recommended for various purposes. Specific references for the best examples of computational procedures were cited in the chapter. Many of these books duplicate information, but they are listed so that some reference will be available to everyone.

ADAMS, GEORGIA SACHS. *Measurement and evaluation.* New York: Holt, 1964.
An excellent and thorough treatment of measurement theory for education and psychology. Of primary concern to the author is developing and understanding concepts for such topics as individual testing, vocational interest and aptitude testing, various approaches to personality assessment, group testing, and educational diagnosis. Although not a statistics book, the statistical methods necessary for the various topics are integrated with the material. Among the outstanding features of this book are the discussions of reliability, validity, and comparability of teachers' marks and the evaluation of student performance in specific skills. It includes, in an appendix, a classified and annotated list of published tests in all areas. Readable and comprehensible for the average student and an excellent source book for the advanced student.

ADKINS, DOROTHY C. *Statistics.* Columbus, Ohio: Charles E. Merrill Books, Inc., 1964.
A good beginning textbook in elementary statistics. Includes the usual types of descriptive statistics, Pearson r as well as six other types of correlation techniques, and a brief introduction to statistical inference. Has normal curve table, t table, and χ^2 table. The chief novelty of this book is its unique

self-testing feature—the incorporation into the textual material of multiple-choice questions.

ANDERSON, K. E., and SMITH, H. A. *Topics in statistics for students in education—first course*. Danville, Ill.: Interstate Printers and Publishers, 1958.
An excellent workbook to be used as a supplement or guide with a textbook for a first course in descriptive statistics. Includes computational procedures for rank-difference and product-moment correlation coefficients in addition to the typical measures of descriptive statistics. All examples and computational procedures are elementary and easy to follow.

BARNES, F. P. *Research for the practitioner in education*. Washington, D.C.: Department of Elementary School Principals, National Education Association, 1964.
An elementary overview of the research process. Includes applications of eleven nonparametric techniques (most of which were discussed in this chapter) to specific experimental designs, but does not include any computational procedures or tables.

BLOMMERS, P., and LINDQUIST, E. F. *Elementary statistical methods*. Boston: Houghton Mifflin, 1960.
A text for a beginning course in statistics. Includes descriptive statistics, *t* tests, and product-moment correlation. Examples are given, but more knowledge of mathematics is assumed than in other elementary books. Has tables for the normal curve, squares and square roots, *t* values, *r* values, and random numbers.

DOWNIE, N. M., and HEATH, R. W. *Basic statistical methods*. New York: Harper & Row, 1959.
An excellent beginning textbook. Involves as little mathematics as possible and stresses computation, application, and interpretation. Includes descriptive statistics, Pearson *r*, *t* tests, χ^2, analysis of variance, rank-difference correlation, and other correlation techniques. Although most elementary textbooks do not, this one does discuss reliability, validity, and item-analysis techniques for test construction as well as the more commonly used nonparametric techniques. Has tables for squares and square roots, normal curve, *t* values, χ^2 values, *F* values, and other less important statistics.

DUNN, OLIVE JEAN. *Basic statistics: a primer for the biomedical sciences*. New York: Wiley, 1964.
Designed as a textbook for a one-semester course in statistics for students in the biomedical fields. Includes descriptive statistics, *t* tests, χ^2, *F* tests, and correlation. Has tables for random numbers, normal curve, *t* values, χ^2 values, *F* values, and *r* values.

EDWARDS, A. L. *Experimental design in psychological research*. New York: Holt, 1950.
Designed for a second course in statistics. Covers χ^2, correlation, *t* tests, analysis of variance, factorial designs, and analysis of variance and covariance. Examples are good, especially those for analysis of variance and covariance. Provides answers to example problems in an appendix. Tables included are random numbers, squares and square roots, normal curve, and significance levels for χ^2, *t*, *r*, and *F* values.

EDWARDS, A. L. *Experimental design in psychological research.* (rev. ed.) New York: Holt, 1960.
The same as the first edition, except that the example for analysis of variance and covariance is not as simplified. New, advanced statistical techniques have been included.

EDWARDS, A. L. *Statistical analysis.* (rev. ed.) New York: Holt, 1958.
An excellent beginning book. For the most part, the examples are excellent. Has descriptive statistics, t tests, analysis of variance, and correlation coefficients. Includes tables for random numbers, squares and square roots, normal curve, t, F, and χ^2.

FERGUSON, G. A. *Statistical analysis in psychology and education.* (2d ed.) New York: McGraw-Hill, 1966.
Provides the technology necessary for the statistical treatment of most sets of experimental data with emphasis on analysis and interpretation. Examples illustrate the discussion of elementary statistical techniques, correlation methods (including partial and multiple correlation), sampling statistics, nonparametric statistics, analysis of variance and covariance, and multivariate problems. All necessary tables are included. In general, an excellent, all-encompassing reference.

GARRETT, H. E. *Elementary statistics.* New York: McKay, 1962.
Another beginning book covering basically the same material as the other elementary books reviewed in this section. Examples are quite good.

GUILFORD, J. P. *Fundamental statistics in psychology and education.* (4th ed.) New York: McGraw-Hill, 1965.
An excellent and very usable source book, but does not discuss the more complex designs. Includes descriptive statistics, t tests, χ^2, analysis of variance, and some nonparametric tests. Has Pearson r, rank-difference correlation, and other less common correlation methods as well as multiple correlations. Has all the necessary tables for the techniques discussed. Almost all examples are excellent, especially χ^2 for goodness of fit.

HAYS, W. L. *Statistics for psychologists.* New York: Holt, 1963.
An excellent source book written for the advanced student, with considerably more emphasis on theoretical than applied aspects of statistical methods. Includes elementary and advanced statistical techniques, correlation techniques, and the most common nonparametric methods. Not recommended for the beginner, but a must for the serious researcher.

JOHNSON, P. O. *Statistical methods in research.* Englewood Cliffs, N.J.: Prentice-Hall, 1949.
An excellent text and source book for the advanced student. Does not include descriptive statistics. Includes most of the methods of statistical inference—parametric and nonparametric—as well as multiple correlation and analysis of variance and covariance. Has tables for normal distribution, t, F, and χ^2.

JOHNSON, P. O., and JACKSON, R. W. B. *Introduction to statistical methods.* Englewood Cliffs, N.J.: Prentice-Hall, 1953.
The first book in a series. Designed as an introduction to statistical methods for use at the elementary level. Includes the basic statistical methods of

descriptive statistics and correlation. Stresses an understanding of the concepts and processes with selected exercises. An excellent book recommended for the beginner.

KERLINGER, F. N. *Foundations of behavioral research.* New York: Holt, 1964. A thorough and comprehensive book describing the entire research process and nearly all statistical techniques including some new ones. Does not include nonparametric tests, tables, or computational procedures.

LEVITT, E. E. *Clinical research design and analysis in the behavioral sciences.* Springfield, Ill.: Charles C Thomas, 1961.

LINDQUIST, E. F. *A first course in statistics.* (rev. ed.) Boston: Houghton Mifflin, 1942.
Although an older book, an excellent beginning text stressing the use and interpretation of elementary statistical methods. Includes descriptive statistics and correlation as well as the application of correlation techniques to the evaluation of test materials.

LINDQUIST, E. F. *Design and analysis of experiments in psychology and education.* Boston: Houghton Mifflin, 1953.
An advanced book that covers most of the more complex designs—factorial designs and analysis of variance and covariance. Only table is of random numbers.

McNEMAR, Q. *Psychological statistics.* (2d ed.) New York: Wiley, 1955.
A very good book encompassing statistical methods from the elementary to the advanced level. Covers descriptive statistics, various correlation methods including multiple correlation, t tests, χ^2, simple and complex analysis of variance, analysis of variance and covariance, and some nonparametric methods. Includes exercises as well as the necessary tables.

RAND CORPORATION. *A million random digits with 100,000 normal deviates.* New York: Free Press, 1955.

SIDMAN, M. *Tactics of scientific research.* New York: Basic Books, Inc., Publishers, 1960.
A book written for the experimental psychology student. Includes some of the methodological problems a person faces in evaluating data. Evaluation procedures are described with reference to specific cases and some case histories. Although not a statistics book, it is excellent for improving judgments in evaluation.

SIEGEL, S. *Nonparametric statistics for the behavioral sciences.* New York: McGraw-Hill, 1956.
The best book available for nonparametric statistical methods. Contains excellent examples, procedures, and tables for twenty-seven nonparametric techniques.

SMITH, G. M. *A simplified guide to statistics.* (3d ed.) New York: Holt, 1962. A simplified elementary book containing descriptive statistics, t tests, χ^2, correlation methods, and a table of squares and square roots.

UNDERWOOD, B. J., DUNCAN, C. P., SPENCE, JANET T., and COTTON, J. W. *Elementary statistics.* New York: Appleton-Century-Crofts, 1954.

Another excellent book for elementary statistical methods. Includes descriptive statistics, t tests, correlation, analysis of variance, and χ^2. Has the necessary tables for those methods discussed.

WALLIS, W. A., and ROBERTS, H. V. *Statistics: a new approach.* New York: Free Press, 1956.

A good introductory book for developing an understanding of statistics. Includes examples of the usual techniques covered in elementary books and discusses more sophisticated designs. Contains a table of squares and square roots and a table of random numbers, the uses of which are explained.

WHYBREW, W. E. *Measurement and evaluation in music.* Dubuque, Iowa: William C. Brown Co., 1962.

Written for the measurement and evaluation of students' musical abilities and performance. Includes only those statistical methods necessary for the evaluation of test scores. Contains a section on available standardized tests.

WINER, B. J. *Statistical principles in experimental design.* New York: McGraw-Hill, 1962.

An excellent, but advanced, book written as a text and a comprehensive reference source for researchers in the area of the behavioral sciences. Includes almost all statistical methods and tables that one would ever need for various experimental designs. One of the two most advanced and comprehensive books reviewed in this section.

39

EXPERIMENTAL RESEARCH STUDIES

A Procedure for Determining the Music Preferences of Mental Retardates *

VANCE W. COTTER
SAM TOOMBS

Introduction

There is no doubt that music is an important factor in human behavior. Gaston (1965, p. 3) has discussed the relationship between music and human behavior from the biological, anthropological, sociological, and behavioral viewpoints. Murphy (1958, p. 33) and Masserman (1955, pp. 616–620) also have discussed the importance of music and the arts for man. All cultures have used music in their societies. Music has probably existed since man's early cultures. "Music is shaped by culture, but in turn, influences that culture of which it is a part" (Gaston, 1965, p. 17).

As music has been important to persons in the general culture, it also has become important in the rehabilitation of patients, because, in some way, it exercises strong control over behavior. Even though little is known regarding the specific effects of music on behavior, music therapy is a behavioral therapy. An individual must understand a patient's responses to music before he can be effective as a music therapist. An observable preference for music offers the therapist an opportunity to begin a relationship with a patient. Gaston (1965) has stated, "we [music therapists] are concerned primarily with human beings, with the many ways they participate in musical activities, and the many ways they are influenced by music" (p. 3). Sears (1965) added that "modern music therapy seeks to establish itself upon acceptable scientific observation" (p. 29), or, as Gaston (1965) stated, "Music and its influences are phenomena, and, therefore, may be studied scientifically" (p. 22).

It seems quite likely that music has at least three kinds of effects on the

---

* This article appeared in *Journal of Music Therapy*, Vol. III, No. 2, June, 1966, pp. 57–64.

behavior of humans. First, it seems to have an emotional effect. Certain music is known for its ability to excite or stimulate the listener, whereas other music is known for its calming effects (Zimny and Weidenfeller, 1962). A second effect of music may be a discriminative or guiding function, such as when a person marches, dances, or taps in time to music. A third effect is that music induces gratification in the listener or performer. It is this third effect that is examined here.

Problem

The term *preferential response* when referring to musical taste is defined by Lundin (1953) as "our preferences (liking-disliking) for compositions, composers or schools of music." He added, "On the basis of some characteristics of the stimulus and functions of the responding organism, choices are made of liking to listen to some works more than others or to music as compared to no music" (p. 154).

Lundin's reference to "liking to listen" means that some type of response is produced by the individual that consistently demonstrates a choice for a specific musical stimulus over other considered musical stimuli. Various studies have been designed that ask the subject to rate music, either in verbal or written form, as pleasant or unpleasant (Downey and Knapp, 1927; Verveer, Barry, and Bousefield, 1933; Krugman, 1943; Washburn, Child, and Abel, 1927). Eysenck (1962), attempting to introduce scientific methods into the study of esthetics, "provides a series of stimuli whose physical properties are known, and asks the subjects to rank these in order of aesthetic merit, i.e., from best liked to least liked" (p. 310).

Apparently, measuring the preferential responses to music presents little or no difficulty when working with subjects who are able to give appropriate verbal or written responses. Unfortunately, this is not the case with a great number of persons. There are 5.5 million mentally retarded persons in the United States (U.S. Department of Health, Education, and Welfare, 1964). The mentally retarded child often has language problems and/or is physically handicapped to the extent that achieving an evaluation of preference for music is difficult. The low probability of optimum physical and/or verbal behavior presents a challenge to the music therapist in his evaluation of the retardate.

A review of sixty-one articles relating to the use of music with the mentally retarded revealed no organized investigation of musical preferences, nor were any specific procedures employed to determine the effects of music as an auditory stimulus to the individuals (Schneider, 1964). The purpose of the study was to develop a procedure to analyze a mental retardate's preferential responses to music in a free-responding setting. The aim was to arrive at a procedure that did not require a verbal or written response.

Sears (1965) stressed the idea of "temporal commitment" regarding the "musically structured experience, and the behavior which is required by that structure."

> . . . the mere commitment to the experience places the individual in a situation where his (future) behavior is determined primarily by musical factors, and not by other factors or persons in his environment. The commitment to the structured experience may be only temporary, for the duration of the music, or some part of it. However, this does not negate the possible continued influence of the music on the individual; it refers mainly to the behavior of the individual which is immediately observable. . . .
>
> The unique structure of music—existing only through time—requires the individual to commit himself to the experience moment by moment . . . (pp. 32–33).

Behavior emitted within the structure of a musical experience provides at least one objective type of measurement, that is, duration of commitment to the stimulus event.

In this study to investigate the preferences of mental retardates for musical stimuli, a technique calling for the subjects to manipulate a mechanical switch was used. Specifically, the following questions to be answered were: (1) Will the subjects show a difference in preference for musical stimuli and noise? and (2) What is the relative proportion of time committed to a specific class?

Method

SUBJECTS

Twenty male and female retardates living at Parsons State Hospital and Training Center, Parsons, Kansas, were used as subjects. The measured intelligence ranged from level 1 through 4, with a mean intelligence quotient (IQ) of 52.5 and a range of 35 to 83. The mean chronological age (CA) was fourteen and the standard deviation was 2.45. The subjects had to be able to respond by pushing or pulling a three-position switch. Only subjects who possessed normal hearing acuity were selected.

SETTING AND EQUIPMENT

The study was conducted in a 12- by 14-foot room containing a table bolted to the floor upon which a metal box 8 by 6 inches was attached. The box contained three 3-position switches in a vertical position. Approximately 2 pounds of pressure overcame the inertia of the switch and ½ pound of pressure maintained the closure of the contacts. One chair was located in front of the table.

There was a cabinet in which five loudspeakers were mounted. The room also contained a junction box in which wires leading from the switch made contact with wires leading in from behavioral-research equipment located in an adjacent observation room. A small window modified for one-way vision was located near the table.

The observation room contained six tape recorders; one microphone mixer; and behavioral-research equipment consisting of relays, timers, switches, digital counters, a discrete event recorder, and a tape programer.

Description of Auditory Stimuli

Six classes of auditory stimuli were selected for the preference evaluation. Three classes were categorized as musical stimuli and three as noise. Three separate tapes were made from three phonograph recordings.

One class of music was a children's record entitled *Let's Join In* (Mercury CLP-1208), which included such songs as "The Hokey Pokey," "The Bunny Hop," and "The Irish Washerwoman." Rhythm predominated over melody, and both vocal and instrumental media were utilized. This type of musical stimuli was labeled children's music.

A second class of music was called adult background music, and the record used was *Romantic Music* by Percy Faith (Columbia CL526). On this record, songs of a popular nature, such as "While We're Young," "I'll Take Romance," and "Invitation," were arranged primarily for strings and woodwinds. Melody and harmony were observed to be predominant over rhythm. The voices of a female choir were used as orchestral instruments, but they never sang lyrics or the melody.

The third type of music was electronic music from a recording of Stockhausen's "Gesang der Junglinge." No definite rhythmic, harmonic, or melodic pattern was predominant, but variations in pitch, loudness, time, and timbre were observed to occur.

The three auditory stimuli classified as noise were white noise, electronic clicks, and ambient noise. A tape of white noise was recorded from a white noise generator. White noise is auditory stimuli consisting of the entire frequency spectrum. There are no changes in pitch, timbre, loudness, and time. The electronic clicks were tape-recorded from an electronic click generator at 300 clicks per second. No changes in pitch, timbre, loudness, and time were observed. The third type of noise used was ambient noise. No tape was necessary for this auditory stimuli; the reasons for including ambient noise as a type of auditory stimuli appear in the next section.

PROGRAMING THE AUDITORY STIMULI

Five tape recorders were operated in the observation room to make each of the five pretaped auditory stimuli available to the subject in the experimental room. Auditory stimulus input was contingent on the subject's closing the contact of any one of the three-position switches in the experimental room. In the off positions, there was silence, but as a switch was pushed or pulled, auditory stimulus input occurred immediately. The auditory stimulus was continuous as long as the contacts of the switch were closed by the subject's response. The subject produced either children's music, adult background music, electronic music, white noise, electronic clicks, or ambient noise (no auditory input by switch manipulation). The subject was able to produce the consequence of silence (ambient noise) by manipulating one of the switches or by not responding on the switches. The silent switch was included as a method of control.

A sound-level meter was used to set the intensity level of the auditory stimuli. The intensity level in the experimental room was 64 to 74 decibels for all stimuli except the electronic music, which varied from 50 to 70 decibels. The ambient-noise level was 44 to 48 decibels.

PROCEDURE

The subject was met by the experimenter at the door of the experimental room and taken to the switches. The experimenter demonstrated how to operate the switches without auditory input. When the subject showed that he was able to emit the response, the experimenter closed the door and entered the observation room. All tape recorders, the discrete event recorder, and the session timer were put into operation, and the experimental session began. Throughout the remainder of the session, digital and graphic records of the subject's manipulatory responses were collected that indicated duration of temporal commitment to the available auditory stimuli.

The question of position responding arose. Position responding resulting from factors other than preference was controlled through a semi-randomization of the six sets of auditory inputs on the different switch positions. The duration of time availability of each auditory input set was controlled by the tape-programer, which automatically changed the operation from one input set to another every seven minutes. There were four such phase changes, and any three occurred in each twenty-five-minute experimental session.

The subject, then, was faced with a different class of auditory stimulus every seven minutes if he maintained only one directional manipulation of a switch. On the other hand, if he preferred any one of the other five classes of stimuli, he was required to produce responses on other switches.

For example, if the subject chose to produce children's music more than any other class of stimuli, he was required to push or pull any one of the other switches at least every seven minutes to be able to continue to produce children's music over the loudspeaker.

The experimental session for each subject lasted twenty-five minutes, and the experimental periods varied from five to twenty sessions. Subjects in the early part of the experimental period participated for twenty sessions. It was observed that by the end of the fifth session, the subject's preference for musical stimuli had stabilized. For this reason, the last two subjects were tested in only five sessions.

Results

All twenty subjects demonstrated a preference for total music over total noise and no response. Table 5 contains a distribution of mean proportions of time committed to each stimulus condition by each subject over all sessions.

TABLE 5

Mean Proportion of Time Committed to Music, Noise, and No Response

Subject	Total music	Children's music	Adult music	Electronic music	Total noise	Total no response
1	0.97	0.58	0.39	0.00	0.00	0.03
2	0.96	0.93	0.02	0.00	0.01	0.03
3	0.96	0.57	0.39	0.01	0.02	0.06
4	0.95	0.85	0.08	0.02	0.01	0.06
5	0.94	0.90	0.02	0.02	0.02	0.06
6	0.94	0.86	0.06	0.01	0.02	0.05
7	0.94	0.56	0.37	0.00	0.01	0.05
8	0.93	0.70	0.21	0.02	0.03	0.08
9	0.89	0.64	0.24	0.01	0.04	0.07
10	0.89	0.27	0.59	0.01	0.02	0.12
11	0.88	0.61	0.21	0.06	0.03	0.13
12	0.87	0.12	0.22	0.53	0.04	0.10
13	0.84	0.79	0.03	0.01	0.04	0.13
14	0.82	0.11	0.70	0.01	0.02	0.16
15	0.79	0.62	0.11	0.06	0.05	0.18
16	0.77	0.67	0.07	0.03	0.08	0.19
17	0.72	0.64	0.05	0.03	0.08	0.22
18	0.60	0.40	0.20	0.00	0.00	0.39
19	0.52	0.26	0.12	0.14	0.03	0.45
20	0.50	0.46	0.02	0.01	0.04	0.46

The binomial test was applied and the probability of twenty out of twenty subjects preferring music over noise and no response was beyond the 0.002 level of confidence. The median proportion of time committed to total music was 0.88 (range = 0.50 to 0.97). The median proportion was 0.02 for total noise and 0.10 for no response.

Three subjects (18, 19, 20), although showing commitment to music the greater proportion of the time, chose not to respond for almost an equal proportion of time. Seventeen subjects clearly preferred music the greater proportion of the time (0.72 or higher).

Within the total-music category, the greatest proportion of time was committed to children's music (median = 0.62, range = 0.11 to 0.93). The next preferred level was the adult background music (median = 0.11, range = 0.02 to 0.70). Two subjects (10 and 14) demonstrated a higher preference for this type of music than any other type of stimuli (0.59, 0.70). Subjects 1, 3, 7, 8, 9, and 11 showed preference for both children's and adult music, but the children's music was over 0.50 in all cases. Subject 12 chose electronic music (0.53). The median for electronic music was 0.01, with the range being 0.00 to 0.53.

Thus, the data show that seventeen out of twenty subjects chose to produce children's music for at least 0.50 of the time they spent in producing all classes of available auditory stimuli. Two out of twenty subjects chose adult music, and one out of twenty chose electronic music. The probability of seventeen out of twenty selecting one type of music out of three by chance alone was less than 0.002.

The total commitment to the three classes of noise was of very short duration (median = 0.02, range = 0.00 to 0.14). The choice of not responding rather than selecting noise was greater for all subjects (median = 0.12, range = 0.03 to 0.46). Thus, the time that was not committed to music was spent in making no response.

Figures 1, 2, 3, and 4 are typical examples of the four types of performances of the twenty subjects. Figure 1 shows a clear preference for music over noise and no response for subject 1 over fourteen sessions. The preference for music is mixed, but the majority of the time is committed to children's music. Electronic music is not shown because of the low preference.

Figure 2 is the performance of subject 10. Again, music is preferred, and the first eight sessions show a preference for adult music. The ninth session demonstrates a change in the preferential response. The preference is now mixed and remains so until the end of the fifteenth session.

Figure 3 is the performance of subject 17. A preference begins to emerge in the fifth session, and children's music is preferred throughout the remainder of the sessions.

Figure 4 is the performance of subject 20, who spent almost as much time not pressing the switch as in producing children's music, which was

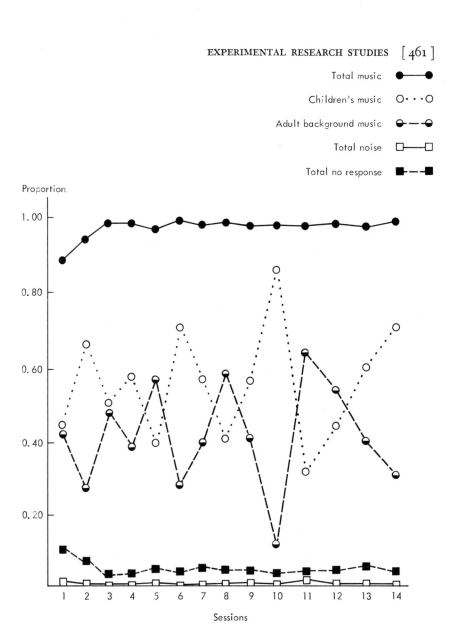

Figure 1. Duration of commitment to auditory stimuli for one subject, No. 1, over fourteen sessions.

preferred the greater proportion of time over other available auditory stimuli.

DISCUSSION

This study demonstrated a reliable technique for assessing music preferences and answered all questions that were asked in the statement of the problem. The subjects were not required to give a verbal or written

Total music   ●——●
Children's music   O· · ·O
Adult background music   ◐— —◐
Total noise   □——□
Total no response   ■— —■

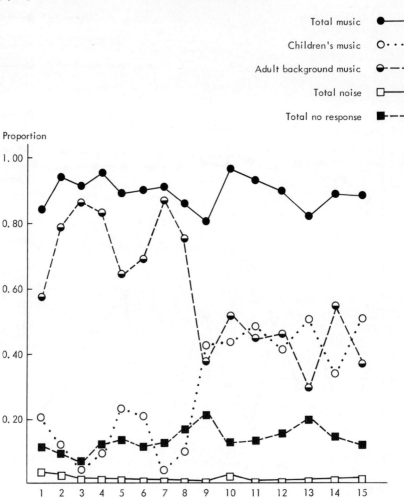

Figure 2. Duration of commitment to auditory stimuli for one subject, No. 10, over fifteen sessions.

response, nor were they asked in any way to rank their preference for the available stimuli. Preferences were obtained, and they assumed a rank order.

There is little doubt about the reliability of the method. If the subjects were position-responding, the data would be equal in all categories. The random response is also untenable because of the three phase changes and the number of sessions.

The use of this procedure as an evaluative technique to place a patient in a music therapy activity seems practical. Not all patients prefer the

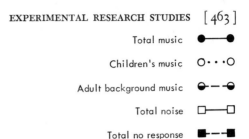

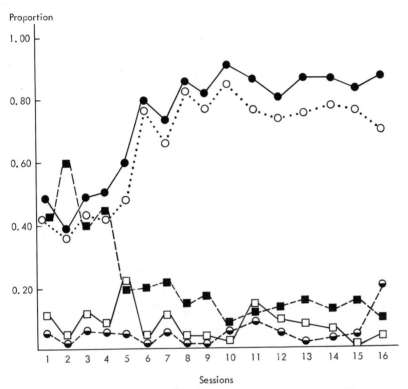

Figure 3. Duration of commitment for one subject, No. 17, over sixteen sessions.

same kind of music or the same amount, and appropriate placement in a music therapy activity is often a problem facing the music therapist. The satiation effect of musical stimuli on the individual is a variable about which the music therapist should be aware.

One subject presented an interesting problem regarding data collection. During the ninth session, the experimenter heard music coming from the experimental room, but digital counters were not operating in corresponding relationship. It was soon discovered that the subject was singing and intermittently manipulating the switch to produce the particular music that he was singing. It was as if he were sampling the music to see if he

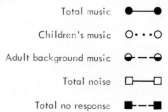

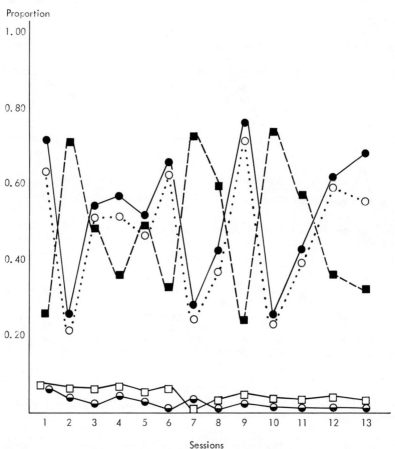

Figure 4. Duration of commitment for one subject, No. 20, over thirteen sessions.

was correct. Such behavior may cause problems in data collection, but it seemed to produce a meaningful type of stimulus control whereby the child was teaching himself the lyrics and melodies of preferred songs.

A technique that employs musical stimuli offers an opportunity to study man's preferential response to music. The objective psychologist may be interested in studying the effects of music as either a discriminative stimulus or a reinforcing stimulus on other aspects of man's behavior.

It is recommended that this procedure be used for further investigation of the preferential response to music. The following is a partial list of possible studies:

1. The preferences of mental retardates and normal children of the same chronological age
2. A comparison of mentally retarded children with different adaptive behavior and measured intelligence levels
3. Preference for different styles of music
4. The effects of tone quality, both instrumental and vocal, on preference
5. The effects of pitch deviation on preference
6. The effects of intensity on preference
7. The effects of rhythmic variation on preference
8. The satiation effects of musical stimuli
9. Factors that alter preference
10. The effects of musical stimuli on the modification of other behavior

Summary and Conclusions

The purpose of this study was to design an accurate and objective method to measure and evaluate the preferential responses of retardates to musical stimuli. The physical properties of sound were discussed, as well as similarities and differences between musical stimuli and noise. The distinction between tone and noise is made by the responding organism.

This experiment used a manipulatory response technique to measure the duration of commitment of the mental retardate to musical stimuli in a free-responding setting. Twenty male and female mental retardates (adaptive behavior and measured intelligence levels 1 through 4 and mean CA 14) at Parsons State Hospital and Training Center, Parsons, Kansas, participated as subjects.

The subjects selected any one of six classes of auditory stimuli (children's music, adult background music, electronic music, white noise, electronic clicks at 300 clicks per second, or ambient noise) by closing the contacts on any of three 3-position switches. The auditory stimulus input was continuous as long as a switch was pushed or pulled by the subject. Thus, the duration of commitment (in proportion) was obtained. Position responding was controlled by changing the auditory input sets from one loudspeaker to another every seven minutes.

The procedure provided a reliable method of measuring objectively and analyzing the mental retardate's preferential responses to musical stimuli in a free-responding setting.

The following conclusions were made concerning the results of this study:

1. The subjects demonstrated a significantly greater duration of commitment to the musical stimuli than to the noise or silence (no response).
2. A rank order of preference for musical stimuli existed for individual subjects as well as for the group. The category labeled children's music was produced the greatest proportion of the time (over 0.50), with adult background music second and electronic music third.
3. The subjects preferred music that employed both instrumental and vocal media and in which rhythm and melody were predominant. Music that emphasized orchestral instruments and in which melody and harmony were predominant over rhythm was not preferred the greatest proportion of time. Music produced by electronic instruments was not preferred a majority of the time.
4. There was no difference in preference for the three categories of noise. Noise, as an auditory stimulus, was not preferred.
5. There was a relationship between the amount of time spent on music and no response. Music as an auditory stimulus was preferred over other available stimuli when the subject responded.
6. There was a unique pattern of preference for each subject over all the sessions.

References

DOWNEY, J. E., and KNAPP, G. E. The effect on a musical programme of familiarity and of sequence of selections. In M. Schoen (Ed.), *The effects of music*. New York: Harcourt, Brace & World, 1927. Pp. 223–242.

EYSENCK, H. J. *Sense and nonsense in psychology*. Baltimore: Penguin, 1962.

GASTON, E. T. Man and music. In E. T. Gaston and E. H. Schneider (Eds.), *An analysis, evaluation and selection of clinical uses of music in therapy*. Lawrence, Kan.: Univer. of Kansas, 1965. Pp. 3–26.

KRUGMAN, H. E. Affective responses to music as a function of familiarity. *J. abnorm. soc. Psychol.*, 1943, 38, 388–393.

LUNDIN, R. W. *An objective psychology of music*. New York: Ronald, 1953.

MASSERMAN, J. H. *The practice of dynamic psychiatry*. Philadelphia: Saunders, 1955.

MURPHY, G. *Human potentialities*. New York: Basic Books, Inc., Publishers, 1958.

SCHNEIDER, E. H. Selected articles and research studies relating to music therapy. *J. Mus. Ther.*, 1964, *1*, 95–96.

SEARS, W. W. Processes in music therapy. In E. T. Gaston and E. H. Schneider (Eds.), *An analysis, evaluation, and selection of clinical uses of music in therapy.* Lawrence, Kan.: Univer. of Kansas, 1965. Pp. 29–42.

U.S. Dept. of Health, Education, and Welfare. *The President's Panel on Mental Retardation.* Washington, D.C.: Author, 1964.

VERVEER, E. M., BARRY, H. JR., and BOUSEFIELD, W. A. Changes in affectivity with repetition. *Amer. J. Psychol.*, 1933, *45*, 130–134.

WASHBURN, M. F., CHILD, M. A., and ABEL, T. M. The effects of immediate repetition on the pleasantness or unpleasantness of music. In M. Schoen (Ed.), *The effects of music.* New York: Harcourt, Brace & World, 1927. Pp. 199–210.

ZIMNY, G., and WEIDENFELLER, E. Effects of music on G.S.R. of children. *Child Develpm.*, 1962, *33*, 891–896.

The Effect of Early Music Deprivation
on the Musical Performance
of Institutionalized Mentally Retarded Children *

RICHARD M. GRAHAM

Introduction

The question of whether mental retardates exhibit more rigid behavior than children with normal intelligence is still unsettled. The view that rigidity is a general characteristic of the mentally retarded has, however, greatly influenced the orientation of the treatment and training of these individuals. Many have considered this assumption of rigidity among the mentally retarded to be responsible for the reluctance of some health personnel to attempt psychotherapy with the feebleminded.

Music educators who teach the mentally retarded are reminded frequently that the emphasis must be on concrete situations, reflecting the attitude that these individuals have difficulty coping with flexible situations. Other aspects of the music curricula reflect the assumption that musical offerings to the retardate should make allowances for his rigid personality structure. Music therapists in training schools and hospitals are faced daily with problems arising from the institutional reluctance to expose retardates to the varied approaches of the activity therapies because of the opinion that these individuals are too rigid to benefit from such experiences.

The many studies that have led to and supported the rigidity hypothesis

* This article is a condensation of Dr. Graham's Ph.D. dissertation, University of Kansas, 1965.

made use of tasks that required subjects to pursue an activity to the point of satiation and to switch in response to familiar stimuli. The lack of influence of initial satiation on the performance of subsequent tasks has been interpreted as indicating a greater rigidity in the personality structure of the retardate.

For a period of about twenty years, these studies supported the traditional view of rigid behaviors in the mentally retarded. Recent studies, however, have interpreted these behaviors as *phenotypic phenomena* stemming from developmental and motivational factors, rather than outgrowths of the inherent rigidity of the mentally retarded, as postulated in earlier investigations.

There is now a need for music educators and music therapists to determine the degree to which developmental and motivational factors contribute to rigid behavior by mental retardates involved in musical activities. The question of rigidity in the musical behavior of retardates is unanswered mainly because studies concerning rigidity have never made use of musical tasks. Nevertheless, music education and music therapy practices continue to be influenced by attitudes based on the hypothesized rigidity of the mentally retarded, although this hypothesis has been reinforced by studies that made use of nonmusical tasks.

Studies of rigidity involving musical tasks must give careful consideration to a retardate's previous experiences with music. Recent studies in deprivation reveal a relationship between the amount of deprivation in a particular area (sensory deprivation, cultural deprivation, social deprivation, and so on) and how an individual will perform in that area. The present study directs itself to the problem of the performance of mentally retarded children on a satiation-type musical task and the antecedent—environmental factors that may be related to any individual differences that might occur.

Problem

Writing on the need for esthetic experience in music, Gaston (1963) states,

Children not only of our culture, but of all cultures, need music for their healthy and normal development. Their motivations for sensory contact from which derive aesthetic experience are just as important for their development into human beings as are so-called visceral and activity drives (p. 62).

Gaston (1958) also discusses the particular need of handicapped children for an esthetic experience through music.

Handicapped children, in most cases, are direly in need of self-gratification, much more so than the ordinary child. The frustrations of their physical condition or mental deficiency will have deprived them of opportunities for gratification available to other children. The simple accomplishment of some sort of musical activity is highly worthwhile for these reasons, but many times more so when the benefits of music are recalled (p. 301).

Zigler (1958) has advanced the position that differences in rigidity observed in normal and feebleminded children are related to motivational differences between the two groups and among individuals in both groups. Zigler's specific hypothesis was as follows:

The greater the amount of social deprivation experienced by the feebleminded child, the greater will be his motivation to interact with an adult, making such interaction and any adult approval or support that accompanies it more reinforcing for his responses than it would be for the responses of a feebleminded child who has experienced a lesser amount of social deprivation (p. 64).

A logical extension of this view into the areas of music education and music therapy is suggested in the preceding statements by Gaston. In these statements, the additional motivational variable of music deprivation is discernible. It would seem that in a satiation experiment similar to Zigler's, but employing musical tasks, some kind of relationship would be revealed between the amount of esthetic deprivation experienced by mentally retarded subjects and the amount of time spent on their tasks.

It thus appears worthwhile to merge the motivational hypothesis of Zigler with Gaston's views of universal music needs into a hypothesis capable of generating testable predictions concerning differences in performance among the mentally retarded. This hypothesis can be stated as follows: *The motivation of a mentally retarded child to perform in a musical situation structured to his abilities will be generally proportional to the amount of music deprivation he has experienced.*

Specifically, the problem of this study was concerned with a musical task designed to bring about satiation. The study used a three-tone musical instrument made up of three resonator bells tuned to the first three tones of a C-major scale (C = 250 cycles per second) and a hammer board. On each task, one subject (S) at a time was required to make similar striking movements with a mallet in one case and with a very similar hammer in the other. Two conditions of reinforcement, each consisting of two parts, were employed. In the first condition, part 1 of the task required S to make one response—to hammer pegs into holes on the board—until he was satiated or until the maximum number of responses were made (all the pegs driven into the board); in part 2, S was instructed to perform a simple three-tone melody ("Hot Cross Buns"), which was learned before the start of the experiment, until satiated. This was designated the nonmusical to musical condition (NM–M). In the second condition, part 1 consisted of S performing the musical task until satiated, and part 2 involved the hammer-board task. This was designated the musical to nonmusical condition (M–NM). From the hypothesis advanced in this study, and by employing these tasks with their two specific conditions of reinforcement, certain predictions were made. These predictions and their rationale are presented here:

1. The more music-deprived Ss will perform longer on the musical task than will the less music-deprived Ss in both the NM–M and the M–NM conditions.

2. The more music-deprived Ss will make a lower proportion of errors on the musical task (play fewer wrong notes) than the less music-deprived Ss. If, as hypothesized, more music-deprived Ss have a higher motivation to perform in a musical situation that is not too difficult for them, they should show greater effort to play the melody in its proper form; the greater effort should lead to fewer errors.

3. The increase in time from part 1 to part 2 will be greater for the more music-deprived Ss than for the less music-deprived Ss under both NM–M and M–NM conditions. This prediction would be true for the M–NM condition, because it is assumed that the nonmusical task following the musical task will result in an increase in the number of responses because S may believe that completion of the hammer-board task would result in a reinstatement of the musical tasks experienced in the preexperimental period. Because the more music-deprived Ss would have the higher motivation for the reinstatement of the musical tasks, it would be expected that they show a greater increase in time than the less music-deprived Ss from part 1 to part 2 under the M–NM condition.

In addition to testing these predictions, the study was concerned with examining certain other factors and relationships of interest.

1. The relationship between the total time spent on the musical task by all Ss and their chronological ages (CAs). Gewirtz and Baer (1958) discovered a positive relationship between the ages of their own children and the effectiveness of certain social reinforcers. It would be of interest to see whether such a relationship exists between the ages of mentally retarded Ss and their motivation to perform in a musical situation.

2. The relationship between the total time spent on the tasks by all Ss and their mental ages (MAs). Stevenson and Zigler (1957) found

that on their experimental task, the CAs of their feebleminded Ss did not constitute a pertinent variable. They advanced the view that in a feebleminded population, it is the MA that is more significant as a determiner of performance.

3. The relationship between the total time spent on the musical task by all Ss and their intelligence quotients (IQs). It would be of interest to investigate whether the relationship of MA to CA is a pertinent variable influencing performance on the musical task used in this study.

4. The relationship between the total time spent on the musical task by all Ss and their length of institutionalization. There can be little doubt that the contemporary condition of institutionalization must be an important determinant of the mentally retarded child's current behavior. The results of such institutionalization are, however, far from clear. One could assume that institutionalization results in music deprivation, allowing one to deduce from the hypothesis presented in this study that length of institutionalization will be positively related to the time spent on the musical task.

5. The relationship between the total time spent on the musical task by all Ss and their CAs at the time of institutionalization. This was undertaken to evaluate a critical period concept. Gaston (1963) has suggested that the child is more vulnerable to the effects of music deprivation at certain periods of his life than at other periods. The importance of critical periods is further suggested by the imprinting phenomena reported by Lorenz (1952) and Tinbergen (1951). This problem becomes especially pertinent to the performance of the mentally retarded in light of Sarason's and Gladwin's (1958) view that "The effects of institutionalization undoubtedly vary with age of commitment" (p. 243).

Method

SUBJECTS

The Ss were thirty-two mentally retarded children residing at a Middle Western state hospital and training center. The conditions for inclusion in the sample were that the individual should (1) have a diagnosis of mental deficiency, familial type; (2) be free of any gross motor or sensory disturbances; (3) have a CA between 8.0 and 14.0 years; (4) have an MA between 4.0 and 9.0 years; and (5) have been a resident of the hospital for at least one month. The hospital's admission ledger was used to obtain the sample. In lieu of random sampling, Ss were selected by beginning with the most recent admissions and including every individual who met the preceding requirements in the sample until the desired number of Ss had been selected. Names were chosen in order, with the sampling procedure continuing until a group of twenty-one boys and twenty-one girls had been formed. The ten extra children were classified as stand-by Ss to be used in the event that members of the original sample were forced to withdraw before completion of the experiment. The birth date, MA, and IQ for each child were taken directly from the hospital's records. Each child's IQ was employed to adjust his MA for any time interval that might have intervened between his MA rating and his participation in the study. In keeping with the practices of the instituion, all Ss were given the same test (draw-a-person) to obtain MA ratings.

THE EXPERIMENTAL TASKS (THE HAMMER BOARD AND THE RESONATOR BELLS)

The hammer-board equipment was the familiar perforated wooden square, 400 small pegs that fit the holes of the square, and a small hammer. This is not a game in the true sense of the word because there is no defined goal for the participants. There may be the implicit, but apparently distant, goal of hammering in all the pegs, thus filling up the board. The musical equipment for the second task consisted of three resonator bells. A resonator bell is a vibrating plate with an individual resonator. The plates are struck with a mallet that is the same size and weight as the hammer used in the hammer-board task. The similarity of the mallet and hammer made the striking aspect of the two tasks as much alike as possible. The musical task was an open-ended one allowing the S to terminate it whenever he wished.

PROCEDURE

Performance Variable. Each S was taught how to play the tune "Hot Cross Buns" on the three resonator bells before the beginning of the experiment.

NM–M Condition. The Ss were tested individually. A nonadult assistant situated each S in a room with a one-way mirror and told him to perform the hammer-board task. The experimenter (E) viewed S through the mirror. Before going into the room, S was instructed in the following manner:

On the table inside the room is a hammer board. You may play with it until you wish to stop. When you finish with it, you may play "Hot Cross Buns" on the resonator bells.

M–NM Condition. In the M–NM condition, S began with the musical task and was instructed in the following manner:

On the table inside the room is the set of resonator bells we learned to play a little while ago. You may now go inside and play "Hot Cross Buns" over and over again until you wish to stop. When you finish, you may play with the hammer board as long as you want to.

The E recorded the responses (number of times S played the melody and the number of pegs driven into the board), the number of errors (wrong notes played in the melody), and the total time spent on each task.

Music-deprivation Variable. An experienced music therapist with music-education experience and a staff psychologist interviewed each S and read his case history. The S was then rated independently by the music therapist–educator and the psychologist on a music-deprivation scale. Ratings were made on 60-centimeter lines evenly subdivided, for reference, into six areas: much experience, experience, limited experience, slightly deprived, deprived, and very deprived. The music-deprivation score for each S was the average of the two judges' ratings. The possible range of scores denoting the amount of music deprivation thus could be from 1 (extreme of much experience) to 60 (extreme of very deprived).

The judges were not instructed as to what constituted deprivation or experience beyond being told that the terms were concerned with the amount and quality of the child's participation in music situations. The judges were then asked to list the specific factors in each S's history that influenced their rating for that S. This last procedure was included in the hope that such a listing would uncover specific factors that might eventually be employed in purifying and making more operational the music-deprivation variable.

The judges were cautioned against using any data other than those contained in the preinstitutionalization history of the child in making their ratings. They had no knowledge of an S's performance on the experimental tasks and E had no knowledge of the Ss' music-deprivation ratings until all had completed their performances.

EFFICIENCY RATIO

A linear relationship between music deprivation and the effectiveness of the music situation in motivating extended musical responses could be predicted. An additional description of the Ss' behavior was obtained by the computation of an efficiency index, which provided a ratio of the amount of time each S spent at the tasks to the amount of time he spent in the experimental room. This ratio was expressed as follows:

$$\text{Efficiency} = \frac{\text{time on tasks}}{\text{time in room}}$$

ATTRACTIVENESS OF TASKS TO SUBJECTS

The problem of whether a hammering type of task is as attractive to female Ss as it is to male Ss was considered. If female Ss showed noticeably less interest in the hammering task, this was noted and allowances were made when the data were reported.

Results

The tasks used in the study proved to be of interest to the Ss. Although there was great variability in the length of time the Ss spent on both tasks of the study, there were no noticeable differences among them in their initial attitudes toward the tasks. No S mentioned that hammering was a significant part of both tasks; and all responded to task 2 of the experiment, whether hammer board or resonator bells, as though it were a completely new, unrelated assignment.

MUSIC-DEPRIVATION VARIABLE

The correlation between the two judges' music-deprivation ratings was .72. (All correlations reported are Pearson product-moment correlations.) The judges reported that it was difficult to rate certain of the Ss because of the meager amount of information contained in their social histories. Both judges commented on the high proportion of Ss who had experienced considerable amounts of music deprivation. The combined ratings of the judges placed eight Ss in the very deprived range of the music deprivation scale; eighteen in the deprived range; six in the slightly deprived range; and none in the limited experience, experience, or much experience ranges. The specific factors in the Ss' histories that influenced the judges' ratings were as follows: Previous exposure to music had been limited mainly to radio or television. The child came from an orphanage or had lived in foster homes. The child came from his original home where conditions were too unstable to permit normal musical growth. The child had no experience, whatsover, in musical performance. The child expressed a great desire to perform musically. The child could not sing or accompany simple tunes with rudimentary rhythm instruments (drums, maracas, rhythm sticks, and so on). The mean of the music-deprivation scores of the NM–M group of 44.2 did not differ significantly from that of the M–NM group of 45.3 ($t < 1.00$).

Because the purpose of the study was to compare the performance of the more music-deprived Ss with that of the less music-deprived Ss, the Ss were divided at the median of the music-deprivation scores (44.7), forming two groups—a high music-deprived group (HD group) and a low music-deprived group (LD group). The range of music deprivation was from 32 to 44.5 for the LD group and from 45 through 56.5 for the HD group.

Analysis of Predictions

The first prediction was that the more music-deprived Ss would spend a greater amount of time on the musical task than would the less music-deprived Ss under both the NM–M and the M–NM conditions. The difference in the average time spent on the musical task by the HD group (18.68 minutes) and the LD group (5.02 minutes) was 13.66 minutes, which is a significant difference ($t = 2.51$, $p < 0.01$). (In all analyses of predictions one-tailed tests of significance were employed.) The formula for all t tests used in this study was:

$$t = \frac{\overline{X}_1 - \overline{X}_2}{\sqrt{\left(\frac{\Sigma X_1{}^2 + \Sigma X_2{}^2}{N_1 + N_2 - 2}\right)\left(\frac{N_1 + N_2}{N_1 N_2}\right)}}$$

The findings relating to the second prediction, that the more music-deprived Ss would make a lower proportion of errors than the less music-deprived Ss, were not found to be significant. The difference is in the predicted direction, although it did not reach the 0.05 level of significance.

The third prediction, that increase in time from task 1 to task 2 of the experiment would be greater for the more music-deprived Ss than for the less music-deprived Ss, was also confirmed. The difference in the average increase from task 1 to task 2 by the HD group (4.50 minutes) and LD group (0.20 minutes) was 4.30 minutes, which was significant ($t = 1.73$; $p < 0.05$).

Thus, two of the three predictions were confirmed. The more music-deprived Ss were found (1) to spend a greater amount of time on the music task and (2) to evidence a greater increase in time from task 1 to task 2 of the experiment. The prediction that the more music-deprived Ss would make a lower proportion of errors was not confirmed, although the findings were in the predicted direction.

Other Findings

This study was also directed toward an examination of the relationship of the performance measures of the Ss to (1) the two conditions of reinforcement emphasized, (2) CA, (3) MA, (4) IQ, (5) length of institutionalization, (6) CA at the time of institutionalization, (7) sex of Ss, and (8) efficiency of performance. The following statements are the results of statistical measurements taken during this study. When correlation between any two factors differed significantly from zero, partial correlation coefficients were computed.

The difference in average time spent on task 1 between the NM–M

(8.60 minutes) and the M–NM (11.60 minutes) groups was not significant ($t < 1.00$). The difference in the average time spent on task 2 between the NM–M (12.50 minutes) and the M–NM (12.90 minutes) groups was also not significant ($t < 1.00$). The difference in the average total time (task 1 + task 2) spent on the experiment between the NM–M (20.70) and the M–NM (24.60) groups was not significant ($t < 1.00$). It was concluded, therefore, that the groups tested with a sequence of NM–M and M–NM did not differ significantly on increase in time spent on task 2 compared to task 1, nor on total time spent on both tasks.

An insignificant negative correlation was found between total time scores and the CAs of the Ss ($r = -.125$; $p > 0.05$). To evaluate the relative importance of CA and MA, a correlation coefficient was obtained between the CAs and the MAs. Because this correlation was found to be significant ($r = .326$ $p < 0.025$), a partial correlation was computed between the total time scores and the CAs, holding MA constant. This resulted in an insignificant correlation between total performance time and CAs ($r_{12.3} = .048$; $p > 0.05$).

A significant negative correlation was found between total time scores and the MAs of the Ss ($r = -.457$; $p < 0.005$). A partial correlation computed between these two measures holding CA constant was also significant ($r_{13.2} = -.482$; $p < 0.005$). To test for a possible interaction effect between music deprivation and MA, an analysis of variance (music deprivation times MA) was computed with total time scores (see Table 6). Even though the F score associated with the music-deprivation variable ($F = 22.05$; $p < 0.01$) was significant, the F scores associated with MA ($F = 0.020$; $p > 0.05$) and the interaction effect ($F = 0.378$; $p > 0.05$) were not.

TABLE 6

Two-way Analysis of Variance of Total Time Scores
(Music Deprivation Times Mental Age)

	Source of variation	Ss	df	MS	F	p
A	Music deprivation	2,764.89	1	2,764.89	22.05	Significant 0.01
B	Mental age	2.55	1	2.55	0.02	Nonsignificant 0.05
A × B	MD × MA	47.40	1	47.40	0.38	Nonsignificant 0.05
	Within	3,510.84	28	125.38		
	Total	6,325.68	31			

The correlation between the total time scores and the IQs of the Ss was not significant ($r = -.115$; $p > 0.05$). The correlation between the total time scores and the length of institutionalization also was not significant ($r = .242$; $p > 0.05$). To test for a possible interaction effect between length of institutionalization and music deprivation, an analysis of variance was computed with the total time scores as the dependent variable (see Table 7). The resulting F score associated with the interaction effect between length of institutionalization and amount of music deprivation was not significant ($F = 0.154$; $p > 0.05$). A relatively high positive correlation between length of institutionalization and increase in time (task 2 to task 1) did not reach significance ($r = .242$; $p > 0.05$).

TABLE 7

Two-way Analysis of Variance of Total Time Scores
(Months Institutionalized Times Music-deprivation Score)

	Source of variation	Ss	df	MS	F	p
A	Music deprivation	2,792.78	1	2,792.78		
B	Length of institutionalization	0.50	1	0.50		
A × B	MD × LI	17.92	1	17.92	0.154	Nonsignificant 0.05
	Within	3,228.74	28	116.02		
	Total	6,039.94	31			

A significant negative correlation was found between the total time scores and the CAs of the Ss at the time of their institutionalization ($r = -.383$; $p < 0.025$). Because the CAs of the Ss at the time of institutionalization are related to both their CAs ($r = .470$) and their MAs ($r = .424$) and because MAs had been found to be significantly related to the total time scores, a partial correlation was computed between the total time scores and the CAs of the Ss at the time of institutionalization holding both CA and MA constant. This resulted in an insignificant correlation between the total time scores and the CAs of the Ss at the time of institutionalization ($r_{12.34} = -.271$; $p > 0.050$).

RELATION OF MUSIC DEPRIVATION TO OTHER VARIABLES

The characteristics of the HD and LD groups were examined further to ascertain whether the two groups differed on variables other than the performance measures employed in the predictions. An analysis was made of the differences between the two groups in regard to CA, MA, IQ, length of institutionalization, age when institutionalized, efficiency of performance (time spent on tasks divided by time in the experimental room), and experience in music therapy. There was also an analysis made of the differences between the performance of girl and boy Ss. None of the *t* values associated with the differences in these factors were significant.

Conclusions

The findings of this study offer support for the view that rigid behavior in mentally retarded Ss may be a product of motivation that results from deprivation. This study offers evidence that the mentally retarded Ss' higher motivation to pursue a musical task is related to the greater music deprivation such Ss have experienced. Furthermore, it is indicated that individual differences among the mentally retarded in the frequency with which they exhibit persistent musical behavior is also related to differences in the amount of music deprivation experienced. Because the persistence exhibited by mentally retarded Ss in musical activity has been found to be related to music deprivation, the prediction can be made that such persistence also would be shown by Ss of normal intelligence who have experienced similar amounts of music deprivation.

A significant negative relationship was found to exist between MA (holding CA constant) and the length of time spent by Ss on the two tasks of the experiment. When MA was held constant, no significant relationship was found between CA and the length of time spent on the total task. This finding supports the view that in a mentally retarded population the MA is a more significant determiner of performance than the CA.

The frequently observed tendency for institutionalized mentally retarded children to react negatively to experimental settings is assuaged by pre-experimental musical experiences. Musical tasks decrease this negative tendency even further, thus leaving the S with a greater positive reaction tendency toward the experimental setting.

No significant relationship existed between the time spent on the experimental tasks and any of the following factors: CA, IQ, sex, length of institutionalization, and efficiency of performance. It was found, however, that the more music-deprived Ss were institutionalized at an earlier age than the less deprived Ss. This factor may be related to the fact that most of the Ss in this study came from homes characterized by a level of social deprivation in which typical musical experiences would not occur. In relation to the earlier age of institutionalization of the more music-deprived group, the following hypothesis is advanced: *Mentally retarded children, even of borderline intelligence, are more likely to be institutionalized if their early environment is characterized by those factors that directly or indirectly constitute music deprivation.*

This study offers evidence that differences among Ss in the frequency with which they may manifest certain musical behaviors that have often been characterized as rigid (perseveration, stereotypy, and so on) are related to differences in the amount of music deprivation the Ss have experienced. It adds support from the specialized area of musical behavior to the position advanced in earlier studies that constructs needed to explain the performance of normal Ss are adequate in explaining the performance of mentally retarded Ss. This study again points out the danger of describing a group as though its members uniformly possess a particular characteristic, that is, rigidity, without considering such factors as historical differences among Ss, variability in motivation, the nature of the reinforcement provided, and the tasks employed.

These results offer further support for the view that the alleged rigid behavior observed in mentally retarded Ss may be just as reasonably attributed to differences in motivation. In music activities, such behaviors may be attributed to higher motivation to receive the special kind of self-gratification that derives from the successful performance of music. The results of this study support the findings of earlier studies on rigidity in the mentally retarded.

References

GASTON, E. T. Functional music. In N. B. Henry (Ed.), *Basic concepts in music education*. Chicago: The University of Chicago Press, 1958. Pp. 292–309.

GASTON, E. T. Aesthetic experience in music. *Mus. Educ. J.*, 1963, 49, 25–26, 62, 64.

GEWIRTZ, J. L., and Baer, D. M. The effect of brief social deprivation on behaviors for a social reinforcer. *J. abnorm. soc. Psychol.*, 1958, 56, 49–56.

LORENZ, K. *King Solomon's ring*. London: Methuen, 1952.

SARASON, S. B., and GLADWIN, T. Psychological and cultural problems in mental subnormality: a review of research. *Genet. Psychol. Monogr.*, 1958, 57, 3–284.

STEVENSON, H., and ZIGLER, E. F. Discrimination learning and rigidity in normal and feebleminded individuals. *J. Pers.*, 1957, 25, 699–711.

TINBERGEN, N. *The study of instinct*. Fair Lawn, N.J.: Oxford University Press, 1951.

ZIGLER, E. F. The effect of pre-institutional social deprivation on the performance of feebleminded children. Unpublished doctoral dissertation, Univer. of Texas, 1958.

AUTHOR INDEX

SUBJECT INDEX